CONTACTS

EDITOR
Jade Tilley
jade.tilley@onecoms.co.uk

GROUP SALES MANAGER
Donna Jenkins
donna@onecoms.co.uk

BUSINESS
DEVELOPMENT
MANAGER
Melanie Bell
mel.bell@onecoms.co.uk

ACCOUNT MANAGER
Sharon Price
sharon.price@onecoms.co.uk

ACCOUNTS
Carole Todd
carole.todd@onecoms.co.uk

RECEPTION
Jo Cluer
jo@onecoms.co.uk

PRODUCTION
CONTROLLER
Emma Coppin
emma.coppin@onecoms.co.uk

EDITOR-IN-CHIEF
& PUBLISHER
R Nisbet
robert@onecoms.co.uk

PUBLISHER'S ASSISTANT
Danny Morgan
danny.morgan@onecoms.co.uk

Produced by Media One
Communications Ltd.
Geneva House, Park Road,
Peterborough, PE1 2UX.
Telephone 01733 756555,
Facsimile 01733 760505,
E-mail info@onecoms.co.uk,
www.onecoms.co.uk

ISBN: 978-1-907394-00-3

INTERIOR DESIGN YEARBOOK 2010

THE ESSENTIAL SOURCEBOOK FOR INTERIOR DESIGN

D0620549

INTERIOR DESIGN YEARBOOK 2010 contributors

GEORGE BOND,
SBID

George Bond is the National Director for the Society of British Interior Designer (SBID) as well as a Fellow of the Royal Society of Arts. George has his own interior design company based in Jesmond, near Newcastle. With a scholar's grasp of centuries of rich tradition and an alchemist's flair for infinite possibility, George Bond is the acknowledged master of modern interior design, mixing the finest English style with cosmopolitan magnificence. **www.georgebond.tv**

NICK AND CHRISTIAN CANDY,
CANDY & CANDY

Nick and Christian Candy are the co-founders of Candy & Candy. Together they drive their award-winning practice forward, delivering a tailored, experienced and thorough interior service. Candy & Candy are leaders in the marine and aviation markets, producing stunning interiors for private clients. **www.candyandcandy.com**

ANNA DODONOVA,
ANNA CASA INTERIORS

Anna Dodonova is the owner and director of Anna Casa Interiors, launched in 2007 at the Design Centre Chelsea Harbour. Anna started her career as a graphic designer after training at college in Germany but soon changed her focus to interior design. Anna worked as an interior designer for several years on projects in Germany and the UK before launching Anna Casa Interiors. **www.annacasa.net**

IRIS DUNBAR

Iris Dunbar was elected on the Board of The British Interior Design Association in 2005 and then made Director of Education and Continuous Professional Development in 2006. As of November 2008, Iris was elected to become the President of BIDA, which has now become BIID (British Institue of Interior Design). Iris is also a Fellow of the Chartered Society of Designers and The Royal Society of Arts. Iris has worked within a cross section of the Interior Design Industry, ranging from a multidisciplinary design consultancy to the independent practitioner. Her experience has spanned all sectors, working on commercial offices and restaurants to residential and exhibition projects. **www.bida.org**

HELEN GREEN,
HELEN GREEN DESIGN

Helen Green is a leading British designer, who founded Helen Green Design in 2002. The company encompasses Interior Design, Interior Architecture and bespoke British made furniture and accessories. Clients include a wide range of prestigious private and commercial projects

GIORGIO ARMANI,
ARMANI CASA

Giorgio Armani is the President and Chief Executive of Giorgio Armani S.p.A., one of the world's leading fashion and lifestyle design houses, Mr. Armani's philosophy of fashion and style together with his entrepreneurial ability have been central to the success of Giorgio Armani S.p.A. He oversees both the company's strategic direction and all aspects of design and creativity. Perhaps best known for revolutionising fashion he has over nearly thirty years of designing, developed a stable of collections, including Armani Casa home interiors, offering a choice of lifestyles to the marketplace. Today, the company's product range includes clothing, shoes and bags, watches, eyewear, jewellery, fragrances, cosmetics and home furnishings. During his career, Mr. Armani has received several local and international awards, including an Honorary Doctorate from London's Royal College of Art. **www.armanicasa.com**

SARAH BEENY

Sarah Beeny is a Channel 4 television presenter on the popular Property Snakes and Ladders prime time show. As well as being a well established property mogul, Sarah also owns mysinglefriend.com, a social dating website and has just launched Tepilo.com, a property website enabling you to buy or sell your home online without any fees, with tips on design, negotiation and marketing, and all the advice you need along the way. **www.sarahbeeny.com**

TARA BERNERD,
CEO & HEAD OF DESIGN, TARGET LIVING

British Designer, **Tara Bernerd** is the CEO and Head of Design at Target Living, which was founded in 2002 by Tara and Architect, Thomas Griem. Tara is a Board Director of Chelsfield Partners LLP and is also a member of the Dulux Creative Board 2009. A worthy winner of the Andrew Martin International Interior Design Award, Tara is a contributing editor on design for British GQ. **www.targetliving.com**

including luxury hotels in the UK and overseas such as the Helen Green Suites at The Berkeley Hotel and the Plantation Suites and the new Spa at The Coral Reef Club, Barbados. **www.helengreendesign.com**

ANOUSKA HEMPEL,
ANOUSKA HEMPEL DESIGN COMPANY

Anouska Hempel's motto is to 'design, refine, repeat'. **Lady Weinberg**, formerly Anouska Hempel, created the London-based international studio, Anouska Hempel Design- AHD. Fundamental to the success of the business is the design approach based on the uniqueness of each project and the importance given to identifying a concept to be carried through from space planning to lighting and furnishing to the smallest detail. **www.anouskahempeldesign.com**

KELLY HOPPEN,
KELLY HOPPEN INTERIORS

Having begun her foray into the design world at the age of just 16, **Kelly Hoppen** has made a name for herself as a world renowned British Designer. As well as designing apartments, houses and yachts for an international list of private clients, Kelly also works on commercial commissions including hotel, restaurant, office and aircraft interiors. Kelly Hoppen was the first winner of the prestigious Andrew Martin International Interior Design Award. **www.kellyhoppenretail.com**

ANDREA MAFLIN,

Andrea Maflin is a renowned Interior Designer who has lent her expertise to many a situation including co-speaking at the Chelsea Design Harbour in lectures and seminars. Andrea trained at the Winchester School of Art, gaining a BA in Textile Design, first producing textiles for fashion. In 1993 Andrea established her own interior design business. Andrea's client list also includes Richmond International and Hirsch Bedner Associates. **www.andreamaflin.co.uk**

CECILIA NEAL,
MELTONS

Cecilia Neal is a member of BIID (British Institute of Interior Design) and the IIDA. Cecilia established Meltons, her interior design practice, over twenty years ago. There is no one single "house style" at Meltons. Cecilia Neal brings a profound understanding of architecture and its components, the requirements of modern technology and, above all, the needs and desires of her clients to each project. **www.meltons.co.uk**

KATHARINE POOLEY

Katharine Pooley is a well-respected and highly creative interior designer. Before settling in London to establish Katharine Pooley Ltd, an interior design company and boutique, she spent 14 years working for Morgan Stanley and Barclays Bank in Hong Kong and in her lifetime has also lived in Vietnam, Singapore and Bahrain. Katharine honed her interior design skills on her own homes, completing three impressive projects in the space of one year: a luxury beach villa in Phuket, Thailand, a 16th century castle in Scotland and a vast ski-lodge in Colorado. Now five years on the company boasts a highly discerning client list and an impressive portfolio of projects. Carving a name for herself among the world's most talented designers, for the past four years Katharine's projects have been featured in the Andrew Martin Interior Design Review. **www.katharinepooley.com**

DAVID SPENCE

David Spence is an Architect and a Founding Partner of SHH and Company Chairman. He acts as client director on all residential projects in the studio and is responsible for the smooth running of all jobs in the studio on a day-to-day basis. David has over 30 years of experience in designing, building and refurbishing residential schemes, from ultra high-end one-off homes to mass housing projects, but his CV also encapsulates everything from offices to hotels and airports. Key projects include the RIBA Manser Medal finalist project Pilgrim's Lane; the Mayfair Penthouse, for which David was shortlisted as the Bathroom Designer of the Year and the Parkcity hotel. **www.shh.co.uk**

SALLY STOREY,
LIGHTING DESIGN INTERNATIONAL

Sally Storey is the Creative Director at Lighting Design International and John Cullen lighting. Sally spends much of her time travelling the world, designing lighting schemes for individual and corporate clients. Sally has written three books and this year her third, 'Perfect Lighting' (Jaqui Small Publishing) was released, which was designed to help people understand the importance of light and to show how to combine effects for the perfect mood. **www.lightingdesigninternational.com**

GAIL TAYLOR AND KAREN HOWES,
TAYLOR HOWES DESIGN

Gail and Karen are the Founders of Taylor Howes Design and celebrated International interior designers. The company was founded in 1991 with a dedicated team of designers providing a comprehensive design service for private clients, property developers and hoteliers. Winners of the prestigious Andrew Martin International Interior Design Award, 2006 was the year for Taylor Howes as they took home the award for their style and effortlessly beautiful interiors. **www.thdesigns.co.uk**

SOURCEBOOK
index:
YOUR A-Z OF **MUST-HAVE** CONTACTS

foreword

By **Iris Dunbar,**
President, British Institute of Interior Design

With the recession still in full grip the property market is forcing home owners to re-assess their present circumstances, with many choosing to improve their homes. Like never before, businesses are under pressure to outperform their rivals and interior design is a pivotal factor in attracting customers. A professional, quality finish by a professional interior designer can raise the value of a property substantially. The enhancement of a property can often make a considerable difference to its value, and can dramatically improve the chances of a speedy and successful sale or lease, for both private and commercial properties.

Projects are being designed with a sense of longevity in mind. There is an increased enthusiasm towards sustainable and ecological issues, combined with a real sense of nesting and comfort in the use of natural materials. Renewed consideration for technical expertise and craftsmanship is encouraging manufacturers to explore new methods. Technology has given us a refreshed approach to the use of materials, introducing greater choices in colour, light, pattern and texture in architectural structure and interior surfaces. Experimental materials such as woven plastics, lace patterned fretwork, and robotic printing processes are just a few of the endless possibilities resulting in new innovative techniques. Interior design is always at the centre of change. Moving home, upgrading the office, restaurant design, performance retailing, new age leisure activities, innovative educational initiatives, state of the art healthcare- the list is endless. Whatever the requirement, design makes a difference to how people experience a space and their surroundings.

Interior designers have often been misconstrued as an expensive luxury and far beyond typical budgets. However, this is not the case. Using an interior designer can actually save money. The British Institute of Interior Design is a leading professional body representing interior designers in the UK. BIID nurtures, recognises and rewards excellence in interior design through education, practical professional support, development opportunities and facilitating the sharing of best practice. With our members, we form a collective of expert interior designers committed to the highest standards of professional practice and furthering the impact and influence of the industry.

By hiring a BIID member, clients will reap the rewards of superior expertise and design knowledge and enjoy the benefits of an established network of trade and stockist contacts. Their network of specialist suppliers also ensures that less available, more exclusive quality furnishings and interiors can be available to their clients at affordable prices. A professional BIID member will also be able to prevent costly mistakes by producing designs that are right the first time, as well as manage the costs of the project and obtain the best results for the budget.

The Interior Design Yearbook 2010 provides great insight into the best companies and is an invaluable resource for those wishing to access products and service companies who are established in the industry.

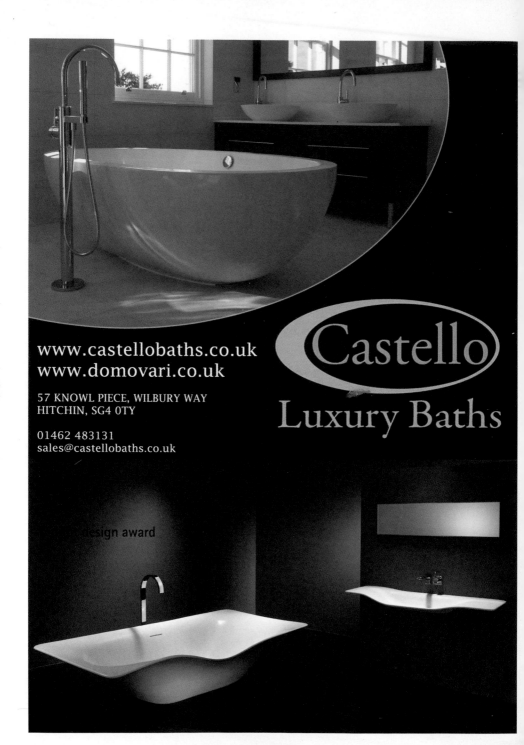

www.castellobaths.co.uk
www.domovari.co.uk

57 KNOWL PIECE, WILBURY WAY
HITCHIN, SG4 0TY

01462 483131
sales@castellobaths.co.uk

design award

Castello
Luxury Baths

INTERIOR DESIGN²⁰¹⁰
YEARBOOK

Photo Casebook

Inspiration for a beautiful interior look can be found in the most unusual of places, a fine dining space or decadent hotel lobby can provide a new outlook on a particular style that translates into a more personal domestic space. The Photo casebook glides across the globe featuring recognizable settings such as the fabulous St Pancras International with its impressive architecture and stylish station dining, or a luxurious hotel with sumptuous suites and eclectic uses of furniture. From London to Tel Aviv, Moscow to LA, recline, relax and take note as the Interior Design Yearbook transports you to a world of global luxury.

DESIGNER: **MARTIN BRUDNIZKI**
CLIENT: **SEARCY- ST PANCRAS GRANDE RESTAURANT**
LOCATION: **ST PANCRAS INTERNATIONAL, LONDON**

ST PANCRAS GRAND

Following its hugely successful £800m refurbishment in November 2007, St Pancras International is truly back on the map and has become a chic destination for rail, retail and restaurants. **Martin Brudnizki** has designed St Pancras Grand as a contemporary take on the classical brasserie, incorporating an Oyster Bar, dining and bar area. The Brasserie creates a timeless atmosphere of quality and refinement by using an appropriate palette of materials and lighting effects. Dark herringbone flooring contrasts with limestone borders, coffered and barrel vaulted ceilings are washed with a warm backlight to accentuate the gold leaf surface. The lighting is augmented with traditional brasserie ball pendant lights. Additional subtle lighting is incorporated into the black lacquered and bronzed wall paneling, and concealed within the bespoke seating.

LA VITA SPUNTINI

La Vita Spuntini is the sparkling new Italian tapas-style restaurant in the heart of Glasgow's West-End that has been redesigned and refurbished by **Surface ID**, offering a new style of dining for the discerning culinary glitterati of the area. Interior designers of the award winning bar, restaurant and entertainment venue Òran Mór, Surface ID worked to the client's brief, developing a style for the restaurant that evokes the feeling of medieval Tuscany mixed with more contemporary elements.

DESIGNER: **SURFACE ID**
CLIENT: **LA VITA SPUNTINI (MR MARCO ARCARI)**
LOCATION: **GLASGOW**

RIVERSIDE RESPLENDENCE

St George, the award winning developer, unveiled one of London's finest riverside penthouses at Imperial Wharf in April 2009. Envisioned by **Taylor Howes** bespoke interior eye, the interior oozes sophisticated luxury that has trend-inspired elegance and comfort dripping from the walls. The interior styling was designed to give the feeling of a unique, luxurious experience, combined with a space that can be lived in. Drama and warmth are fused together by the clever choices of colours and the depth in the fabrics and detail adorned across every element of the space. Metallic walls, a beautiful black lacquer console and a stunning Swarovski crystal chandelier that descends from the top floor is all part of the dramatic opulence of the penthouse.

DESIGNER: **TAYLOR HOWES**
CLIENT: **ST GEORGE**
LOCATION: **IMPERIAL WHARF, LONDON**

Image: Antoine Bootz

DESIGNER: BENJAMIN NORIEGA ORTIZ, LLC
CLIENT: MANZANITA CAPITAL, DIPTQUE
LOCATION: PARIS

UNIQUE DIPTYQUE

The design of Diptyque's New York "pop-up" store was inspired by a painting of a tea party with Poirot entertainers by Francesco Beda (1840-1900), an Italian painter who was known for his French Rococo decorative style of the 18th century. Benjamin Noriega Ortiz has created a set for human interaction, where the rest of the store is in the brand's signature black and white. Alternatively, by limiting the color palette to black and white, they were also paying homage to the quintessential New York artists, such as Louise Nevelson with the black table on black floor and Donald Judd with our white shelves and furniture against black walls and black floor. Yves Couleslant, one of the three original founders of Diptyque was a set designer. The entire store has been designed as a window display and the "Tea Party" guests, the customers, are the actors in front of a backdrop.

DESIGNER: **CAULDER MOORE**
CLIENT: **MICHAELJOHN SALON**
LOCATION: **MAYFAIR, LONDON**

THE CUTTING EDGE OF CREATIVITY

The interior concept of the Mayfair MichaelJohn salon puts a contemporary twist on the classic glamour of the 1940's to create a luxury environmental experience with sophisticated, understated elegance and discrete glamour. A palette of champagne, gold and bronze combines with luxurious reflective fabrics. Subtle, harmonious, curved shapes and lines contrast with the "square design philosophy" often seen in modern luxury hair salons. **Caulder Moore** were the creative agency behind the design of the salon, which emulates beautifully that of an authentic 1940's backdrop. Walls have been adorned with a sumptuous gold, dark walnut features as key accents in furniture and the adorned crystal is reflected in the extended use of mirrors throughout. Bespoke seating is true to the era with white high gloss tub chairs, feature styling units are used in column form with yet more mirrors and crystal chandeliers. Further metallic's are used throughout the different areas of the salon, in the colour area there is a stone topped platinum veneer, feature circular table, circled with gold oval mirrors, the backwash area depicts a bronze laminate with silver leaf lined recessed doors, woven ceramic tiles are also integrated. Other areas such as the VIP room boast champagne coloured walls with diamond mosaic patterned steel and in the basement lounge, clients are treated to Philippe Starck Passion Chairs, on a platinum timber flooring. The intricate design appears endless as it flows seamlessly through each room, paving the way to pure luxury, which is emulated in the quality synonymous with the Michaeljohn brand.

NICHE 'NEIGHBOURHOOD' DESIGN

Jamie Oliver's Italian, part of the 'neighbourhood' collection opened this year and is a perfect example of **Martin Brudnizki's** Design Studio work. The environment combines a rustic Italian feel, synonymous with the food served, complemented with a relaxed yet contemporary setting. Quirky furniture and decorative elements defined in the materials used, creates a spot on look.

DESIGNER: **MARTIN BRUDNIZKI**
CLIENT: **JAMIE'S ITALIAN RESTAURANT**
LOCATION: **OXFORD**

AN URBAN OASIS

Completed in the Autumn 2008, **Yasumichi Morita at GLAMOROUS co.,ltd** collaborated with other designers to create certain elements of the W Hong Kong hotel. The hotel design is inspired by nature. The aim for the five star urban hotel, was to express nature transformed into a modern, glamorous and abstract urban oasis. The elements of nature are expressed in rich materials, transformed into the glamorous appearances and scattered everywhere to become series of WOW impressions. The glass box made of twigs becomes signature at the façade. It consists of two layers of twig screens and gives an impression of abstract forest. From the inside, the cityscape of Hong Kong is seen beyond the forest; from the outside, it becomes a beautiful lantern to wrap the podium floors. A part of twig forms the brand logo and LED embedded into twigs emit sparkles. Sparkles of LED are found as if thousands of fireflies fluttered over this beautiful screen. The drop-off is designed to be masculine and formal to clearly define gate into the enchanted forest.

FIRE, the name and concept of this specialty restaurant, is the keyword for design without doubt. To express the energy, Glamorous appointed three Japanese artists; Isshin SUSA, Masataka KURASHINA and Takahiro KONDO. FIRE photos by Isshin SUSA successfully captured lively fire dance into the scenes. These photos overflowing of the energy became the wall partitions to wrap the space with intimacy. KURASHINA spreads his original FIRE flower onto his ceiling campus. His bold but abstract expression of FIRE built the gastronomic enthusiasm. KONDO extracted mist out of the FIRE. The dark room surrounded by "mist" is calm and mystic, yet representing sophisticated impression of FIRE.

photos by Nacasa & Partners, Inc

DESIGNER: REARDONSMITH/ GA DESIGN/PETER SILLING/ R.P.W DESIGN
CLIENT: GROSVENOR HOUSE- J.W.MARIOTT HOTEL
LOCATION: LONDON

LONDON PRESTIGE

After a four-year, multimillion pound restoration programme London's largest five star hotel re-launched as Grosvenor House, A JW Marriott Hotel in September 2008. **ReardonSmith** were the restoration architects on board with **GA Design, Peter Silling and R.P.W Design** prodiving the interior design.

Where Grosvenor House, A JW Marriott Hotel stands today was originally the London residence of the Grosvenor family. It first opened its doors to the public in May 1929 and quickly established itself as the glamorous home of the society set and wealthy Americans, attracting a fashionable crowd from Edward VIII and Mrs Simpson to Ella Fitzgerald and Jacqueline Onassis. Fast forward to 2008 and the hotel finds itself at the culmination of the most extensive renovation of its kind. Grosvenor House, A JW Marriott Hotel has resumed its place amongst London's most desirable hotels and is restored to its former glory. The extensive restoration programme included five bar and four dining options, ranging from classic French brasserie BORD'EAUX run by La Trompette's former head chef, Ollie Couillaud to award-winning afternoon tea in the scenic Park Room that rivals any in London. The style of the interior is that of classic contemporary with rich and soothing colours in the furnishings. Many original features of the period have been retained, and opulent marble bathrooms acknowledge an Art Deco influence.

FOUR SEASONS HOTEL MACAU, COTAI STRIP

Architects Paul Steelman Design Group and Interior Designers **Hirsch Bedner Associates** worked together in 2008 to deliver the stunning Four Seasons Hotel, Macau on the Cotai Strip. HBA/Hirsch Bedner Associates blended Port-uguese and Chinese influences to capture the traditional Macanese culture in the Hotel in Southern China. It is a jewel amidst Asia's Las Vegas, as the Cotai Strip® has become known.

Four Seasons Hotel Macau, Cotai Strip® is part of a mixed-use lifestyle and entertainment complex, comprising serviced apartments, high-end shopping mall, a boutique-sized casino, fine dining and other entertainment options. Contemporary design mixes with old world ornamentation with Oriental accents, vibrant colours, lush brocades and jewel tones, reminiscent of the days when the city was a major trading center for Portuguese silks and ceramics between China, Japan, India and Europe. "No other hotel encapsulates the Macanese culture like Four Seasons," said Tracie Co, senior designer from the firm's Hong Kong office. "This design and style is being done for the first time to show off.the rich culture and history of Macau."

Inspired by the beautiful, ornate colonial architecture that makes Macau distinct, HBA/Hirsch Bedner Associates utilized a residential approach in the design and style of interiors that blends seamlessly with the building's architectural style.

DESIGNER: **HBA / HIRSCH BEDNER ASSOCIATES**
CLIENT: **LAS VEGAS SANDS. FOUR SEASONS HOTEL**
LOCATION: **MACAU**

THE EUROPE HOTEL & RESORT, KILARNEY, IRELAND

The London-based studio, **HBA**, has added another feather to its cap with the striking redesign of Hotel Europe. Completed in the Summer 2008, the resort hotel and spa exudes contemporary, natural luxury as it overlooks Killarney's majestic Loch Lein. The renovation, started in November 2006, covered all of the resort's public areas including the Crystal Bar, Brasserie, spa and café, suites and guestrooms. A contemporary style adorns the walls of the hotel and spa that reflects Irish beauty and a sense of calm in its design. The architects for the project, Gottstein Architects worked with lighting consultants DPA Lighting, with Hirsch Bedner Associates taking the lead on interior design. The '60s-style box building offers breathtaking lake views from the lobby, made cozy with plush sofas, huge log baskets, cavernous wood-burning fireplaces, and natural-white and bitter-chocolate limestone floors. Custom-made light fittings and carpets are accented by strong, bold colors defining the 35-year-old hotel, synergizing modern with classic sensibilities.

DESIGNER: **HBA / HIRSCH BEDNER ASSOCIATES**
CLIENT: **THE EUROPE HOTEL & RESORT KILLARNEY**
LOCATION: **IRELAND**

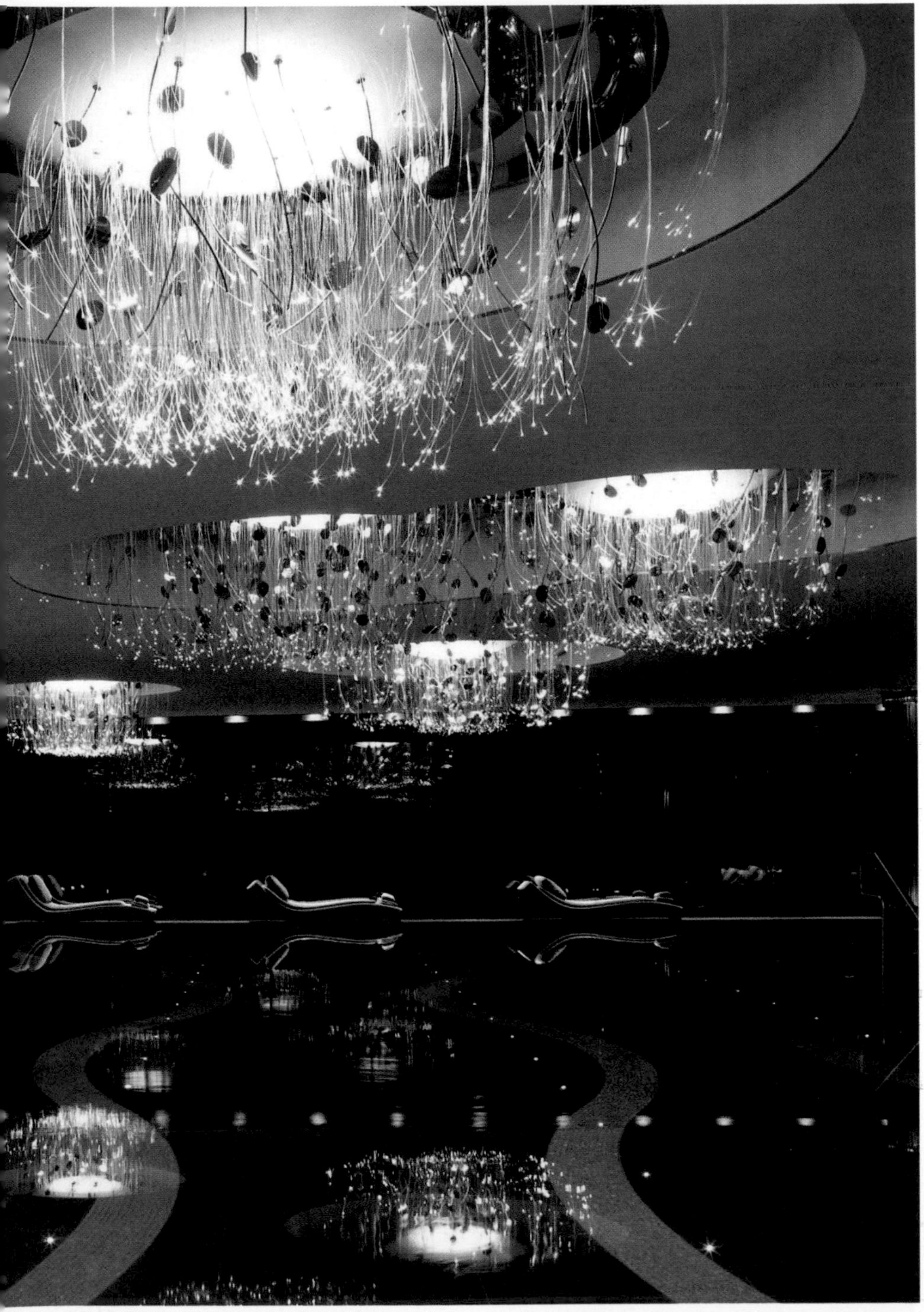

Photography: Christoph Koester and Olaf Lummer

BOND AT THE LANGHAM

In what was originally a federal bank, the design for this 2,200 square foot lounge and bar plays on the old and new, building upon and enriching the existing architecture. An intricately detailed coffered ceiling, soaring 20' above the space, was carefully restored, while original limestone walls, columns, and pilasters were also preserved. A 400 square foot mezz-anine lounge provides an intimate view of the activity below. Prominently featured is a large, half-circle bar at one end of the lounge, dramatically highlighted by a 17' tall illuminated back showcasing top shelf liquors. Taking advantage of the space's majestic windows, custom pieces of artwork on resin panels have been suspended, illustrating bonds as a reference to the history of the space. Rosewood niches with floating beveled mirrors act as partitions between each window, adding depth and drama to the space, while custom lighting pendants draw your eyes upward. **Jeffrey Beers**-designed custom furniture and carpet complete this luxurious lounge.

CELEBRATED DESIGN

The renovation and restoration of Fontainebleau Miami hinged on the reinterpretation of Morris Lapidus' celebrated design, imbuing the property with new visual energy and a modern spirit. It was important for **Jeffrey Beers** to create a pleasurable and stimulating environment for the public – to compose a journey, a sensory experience for each guest. Integral to the design were a consideration and attentiveness to Lapidus' original vision for the resort. Fluidly curving sculpted ceilings evoke Lapidus' shapely structure, while the irregular plan of the space itself provides guests several unique dining options. A wall of recessed U-shaped booths along another wall offers a feast for the eyes, with a fantastical wall covering depicting a black and white kaleidoscope of organic material. The visual palette of crisp and subdued natural materials – white marble floors and columns, river stone, wood-topped tables and paneling and neutral textiles – handsomely sets off the theatrical activity of the restaurant.

LAPIDUS INSPIRED LOBBY

Located adjacent to the main lobby of the resort, Bleau Bar embodies a forward thinking version of Lapidus' vision for glamour, luxury, and vibrancy. Where the floor was once covered in blue carpet, a new, illuminated blue-glass floor glows underfoot. **Jeffrey Beers** has designed the room yo take on a surreal, dreamlike atmosphere, cast in a blue glow. Central to the space is a bold, 18' tall column framed by the circular bar. Glowing internally, the pillar is dressed with strands of crystal, as though a column of cascading water in front of which are lined the glass shelves of the liquor display. A crisp white stone bar is supported upon a fascia of custom undulating polished metal paneling, reflecting and refracting the light cast from below. Floor to ceiling windows look out over the pool deck and towards the boardwalk and beach beyond; draped with sheer white curtains, they encourage a fluid relationship between interior and exterior.

RONDA LOCATELLI DUBAI ENERGY

Blending the enchantment of the Italian countryside with Dubais' energy and pizzazz is what sets apart this warm and inviting eatery of esteemed chef Georgio Locatelli. **Jeffrey Beers** has featured a central, stone-clad structure, housing four wood-fired ovens, the rest of the dining room emanates forth with dark wooden arcs and rustic lattices. To create a rustic yet stimulating environment for Ronda Locatelli, Beers blended the charm of the Italian countryside with the modernity of Dubai. A calming water pond juxtaposed with a custom built fireplace greets guests upon entering, while a central stone clad structure houses four pizza ovens and grounds the space. Diners will relax on specially designed wood basket seating pods, and various sized circular wood trellises adorned with fiery custom glass light fixtures hang suspended over the entire space, lending a sense of intimacy.

A FUSION OF CULTURES

Fuse is the first nightclub of its kind in Nashville. Conceived to bridge the gap in the city's hotel nightclub culture, the 14,000 square foot space – originally a buffet restaurant – has been transformed into an oasis of sensuality within the renowned landmark Opryland resort. **Jeffrey Beers** used a sultry palette of deep rich reds and black, Fuse transports its guests to a shadowy sophisticated ambience. Oversized plush leather black sofas and ottomans rest on an exotic zebra wood floor and are strategically placed in groupings and semi-private alcoves, producing an urban living room experience. Customized LED red lights add a sensual allure, further enhanced by lit columns and architectural rib-work. Ceiling coffers that continually change color produce a dramatic light show within the club's dusky environment. A 120-foot vivid red bar is the central feature in Fuse where twenty curving ebony millwork ribs race up the wall and over the ceiling.

DESIGNER: **BENJAMIN NORIEGA ORTIZ, LLC**
CLIENT: **MORGANS HOTEL GROUP**
LOCATION: **MONDRIAN, LOS ANGELES**

THE ORIGINAL MONDRIAN

In 1996, Morgans Hotel Group and the iconic designer Philippe Starck, left the hospitality industry star-struck with the opening of the dazzling Mondrian Los Angeles. The design untied a quintessentially Californian embrace of nature, the outdoors and the casual within the West-Hollywood tradition of glamour and fantasy. Last year, Morgans Hotel Group commissioned visionary designer **Benjamin Noriega Ortiz** to rejuvenate the Hollywood destination. Upon entering the Mondrian, Philippe Starck's original thirty-foot Mahogany doors reveal the designers signature. Highlights of creams and magnolia's is emphasised by the floods of daylight that moves throughout the entrance. Glamour and sophistication are defined throughout the space with gold leaf vines running across ceilings and columns, referencing nature entangled with fantasy.

LONDON'S LANGHAM

Richmond International was responsible for the transformation of the interiors of the historic Langham in London, including the entrance lobby, reception, the Palm Court lounge, extensive conference and banqueting facilities, bedrooms and suites. Reflecting the Asian and Eastern influences on English Society in the late 19th and early 20th centuries, a hint of the Orient is evident in today's design, mainly in the form of specially-commissioned artwork by leading contemporary artists from Hong Kong, China and the UK but also as decorative elements in the new Guestrooms. A key part of the design concept is the reinstatement of the Palm Court lounge as the heart of the hotel. Here the sophisticated design sees contemporary materials and feature finishes mixed with the classic sparkle of cut mirrors and crystal.

DESIGNER: **RICHMOND INTERNATIONAL**
CLIENT: **THE LANGHAM HOTEL**
LOCATION: **LONDON**

CONTINENTAL CUBISM

The London-based Interior Design Firm, **RDD**, has just completed The Augustine Hotel in Prague, which is the most recent jewel in the Rocco Forte Portfolio. The renovation saw a complex map of old buildings, including an Augustinian monastery and a brewery be skillfully re-mastered by RDD. The design has weaved the beautiful location with Czech design influences and an all important burst of heritage and history to perfectly demonstrate the Rocco Forte mantra and foundation for their global success- The Art of Simple Luxury.

DESIGNER: **RDD**
CLIENT: **ROCCO FORTE**
LOCATION: **PRAGUE**

DESIGNER: **ROCKWELL GROUP**
CLIENT: **NOBU RESTAURANT**
LOCATION: **DUBAI**

MIDDLE EASTERN NOBU

In November 2008 there was a sake ceremony in celebration of the first Nobu restaurant in the Middle East in Dubai, U.A.E., a continuation of the longtime collaboration between Rockwell Group and Nobu that has evolved into Nobu restaurants all across the world, including New York, Melbourne, Moscow and Hong Kong. Nobu Dubai was an evolution of many of the concepts Rockwell Group developed for the flagship Nobu Fifty Seven in New York, such as the emphasis on craftsmanship, natural materials and storytelling. The textures and materials in this particular location were chosen to reflect the finely crafted cuisine and Nobu's roots in the Japanese countryside, while also celebrating the Dubai beachfront context. David Rockwell, Founder and CEO of Rockwell Group, explained: "The context, landscape and history of this new restaurant brought about all sorts of new and exciting challenges. We had to think about its location not only in the Middle East, but also in Dubai as the epicenter of an ever-growing and flourishing environment for building, not to mention being more specifically in the larger-than-life Atlantis resort on Palm Jumeirah."

DESIGNER: **PETER MARINO ARCHITECT**
CLIENT: **CHRISTIAN DIOR**
LOCATION: **NEW YORK**

J'ADORE FLAGSHIP STORE

In 1997, the American Architect, **Peter Marino**, directed the greats works for the fiftieth anniversary of the Flagship Christian Dior store. Ten years later and Marino once again set to work on the evolution of the Dior boutique, a third change in décor has occurred in this beautiful space, combining the future with elements of the past. After eight months of work transforming the interior, the space has morphed into a luxurious contemporary apartment, with each department treated as a salon in a 1,200 square meter private home. The design corresponds to the evolution of society, fashion and contemporary design. The décor is warm and bears the stamp of contemporary artists to have marked the century including the decorator Herve Van Der Straeten, who created the Dior perfume bottle for 'J'adore'. Every detail, colour, fabric and piece of furniture have all come together to create a universe of luxury elegance and joy.

NOBU MOSCOW

Ever since the original Nobu first opened its doors in New York's fashionable Tribeca district in 1994, the name has required little introduction to gourmands worldwide. Nobu Moscow opened in April 2009. The interior of the restaurant was designed by leading design bureau **Rockwell Group** and follow the traditions of Nobu worldwide. It will reflect the personal taste of Nobu Matsuhisa and his love for combining contemporary materials and hand-made design. "The restaurant will be a refreshing and unexpected contrast from the serene, urban Moscow street outside, with an endless bamboo forest at the entrance, mother-of-pearl accents, sea urchin-inspired chandeliers and curvilinear walnut walls that create the illusion of an ocean wave" — David Rockwell, Founder and CEO Rockwell Group.

DESIGNER: **ROCKWELL GROUP**
CLIENT: **NOBU RESTAURANT**
LOCATION: **MOSCOW, RUSSIA**

DESIGNER: **TARRUELLA & LÓPEZ +TRENCHS**
CLIENT: **GRUPO MAIRELES, EME FUSION HOTEL**
LOCATION: **SEVILLE, SPAIN**

GRANDES JAVIER ORTEGA and INSTALACIONES-ANTONIOACEDO

A COSMOPOLITAN FUSION WITH HISTORY

EME Fusion hotel is a representation of a cosmopolitan environment and a renovated concept of lodging industry, which makes the luxury accessible. Combining a sophisticated mix of international fashion influences and an intimate spirit of an ancient city, the design concept invites its guests to listen to the dialogue between the past and the future. Opened in March 2008, **Tarruella & Lopez + Trenchs** worked to create a hotel that fuses old with new in an eclectic and sophisticated culmination of design influences. With 54 rooms and an incredible gastronomic complex of four restaurants, a copas´ bar, the wellness cabinet, panoramic terraces, a swimming pool and multifunctional spaces for events, EME Hotel is located in the very heart of Seville.

A SWISS NIRVANA

The Nevai is a striking four-star Hotel situated at the heart of the Alps in Verbier, Switzerland. **Yasmine Mahmoudieh** was at the centre of the architectural and Interior design for the hotel, which opened in December 2007. The result of its intuitive design is a lifestyle design hotel with a fusion of cutting edge design and Alpine influences. The materials used were designed to reflect elements from the surrounding landscape and to introduce the latest developments in Interior design with a combination of traditional wood and high quality synthetics. The hotel has been designed to provide the ultimate in accommodation through both the ski and summer seasons. The terrace opens up onto panoramic views of the Swiss Alps from beautifully designed seating areas, which are heated throughout the winter.

DESIGNER: **YASMINE MAHMOUDIEH**
CLIENT: **THE NEVAI HOTEL**
LOCATION: **VERBIER, SWITZERLAND**

RIVERHOUSE-GREEN LIVING

One of **Thom Filicia's** most distinctive and acclaimed projects is Riverhouse, a luxury waterfront condominium that differentiates itself from the rest with its innovative design, high standard of living, and cutting-edge technology. It is one of New York City's preeminent LEED Gold certified condominium and demonstrates that green living and luxurious living need not be mutually exclusive. Filicia was able to utilize interesting "green" solutions, such as an industrial modern chandelier made of titanium jet-engine parts. TFI was responsible for incorporating the green way of life into the model apartment, using sustainable materials, such as reclaimed wood, low-VOC paint, recycled pieces and antiques. www.thomfilicia.com.

DESIGNER: **THOM FILICIA, THOM FILICIA INC**
CLIENT: **RIVERHOUSE**
LOCATION: **ONE RIVER TERRACE, NEW YORK**

ZEPRA MELTING POT

Irene Kronenberg, Alon Baranowitz Architecture.
Located in an upcoming business center in Tel Aviv, Zepra sits at the ground floor of a brand new office building running a full city block. There are two main axes' in the heart of the layout plan; the" Day axis" inspired by Asian markets where life simplest needs are served; commerce, food, socializing and daydreaming…This is where the seating is developed supported by a busy open kitchen and the "Night axis", located perpendicular to its former introduces two lounges at its very ends embracing a mega bar in between. The day and night axis cross over at the entrance floor allowing the clients to choose their way.

DESIGNER: **BARANOWITZ & KRONENBERG**
CLIENT: **THE ZEPRA GROUP, ZEPRA RESTAURANT**
LOCATION: **TEL AVIV**

CLOCK ROYAL TOWER

Richmond International was commissioned to design a luxury hotel and apartment interiors at the Makkah Clock Royal Tower at Makkah in Saudi Arabia. The Makkah Clock Royal Tower complex includes over 500 shopping outlets and food courts over five floors in the lower 'Podium' section, luxury apartments on levels 30 to 52, five 'Royal' floors, the 1005-room Fairmont Hotel over 28 floors and utilises the 76 elevators to ensure smooth departure for guests, particularly during calls to prayer. The hotel has extensive conference and banqueting facilities, eight food and beverage outlets and a number of dedicated prayer halls. The hotel is due to open early 2010.

DESIGNER: **RICHMOND INTERNATIONAL**
CLIENT: **FAIRMONT HOTELS AND RESORTS**
LOCATION: **MAKKAH, SAUDI ARABIA**

Trend Concepts

The Interior Design Yearbook has worked with some incredible talents in the design industry to bring you the very best trend forecasts. Whether it is a new roll of fabric or a set of sculptures placed with precision in the home, a small change can make a big difference to any interior space. Here, we take you through the fundamental trends of the New Year, with ideas on furniture design, concepts for clever lighting or a prevailing pattern in a luxurious fabric, our professionals discuss the ideas to carry through in 2010.

trends:

TREND: FABRIC, TEXTILES & WALLCOVERINGS
by Andrea Maflin

Andrea Maflin runs a successful interior designer practice as well as being an accomplished artist, broadcaster and author. Her friendly and innovative approach to interior design has led to many commissions worldwide. Andrea discusses influences in her own work and trends in fabric, textile and wallpaper designs for 2010.

www.andreamaflin.co.uk
design@andreamaflin.co.uk

With my own work I am influenced by trends but I'm also not a slave to them. I may use elements from all trends and use them, as my clients require, from tiny elements through to bold statements entirely worked to the individual needs of each client. In my own home I choose a backdrop of neutral tones, from dove greys blended with shades of clay, putty, biscuit and twine in the form of paint, textural and tactile surfaces with wallpapers, fabrics and carpets. Modern day classics sit along side understated tailored furniture with clean lines and unfussy shapes, which I find pleasing and comforting. The space constantly evolves and changes with my growing collection of accessories and eclectic pieces of furniture. I incorporate intense bejewelled splashes of colour, pattern and texture on all surfaces to suit the changing seasons or simply my mood. I like to incorporate sculptural textures and patterns where possible on to walls that create a stunning backdrop for artwork and sculpture, mimicking delicate woven silks, linen weaves, faux skins as well as the exotic crocodile, textural wood and leather.

TRENDS 2010

Trends naturally evolve and develop just by the very nature of the world around us, influenced by many different factors from fashion and popular culture through to economic change and even politics. Environmental concerns and economic downturn have all contributed towards the evolution of current trends. Never before have we been so concerned and aware of our consumer purchasing power. We now want to know where things come from and how they were made and what from and by who has made them, let alone what environmental and ethical factors these questions raise.

In the coming year we will see strong Global trends filtering through from Countries who have ever-developing markets. 'Russian high glamour' and 'exotic India' will emerge as strong trends from high-end interiors all the way through to the high street. 'Russian high glamour' is a highly theatrical trend with high gloss; contemporary furniture blended with high patent finishes that sit along side ornate traditional carved gilt

furniture and accessories. Black has been around for a while and continues as a key colour but is off set by deepest reds, damsons, emeralds and cobalt blues. Traditional inspired fabric designs in the form of damasks are used to decorate wall ties and sanitary wear in embossed gloss pattern adding an ornate and three-dimensional quality. Upholstery is unashamedly embellished with buttoning in deep pile velvets, silk satins. Fur and feather trims will adorn curtains with vast collections of ornate patterned cushions.

The other Global sensation, 'exotic India' is highly ornate and exotic styling, is exuberant in everyway you would expect, achieved by clashing colours and highly patterned fabrics used on cushions, curtains and upholstery, off set by dark wooden furniture. This trend is not about coordinating; it is about lively mixes of many different patterns being used together on upholstered seating, wallpaper fabrics and carpets. Areas of strong, plain colour that stop room schemes from booking chaotic balance the abundance of pattern.

'Russian high glamour' and 'exotic India' will emerge as strong trends

In the summer months we will see a revival of the quintessentially English eccentric at it's best, influences will be classic floral and chintz reworked into voluptuous over sized, botanical garden inspired prints that cover every surface of the home in the mouth watering pastel and candy shades. Bringing the outside indoors with feminine large-scale floral patterns. Statement wallpapers are also key. Wall coverings continue to delight and enhance our homes. This trend is cheerfully reassuring and playful enough not to take it's self too seriously.

trends:

TREND: COLOUR AND PATTERN
by Cecilia Neal

Cecilia Neal is a member of BIID (British Institute of Interior Design) and the IIDA. Cecilia established Meltons, her interior design practice, over twenty years ago. There is no one single "house style" at Meltons. Cecilia Neal brings a profound understanding of architecture and its components, the requirements of modern technology and, above all, the needs and desires of her clients to each project.

If we believe that trends come from political, economic and ecological backgrounds, we must suspect that some changes of direction in style will emerge from the difficult period and tough financial times through which we are living, and from which we hope we may gradually recover during the next decade.

Trends in interior design over the last ten years have emerged as an enormous and radical simplification of the chintz and frills era of the 1990's. During these years lax lending inflated a huge debt bubble as people borrowed cheap money to plough into property and clients were persuaded by euphoric Estate Agents to decorate their property's in a different way, reacting against what was seen as English in favour of what was deemed to be more international. By default, this became a universal style often described as "String and New White" or "Boring Beige". Initially this was interesting, young and different, although hardly modernist – open plan rooms, with much use of glass meant that family antiques went to the sale rooms or the skip, and contemporary commissioned furniture and art work became requisites. Pattern and colour were out, in favour of neutral plains. Relatively new kitchens were ripped out only to be replaced by a later model, and restraint went to the wind.

Now as another cycle has run full term, a reaction against this can be discerned in the best design magazines. Clients generally with reduced budgets, seem to set a premium on individualising schemes

Colour is becoming more and more important. Neutrals and natural mediums are adorning walls with options such as polished plaster being used.

for their homes using the best in classic design. Extravagance is out, but making the most of a beautiful but expensive fabric, sparingly but effectively used, is in. Changes to the architecture of a building are less aspirational, more gentle, and tuned to personal ideas with quirky decorative extras and a lack of pretentiousness. Colour becomes more and more important –possibly a neutral entrance hall in a natural medium such as polished plaster, with jewel colours for the rooms leading off it. Hand blocked wallpapers, such as those from George Spencer or Coles in special colours are popular requests. Carefully designed bespoke joinery, of very high quality, to suit the needs and personality of the client and unique to him or her, is rightly believed to be a justified expense.

There is much interest in the historic styles of the 1930s - another time of austerity but also the fertile ground in which Sibyl Colefax and Syrie Maugham built their iconic practices that are the bedrock of the modern Interior Design profession.

To look at trends in soft furnishings – colour and grand scale is back. The current Decortex collection looks back to the 30s with strong pattern, some in primary colours, in a scale which is large and unfussy. Neisha Crosland's gorgeous cut velvets are baroque classic, but of the moment, creating an immediate impact. Designers Guild have a wonderful collection adapted from the archive at Windsor Castle,18C damasks and chenilles, overscaled and re-invented in rich strong colours.

These are reasonably priced, as are the modern classics with a French twist from Pierre Frey. Collections at Tissus d'Helene are modern, mouthwateringly smart and seem to fit the current mood.

Furniture of the 30's and 40's continues to command premium prices. Pieces by Jean Michel Franc or Betty Joel are hard to find in the sale rooms but much sought after as a period focus in an otherwise simple room. The furniture trade has had a hard time recently but the very enjoyable Decorative Antiques Fair in Battersea Park enjoys steady trade and is a wonderful source for the quirky one-off piece that can make a room unique.

Clients seem anxious not to be extravagant but to do what is right in terms of the environment. There is a sense of urgency about individual responsibility to be eco-friendly, and to adopt some of the growing number of systems for saving energy, such as geothermal heating and re-cycled water. Organic fabrics are also increasing in popularity, such as the Pangea collection by Old World Weavers. In practical terms Interior Designers are usually the first to interpret this trend and to include relevant systems into early plans and drawings.

trends:

TREND: LIGHTING DESIGN
by Sally Storey

Sally Storey has written three books and this year her third, 'Perfect Lighting' was released, which was designed to help people understand the importance of light and to show how to combine effects for the perfect mood.

Sally Story. Photo: James Winspear

*This year **Sally Storey** designed the new John Cullen Lighting showroom on the Kings Road as a showcase to help the interior designer visualise the difference between new technologies. With different illustrations in effects such as shelf lighting to compare LED technology with fluorescent and incandescent, it really enables the individual or designer to know what they are getting! Also in the showroom is a unique lighting pod that can literally illustrate the different ways to light an object, with different light sources showing how to front light, cross light and back light to really help anyone understand the true meaning of light!*

I do not think there has been such a revolution in the lighting industry as we are seeing now compared with that of the early 1980s when the halogen lamp was introduced and we had miniaturisation of the traditional light source, giving a whiter light and greater control of the beam of light.

Now the 'buzz' word is LED's - the great development resulting in us all now actively wanting to reduce our energy consumption. This year brought in 'Ban the Bulb!' with everyone worried about what they would re-lamp their table lamps with. Together with the Part L

This page: a stunning example of decadent lighting

regulations requiring a certain percentage of luminaires within interiors to be energy efficient, this has forced lamp manufacturers to develop new sources. There has been a flood of compact fluorescent sources hitting the market but also soon there will be halogen based more efficient replacements to the standard GLS that will provide the soft warm light when dimmed.

So, do not think that we will be entirely reliant on compact fluorescent 'CFL' sources. Although these have to be improved they are already working on the colour temperature and dimmability so soon they will be able to be

dimmed on a standard rotary dimmer. If used, I feel they are best concealed by a shade.

It is, however, the development of LED's that really interest me and since last year I am even more confident on their colour. I still however would not use them for general downlighting in a living room or a restaurant for example, as when dimmed they still do not take on that wonderful candle like, yellow quality of halogen. But they are successful for discrete lighting effects and accent lighting whether used as a recessed uplight, steplight or shelf light. LED's can seriously add to ones part L calculation (as long as the right quality type are

This page: recessed lighting can create stunning focal points just for show

used, as not all LED's are compliant) and are able to achieve a huge wattage reduction with maximum effect. I recently lit my own roof terrace with only seven Watts of light! If I turned off the blue uplight it would be four Watts! Other trends are to be more minimalistic and to be less extravagant with light sources so that more impact can be created with simpler effects. I feel this reflects the current general world economy of less extravagance and really trying to design simpler, more beautiful installations that can endure the test of time.

Last year's tips of simple control and using PIRs in bathrooms and corridors to bring on low level lighting is still useful and, if used successfully with a dimmer system, can be subtle and look impressive whilst still being energy efficient as lights are not wastefully left on.

This year is one to review, analyse and simplify. Use good materials and products as they will last longer. Designs should be more timeless as I believe fit out terms for retailers, hoteliers and even houses cannot keep changing at the rate we have seen. Designers need to design for the future not for the present and ensure by this time next year a scheme, whether lighting or interior, looks as good then as it does now!

trends:

TREND: RESIDENTIAL INTERIORS
by Taylor Howes Design

Taylor Howes are winners of the prestigious Andrew Martin International Interior Designer of the Year Award. Headed by Gail Taylor and Karen Howes, who together create stunning interiors for a host of private clients

Taylor Howes Designs provides a comprehensive design service for private clients, property developers and hoteliers. Founded in 1991, the practice has grown into one of the most respected businesses in its field; carving a unique niche in the market with the continual production of some of the most stunning interiors of the moment.

The World of Interior design continues to be driven forward by exciting trends from the fabulous furniture shows from around the world and the fashion industry. Needless to say private clients appreciate our design team being constantly on top of these trends and they feature heavily when we are at the planning stages.

Milan saw the top interior brands injecting a rainbow of colours into their designs including hot pinks, citrus green and a very bold orange. These colours have also been combined in certain pieces, mainly fabrics, to produce a dramatic effect. The impact on our industry has allowed us to experiment with combinations of these colours and different patterns, however always used in subtle settings to ensure that the look has durability. Materials and textures have seen a return to a more natural and raw state with the re-emergence of classic marble, un-polished woods and rough stone. This has been welcomed in the world of interior design as the look is so flexible and natural materials are so wonderful to work with.

The 'honeycomb' pattern was everywhere at all the furniture shows featured on fabrics and in furniture. At Taylor Howes we source a lot of product from the furniture shows especially Maison et Objet where we always find

*Taylor Howes
dress
interiors to
rent, sell and
live.*

wonderful unique, individual and wonderfully stylish pieces. We aim to have an open mind when travelling around the world otherwise you find your style becoming too narrow and predictable. This does not mean however that we neglect our UK craftsman. Across the UK we are so fortunate that we have some wonderful suppliers and craftsmen and year on year we rely on them to produce one off works of art for our interior design projects.

At Taylor Howes we are known for working with leading property developers, predicting and setting trends often two to three years ahead of the market. This is always a challenge we relish and the knowledge we bring to the table is that we have an inherent understanding of what the prospective purchaser is looking for be it a one bedroom flat or a top end penthouse. Developers, naturally always want the next, best look and within our multi-disciplined practice we are always forward thinking and are able to rise to the challenge.

TAYLOR HOWES DESIGNS
Gail and Karen are equal partners and best friends; both with natural talent and differing, distinctive styles that combine perfectly to give their spectacular trademark · finish to every

project. The ethos of the company stems from their easy-going approach, never forcing a client to take on any design feature that they do not feel comfortable with.

In addition, the attention to every final detail has brought them their loyal customer base "our commitment to providing a first rate service and only using the best materials and craftsmen has helped to build our reputation. "We, and every one of our design team, are meticulous about detail and will go to great lengths to find that little something that just finishes the job perfectly" says Gail.

The number of projects taken on at any one time is limited to ensure that every client receives this same level of attention. Gail and Karen oversee every project working

Attention to detail, such as the placing of decorative pieces and a strong combination of textures can really make a room

hand in hand with their team of designers, including Design Director Sheila El-Hadery, who has been with Taylor Howes Design since the early days and has helped to shape the company's stylish image.

Recent commissions include the complete refurbishment of a West City six-storey show home at Phillimore Square, Kensington; two apartments at 'The Knightsbridge', described as 'The World's most desirable new address'; a redesign of a cutting-edge hotel in Ireland as well as delivering inspiring results for many private residences in the UK.

Top tips from Taylor Howes

Taylor Howes designs recently revealed their latest interior design project for one of London's finest riverside penthouses at Imperial Wharf. The penthouse embodies everything that Taylor Howes as a company strives to maintain, with the highest of quality and most useable of design. The design of each room sparked some interesting trend ideas for a residential interior.

Impact - Look to focus on one impact piece in each room whether it be art, a collection of stunning vases or a display of beautiful cushions

Colour - Bold combinations of colour can create drama so long as everything else is kept simple Red and Black for example can be stunning so be brave and experiment

Detail - Use detailing where possible on simple affordable pieces upholster a plain chair with great fabric and ribbon detailing for an affordable solution

Hotel Chic - For the master bedroom think hotel chic no clutter! Beautiful hand lotions and creams always appeal and display only your favourite clothes and shoes

Mirror – Mirrors are incredibly important in any property and must be carefully considered. The age old trick of mirrors creating space will never tire. In our opinion mirrors are as important as art.

Pairs - Think about investing in pairs two identical vases, two unusual

chairs when placed in a simple setting can create real drama

Lighting - Never underestimate the importance of lighting if you have good natural lighting then great but if not you need to create atmosphere through lighting. Investing in one stunning chandelier can be just as good as investing in a piece of art

Storage – Finally when planning a space ensure that storage is something that is considered at the outset. Miscalculating the amount of storage that is needed is quite easy to do so always provide a bit more than you need. A carpenter can provide great storage solutions at affordable prices.

trends:

TREND: LUXURY INTERIORS AND FURNISHINGS
by Giorgio Armani, Armani Casa

First launched in 2000 in Milan, Armani/Casa represents Giorgio Armani's vision of the perfect home environment

Armani/Casa features a permanent collection of furniture, accessories, lighting and fabrics as well as kitchen and bathroom systems. This is expanded on a seasonal basis with more updated lines of accessories and fabrics. The Armani/Casa Limited Edition collection presents clients with the opportunity to invest in the antiques of tomorrow; pieces personally signed by **Giorgio Armani** *include chaise longues and bar cabinets.*

2009 sees the launch of two exciting collaborations. At the Salone del Mobile in April 2009, Armani/Casa unveiled its first collection of exclusive home fabrics with Rubelli, the leading Venetian textiles house. Armani/Casa has also collaborated with the Molteni Group to design kitchen systems under the new brand name, Armani/Dada. Armani/ Casa maintains an International presence based on 80 outlets in 45 countries. Giorgio Armani discusses his inspiration behind Armani/Casa and the growth of personalisation within the luxury design market.

A*rmani/Casa perfectly embodies my aesthetic and ideal of interior design: it is pure, essential and rigorous, yet also warm and welcoming. Almost 10 years since its creation, Armani/Casa now has a very defined look with iconic products that are immediately*

"People like personal service and everyone dreams of the opportunity to have things created in a bespoke way for them. I therefore believe that the big thing in luxury interior design for 2010 will be the growth in customisation."

recognized as my own designs. My collections combine beauty with function and value elegance and sophistication over transient trends. "It is always my aim to deliver a collection with these qualities, but it seems more important to do so now than ever before. In the context of the current economic crisis – and as a response in general to the mass-production, standardization and homogenisation of design styles we have seen over recent years – I feel that we need to elevate the quality of products and make them special and unique. We should treat them as if they were jewels, or artworks.

"Because of this, I believe we will see a re-emergence of traditional craftsmanship, sophisticated research and creative originality in 2009. This philosophy can be expressed through skilfully chosen details, fabrics and materials. I constantly search for new

inspirations and innovative combinations, working on each piece of furniture to see what sensory and emotional response it can evoke.

"My 2009/2010 collection represents this quest for uniqueness, preciousness and exclusivity. Instinctively I am attracted to natural materials, treated with sophisticated techniques to make them more functional. I have introduced precious woods, leathers and sumptuous fabrics in a palette of warming earth colours, which are complemented with cutting-edge varnishing techniques, such as liquid metal or black nickel. Product highlights include an exceptional lizard skin and rosewood writing desk and a 24-carat dipped gold finished table.

"This essence of quality should also be reflected in the way that we address our customers as individuals rather than as an anonymous,

Right: Calyx kitchen for Armani/Dada.

abstract clientele. People like personal service and everyone dreams of the opportunity to have things created in a bespoke way for them. I therefore believe that the big thing in luxury interior design for 2009 will be the growth in customisation."

Armani/Casa offers a bespoke Interior Design Service to provide consultancy on interiors projects, from room decoration to total home planning and design. Launched six years ago, the service is primarily aimed at private clients, but is equally relevant for interior designers and property developers looking to integrate the

lifestyle philosophy of the Armani/Casa brand into a project. The Armani/Casa Interior Design Studios are currently working on a variety of exciting global projects spanning across New York, Hong Kong, St Petersburg, Moscow and Hawaii.

Armani/Casa: 0207 079 1930
www.armanicasa.com
113 New Bond Street, London W1S 1DP

No comparison
No compromise

Make no mistake!

Today we have access to music quite literally everywhere its influence seems to be all pervading. Music excites us, it relaxes us, we can enjoy it live, we buy recording and 'downloads' by the million. Music underpins every conceivable aspect of our lives. Music is our second language and **'without it life would be a mistake'** Yes philosophical we know - but true.

At KJ West One we are all exposed and privileged to indulge our senses in the absolute finest audio equipment available today. From time to time we are introduced to certain new products whose performance pushes back the boundaries to provide new higher levels of sound reproduction, which exceeds all our expectations. Recently we have seen the release of several new and exciting products, these range from comparatively modest to outrageously expensive. At KJ West One we have taken the time to audition & create our 2008 **'Absolute Sound Collection'** Please visit our website **www.kjwestone.com** for a 'preview'.

Once again we invite you to share the experience with us, so call in soon or better still make an appointment for a personal demonstration at your convenience.

Make no mistake - Visit KJ West One

trends:

TREND: LIFESTYLE INTERIORS
by **Tara Bernerd**, CEO and Head of Design at Target Living

*Target Living was founded in 2002 by British Target Living was founded in 2002 by British Designer, **Tara Bernerd** and Architect, **Thomas Griem**. The duo met whilst working with Philippe Starck on both interior architecture and design for international projects.Tara Bernerd is a Board Director of **Chelsfield Partners LLP**. She has recently been appointed as the Design Editor of British **GQ** in acknowledgement of design achievements. Tara is also a member of the **Dulux Creative Board** 2009. Andrew Martin International Interior Designer of the Year Award winner, Tara Bernerd is a woman at the very top of her game. Focusing on space planning, interior design and styling, Tara's portfolio of work spans unique private residences to large property and leisure developments as well as designing a bespoke range of cushions and rugs for **The Rug Company**. Tara is, by her own admission, a 'forceful character', with strong ideas of what works and what doesn't. She is known for her bold designs, strong use of colour and texture and seamlessly fusing contemporary with traditional. Tara's expertise, enthusiasm and talent have resulted in her seat on the design board of mydeco.com. Other highlights this year have found Tara included on the Dulux Creative Board, as well as being on the committee for **ACT**. Tara talks trends and tapping into spiritual style.*

Tara Bernerd image by Alex Lake

The use of black, mixed with technology give this bathroom the edge.

2009, this year is all about attitude. It is all about feeling empowered, confidence and making a statement. Don't underestimate the number nine. The Chinese, who I have the utmost respect for, see nine given that is the highest single digit number as "the highest", as well as the most. Spiritually nine includes being visionary, imaginative and creative.

Colour is certainly always a challenge to use successfully, whether in abundance or discretely and one step beyond for many is, in my opinion, the daunting process of making it black. However there is a certain punch, depth and seductiveness that a black room can achieve and it is this fundamental message of confidence that it delivers that I feel makes it a mood worth exploring this year.

From my experience, I have used black or dark materials successfully in bathrooms, kitchens, private club rooms, board rooms and indeed offices. In my opinion it is

"2009, this year is all about attitude. It is all about feeling empowered..."

about pushing our comfort zones, not working to a set of rules and keeping an open mind.

When working with a monochrome colour and for those readers recoiling at the

Target Living is now reputed as one of the UK's leading design consultancies, generating the most current design. The company's strengths are combining architectural skills with interior design. This allows for a more substantial role and involvement with projects. Target Living is revered for its understanding of budgets without compromising creating aspirational design.

Target Living brings carefully designed interiors to the market. The practice divides between architects and designers and the teams role includes running projects, to producing detailed concepts; working in collaborations with project architects on international jobs.

"Always be conscious of lightening it up, either through great lighting, knockout art, or perhaps the introduction of white leather furniture."

thought of black, this monogamous commitment to one colour translates into any colour i.e. you could go all grey, all burgundy, certainly all white and for those braver than I, all yellow.

Fundamental to this is exploring the range of materials in the room. A colour will change depending on its texture; for example, a black lacquer will look different to a black velvet, or indeed a black wood. Thus the subtle mix of materials and texture is key to this palette.

I would also warn not to get too heavy, especially in a black room. So always be conscious of lightening it up, either through great lighting, knockout art, or perhaps the introduction of white leather furniture, such as the B&B Italia chairs in the image shown of a private club (see above), where I have also sneaked in a little dark green and brown.

Going forward for a look for the year ahead, I feel that it is about moody atmosphere, moody colours and, as said, if black is not for you or indeed you have the rest of the house to

do, it's about earthy tones that black certainly sits in with its volcanic temperament. From Molteni and Co's latest When side tables in their smoky browns and sagey greens, or great

"If black is not for you or indeed you have the rest of the house to do, it's about earthy tones that black certainly sits in with its volcanic temperament."

art by artists like Guido Mocafico, it's all about making a presence.

I am exploring more with colours like sage greens, metallic greys and a little bit of black, but it's all about not overdoing it.
www.targetliving.com

trends:

TREND: FURNITURE DESIGN
by Anna Dodonova

Anna Dodonova's interest in art and design started when studying art at school as a young girl and she continues to paint and draw in her own time. Anna started her career as a graphic designer after training at college in Germany but she soon realised that her interest in design was mainly focused in the interior design industry and she retrained as an interior designer in the UK. Anna then worked as an interior designer for several years on projects in Germany and the UK. Anna wanted to start her own business and decided to open Anna Casa Interiors in 2007 when she realised that there was a lack of central London showrooms offering a variety of contemporary furniture. Anna Dodonova discusses furniture design for 2009.

Starting with colour, natural colours in muted tones were a big trend at the furniture fair in Milan this April and we will be seeing this coming strongly through in coming furniture collections and in the UK's interior shops.

I see this trend manifesting itself in the use of natural coloured fabrics and decoration elements like wallpaper, lighting, furniture and accessories. It is almost impossible to go wrong with natural colours and I like to use different shades by mixing them. Working with clients and decorating their homes, I can see this trend working very well in most types of interiors. Natural

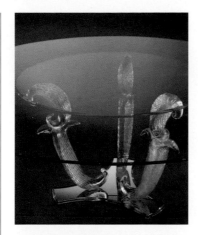

wood and raw materials will be used more and more. Untreated wood was very big at Milan, being used in a wide variety of ways, from wardrobe door to chairs and bedsteads.

Secondly, colours such as a lot of bright colours like yellow, pink, green and purple mixed with white are something we will see more of. You have to be careful when using these colours though as you can get tired of the effect very fast. I always suggest that bright colours are best in bigger spaces, and always to use a white or neutral scheme and then add bright accessories, objects and furniture to add some spice without going overboard. A feature wall in a block colour is a perfect way to add tone and is perfect for hanging art and mirrors as it creates a frame.

"Interesting angular shapes and sharp lines are also seeing their way back into vogue."

High glossy is also very popular; when furniture is lacquered in bright interesting colours it instantly transforms them to ultra-modern pieces with a hint of retro. This is especially true in commercial interiors, at the moment hotels and designers in charge of public spaces want super slick, polished furniture, the more modern the better. I have chosen some fabulous pieces from an Italian company called Creazioni which creates traditional French furniture with a modern twist, adding bright coloured glosses or metallic finishes. The contrast between traditional and modern works incredibly well in any interiors and creates statement pieces, which will last. In the residential market, the difficult economic climate means that long lasting and iconic pieces are essential, people do not want to spend on pieces, which they will get bored with after a short period of time. When choosing any piece for my showroom I always think about the longevity of a piece, and if I have any doubt then I will not choose it. I pride myself in being able to choose and put together pieces, which people can keep forever.

Interesting angular shapes and sharp lines are also seeing their way back into vogue. As raw materials are moving in, so are their sharp lines, furniture is taking on a harsher design which creates striking pieces which stand out. I have designed a table for Reflex called the G collection, which will be followed by a whole collection and it is very angular. I have used straight lines and glass to emphasise the strict design, I think that when glass is used in such a neat and undiluted way it creates a very striking effect. I think that my G Table would be a great contrast as an occasional table next to a soft upholstered table. When working on interior spaces I like playing with contrast, soft fabrics together with hard lines, cold metal and glass teamed with warm woods.

"Untreated wood was very big at Milan, being used in a wide variety of ways, from wardrobe door to chairs and bedsteads."

Artisan skills are a key trend for contemporary interiors in 2009 with craftsmanship differentiating individual pieces of furniture and adding personality. Our clients want authenticity in the furniture we provide and an element of artisan skill really adds character to each piece. I look for the story in all the pieces I choose for Anna Casa Interiors. Even very contemporary furniture can have elements of real craftsmanship and the blend is truly interesting. The Casanova table designed by Reflex/Angelo makes the most of the skills of the Murano glass-masters, an art, which is slowly disappearing, with its intricately designed table base made from hand-blown glass. Each table is made to specification and is signed by the glass-master. No two are the same and the declining number of Murano glass-masters adds a rarity to these stunning tables, this is something I find incredibly fascinating and each piece they make I find awe-inspiring like seeing a masterpieces by a famous painter.

Anna Casa Interiors is the culmination of the intuitive and creative vision of owner and Director Anna Dodonova. Anna is passionate about art and design and wanted to bring a new and contemporary element to the Design Centre and created a distinctive and stylish showroom with Anna Casa Interiors. "I am passionate about contemporary furniture and design and saw that this was missing at Chelsea Harbour. I felt I could bring something really different and unusual to the existing mix with my own showroom of top end international contemporary brands" comments Anna Dodonova. Anna Casa Interiors offers a wide range of furniture from the internationally renowned brands Reflex / Angelo, Creazioni, Gurian and Mimo.

The showroom at the Design Centre is currently the only Anna Casa Interiors showroom; however Anna plans to open other showrooms across Europe over the next few years. Anna Casa Interiors prides itself on a quality product with a professional service to back it up and will work with both interior designers and customers direct, offering outstanding quality and expert advice with a comprehensive aftercare.

trends:

TREND: FURNITURE TRENDS
by Lady Weinberg, Anouska Hempel Design

Anouska Hempel Design – AHD, is the London-based international studio created by the illustrious designer, with an unrivalled international reputation for architecture, interiors, landscapes, products and graphics. Anouska Hempel Design has been responsible for the entire creation of three significant and influential hotels, which have been acclaimed as masterpieces - Blakes Hotel in London and in Amsterdam and The Hempel in London, alongside residential work in numerous countries. Fundamental to the success of the business is the design approach based on the uniqueness of each project and the importance given to identifying a concept to be carried through from space planning to lighting and furnishing to the smallest detail. The studio is currently engaged in numerous innovative ventures globally, including projects in Dubai – Havana and Cuba in 'The World' development, Mauritius and on the north coast of Brazil where Anouska Hempel's fourth hotel, Warapuru, a highly anticipated state-of-the-art hotel and villa complex in Bahia, due for completion in 2010 is being designed and constructed.

Lady Weinberg, Formerly Anouska Hempel discusses furniture trends and the influence of our surrounding architecture.

CURRENT PROJECTS:
Anouska Hempel
Design's team is
currently working on
extensive projects,
ranging from a spa in
Santa Domingo to the
Infamous 'Cliveden
House Hotel' and 'The
Grosvenor House
Apartments' on Park
Lane. Grosvenor House
Apartments are being
given a very individual,
distinguished look that
draws inspiration from
English Traditionalism
whilst embracing the
moderninity of today
and the cosmopolitan
culture of London.
Quality, attention to
detail and atmosphere is
the cohesive factor of
these styles. Walking
into the building is an
Alice in the looking glass
experience. Each step
takes the guest deeper
into an ever expanding
space, starting with the
horizontal simplicity of
the lobby, whose
monolithic purity alludes
to the bigger reception
hall above, while all the
time, slotted walls reveal
and conceal the outside
world – a veil to privacy
and curiosity. The
courtyard is the core of
the narrative adventure.
The atrium is tall and
vast, soaring upwards
and creating a sense of
infinite space. The chalky
stone walls are softened
by a gossamer mesh that
drapes like a mist on a
midsummer's morning,
offering just a glimpse of
here and there of people
moving behind the
rooms above. From time
to time, this
extraordinary vaulting
space will be clothed
with a virtual library of
antique books, volumes
in which the essence of
Britishness was created -
Shakespeare, Milton,
Donne, Tennyson and of
course, William Blake,
who first imagined what
it would be to build
paradise here in
England's green and
pleasant land.

Furniture design is becoming more influenced by the architecture that surrounds it, moving away from trends in which furniture has frequently contrasted to or dominated its surroundings.

These trends have been driven by the same style magazines being read throughout the world and manufacturers and retailers distributing the same furniture across the globe. Although these conditions remain unchanged we anticipate more emphasis on combining this furniture with more bespoke pieces to create a more integrated interior.

We are anticipating this development going a step further with furniture design becoming more architectural. Materials, colours and finishes are being selected to integrate with the surroundings. Legs are out - rather than a sea of table and chair legs dominating an interior, the legs will be disguised or seating more integrated. After all, aren't the legs of the pretty lady seated on the chair more interesting than

the inanimate chair itself?

There's a growing realisation that interiors should be a backdrop to human activity rather than an end in itself with a primary purpose of looking good in a photo shoot for a magazine.

In our project for the Grosvenor House Apartments in London we have created a muted palette of greys with subtle variations in textures and finishes. Honed and ribbed stone, soft lacqueredl leather and soft sensuous flannel fabrics which result in a coordinated interior. The fabrics appear on walls as well as the furniture; the same timbers are used in the architectural joinery, screens and furniture; and the stone on the floors and walls is used for creating bathroom sanitary ware, table tops and accessories. The palette is consistent throughout the public spaces of the lobbies to the apartment interiors although the manner in which they are used develops and changes.

The focus of the project is a central

courtyard which is treated as an oversized living room – a little Alice in Wonderland like with a huge fireplace in scale with the courtyard over which a massive pendant lamp we have designed provides a focus for the seated guests below and the rooms above that look into the courtyard.

Conceptually this sounds rather contradictory to what I've said above about interiors not dominating human activity, which is why it's an interesting example. For despite the scale of the key interior elements they are treated in a harmonious manner in which there is an ambiguity between what is architecture and what is furniture. The fireplace is a simple wall of honed grey stone and perimeter seating around the courtyard are benches in the same material that morph between being sofas, planters and staircases and ramps. Chairs in the middle of the courtyard are upholstered in greys to complement the stone with skirts to the chairs to disguise their legs, linking them to the architecture rather than sitting within it. Free-standing glass screens punctuate the space and reflect the material qualities of the pendant overhead and architectural wall elements to the courtyard bar and the reception area.

And if the sun is shining you can always cross Park Lane to sit in Hyde Park, a tree as a backrest, a canopy of leaves overhead and a carpet of grass beneath you. Nature's got the right idea.

"Legs are out- rather than a sea of table and chair legs dominating an interior, the legs will be disguised or seating more integrated."

BLAKES HOTEL, LONDON

Anouska Hempel first established her reputation as the designer and owner of Blakes Hotel, originating the concept of the 'Boutique Hotel'. Its distinctive style and service has built up an international reputation, which attracted and continues to attract leading figures from the world.

Blakes, London, a seductive design exploration through India, Thailand, China, Jakarta, Cambodia and then to the Pyramids and back through Italy. An elegant, eclectic, ethnic story, whispered in the abundant luxury of accessories, furniture and artefacts found personally all over the world by this renowned designer during the many years of her travels. Aesthetically chosen and positioned in her Boutique Hotel, the first of its kind in London and the World, Blakes evokes past and current intrigues and dark mysteries. The 'Opium Den' named after Coco Chanel and the shadow of Marlene Dietrich, pervades the Chinese Room, in certain lights she can still be glimpsed leaning on the piano.

Napkins dressed with ginger and black grosgrain ribbons facing each other like soldiers are to be found in The Chinese Room, with a myriad of slipper orchids running along the centre…candles, books in profusion, Chinese Ancestors smiling knowingly down from the walls, black lacquer trays with colourful canapés, then Black Beluga Caviar served in glass boxes with a beautiful 'B' etched on the top, all gives the background for gentle and elegant service that glides unobtrusively from room to room to give the most discreet attention one could ever wish for. Yet it is busy, bustling, bohemian and beautiful.

Blakes' rooms are dramatic interpretations of deep, rich tones that are often paired for subtle contrasts. The compositions are startling, luxurious and operatic. Some of the most astonishing interior spaces anywhere in the World. What might easily have slipped 'over the top' is somehow neither too saccharine nor too precious. Rather, these interiors are fascinating exercises in design imagination, choreographed by a masterly eye. Right down to the smallest scale of carefully placed accessories or cushions, the relationship between objects and between forms and fields, is studied and carefully resolved.

With Concierge service day and night, Room Service day and night, nonsense and happiness day and night, Blakes is a romantic whirlwind the minute you step in the door, full of fantasy and full of fun. You just have to have a great time!

Everywhere one discovers the mystery and magic that has been created. If the term 'Design Hotel' means attention to the entire aesthetic experience, Blakes veritably deserves that title.

THE HEMPEL, LONDON

Anouska Hempel did it first – and nobody does it better: The Hempel is a pioneering masterpiece. Behind a row of white Georgian houses blooms London's first minimalist hotel, a Zen sanctuary inspired by ancient aesthetics, to cater to the modern traveller.

Her architectural creation awakens, and then soothes, the senses. A monumental atrium seems as light as a piece of Japanese origami; every detail, like walls that appear to float, makes this a hotel of surprise, wit, and magic: sophisticated and a truly satisfying place to stay.

trends:

TREND: BEDROOM DESIGN
By David Spence, Chairman SHH

*SHH is an Architectural practice and design consultancy run by its three Directors and Co-Founders; **David Spence**, **Graham Harris** and **Neil Hogan**. The company, based in its own West London studio, employs a highly talented and cosmopolitan team of architects, interior designers, graphic designers, technical and administrative staff. SHH offers a full architectural, interiors and branding service – from planning, architecture and interior architecture right through to styling, decoration, environmental and 2D graphics. They specialise in creating cutting-edge, design-led solutions that are elegant and long-lasting and which perform both financially and aesthetically for their owners and end-users. Building on a reputation for creating high-end luxury housing, the SHH portfolio now covers shops, bars, restaurants and hotels, offering a branding service as well as professional interior design skills. Here, David Spence discusses trends in the bedroom.*

Where open-plan living spaces were once the main focus in the design or redesign of a house – and home to the most exciting and radical elements of that design - we find increasingly that our clients are turning their attention to the master suite, with ever–more ambitious demands for showstopping combinations of bedrooms, bathrooms and walk-in wardrobes, in order to provide a place of sanctuary from life's daily stresses and strains. Influenced by the hotel

sector and our clients' jet-setting lifestyles, master suites are subsequently becoming one of the most exciting and interesting spaces to design in a residential project.

Even in the refurbishment of a more classical townhouse, for example, whole storeys are now being given over to master suites, which are sometimes completely open-plan. Alternatively, his'n'hers bathrooms are located to either side of a master bedroom, with adjoining his'n'hers walk-in wardrobes. Everything is controlled from the bed, with three-way lighting switches

> **"In the refurbishment of a more classical townhouse, for example, whole storeys are now being given over to master suites, which are sometimes completely open-plan."**

by the door and at each bedside. TV screens and surround-sound music systems are also controlled from the bed, with one client even asking for a woofer beneath the bed and a full colour under-bed lighting system, for that intimate disco feel! For our very richest clients, bedroom electronics can even extend to panic buttons, to lock down the whole house in case

of unlawful entry! For those with live-in staff, a discreet dumb waiter station is not unheard of…

Carpets, whilst still insisted upon for those who like the softness of shagpile beneath their feet, are generally waning in popularity because of their tendency to retain dust and irritate those with breathing difficulties. Underfloor heating has taken the chill out of wooden or other

types of flooring and the desire for soft furnishings or pattern is being increasingly replaced by rugs instead. Plain white painted walls are still the most requested wall surface, but a single feature wall, either papered or in the form of huge-scale fabric bedheads, is increasingly popular to animate a room.

Although the era of Feng Shui seems mostly to have had its day, bedroom layouts are also susceptible to individual clients' beliefs. Some Jewish clients, for example, don't like beds to face the door directly, whilst others don't like to face east, although facing the early-morning sun would be our usual layout preference, as it certainly lifts the spirits too!

Ensuite bathrooms are often open-plan now, with toilets set to one side with their own fan systems. Sometimes baths – especially of the roll-top or standalone variety – are making it into the bedroom itself so that bathing can become a sociable activity for a couple. On another SHH project, a client asked for a bathroom with both a chaise longue and a chandelier over the bath to enhance a sense of luxury and shared relaxation.

Sometimes bedrooms are microcosmic expressions of different individuals within a family unit. For our Kensington House project, where the main spaces are huge, grand and imposing, with layers of textured whites and creams, a series of bedrooms for the clients' teenaged children was an opportunity to experiment with completely different design styles and colourways, suitable to the character and interests of each. These ranged from ultra-girly pinks with perspex console tables and study areas, to a boy's room with severe lines and a Far Eastern aesthetic.

One thing is for sure – we haven't seen the end yet of exciting trends and permutations in bedroom design. They are fast-becoming a home within a home for those who actually live in the house, with open-plan kitchen, dining and reception rooms increasingly used solely for entertaining and in order to present an outward-facing aspect to the world.

Above:
Incorporate personal desk spaces for a more individual room

Right page:
Lighting under the bed is unconventional and yet can completely change the mood

"Sometimes bedrooms are microcosmic expressions of different individuals within a family unit."

trends:

TREND: KITCHEN AND BATHROOM DESIGN
By Katharine Pooley

Katharine Pooley is a renowned Interior Designer and businesswoman. Before settling in London, Katharine spent many years abroad in such places as Hong Kong and Singapore before moving to the UK and setting up Katharine Pooley Ltd Interior Design Company and boutique. Katharine honed her interior design skills on her own homes, completing three impressive projects in the space of one year: a luxury beach villa in Phuket, Thailand, a 16th century castle in Scotland and a vast ski-lodge in Colorado. Now five years on the company boasts a highly discerning client list and an impressive portfolio of projects. Katharine has developed a unique style influenced by the experience of spending many years abroad. Each project she undertakes shows an appreciation of comfort, fine finishes and rare and exquisite objects whether contemporary or classical. Katharine points out her aim is to make each project a home above all, and loves to combine modern pieces with antiques and personal treasures sourced from her travels. Here, Katharine lends her expertise to the subject of kitchen and bathroom design.

For the modern lifestyle, kitchens and bathrooms are the two of the most important rooms in the home; the kitchen is not only used for cooking and eating, but is often a hub for social activities. Likewise, the bathroom is for many not only a place to get washed and changed but a sanctuary/space in which one can get away from the rest of the world, relax and enjoy 'down time'. Consequently, the décor, planning and ergonomics of these rooms are vital for them to be successful environments and as our requirements develop, likewise do trends and fashions.

THE KITCHEN

A kitchen design should be planned to suit the individual and their lifestyle. The layout should not only be safe but also make life in the kitchen easy and practical. The ergonomics of the kitchen have become much more important as kitchens become more sophisticated. The height of cupboards and distance between cupboards are basic but important considerations and part of the essential planning process. Often the kitchen is one of the single most expensive purchases in the home and it is crucial that it functions as well as looking good.

The minimal look is popular in urban environments and as such there are many handle-less designs available. Push-touch release catch doors or hidden handles in concealed grooves are modern options that help to keep clean lines.

"Gloss kitchens are slick with the convenience of being easy to keep clean."

Gloss kitchens are slick with the convenience of being easy to keep clean, Parapan is a relatively new material which is perfect for the kitchen environment. This is a man-made material, which is available in a wide range of colours. Parapan is highly reflective which has the effect of making smaller kitchens seem a lot larger than they really are. The black gloss option offers an ultra sophisticated choice. These materials give more choices than ever before and the capacity to choose versatile materials that are functional as well as also looking good.

"Travertine, marble and stone are enduringly popular for natural, organic materials are fitting in the bathroom environment. A contemporary bathroom design might not only have the travertine on the floor but also on the walls."

THE BATHROOM

There are many different styles and designs to choose from in the bathroom and the choice should be based on the lifestyle of the individual. From modern, clean-lined spaces with minimum detail to luxurious, pampering rooms with roll-top baths the choices are endless and completely dependent on how the room will be used. The style and choice of sanitary ware is important – choosing between a power shower and a free standing bath may be necessary if space is tight and the style that you decide on will be a starting point for the whole design.

The style of the bathroom is very much down to

This page:
Minimal
bathroom
styles for
space saving
solutions

Left page:
Bathrooms
evoke luxury
and
decadence, a
place to lose
yourself in

individual taste. Trends come and go and whether you want a contemporary minimal space or prefer traditional fittings it is a personal choice. Travertine, marble and stone are enduringly popular for natural, organic materials are fitting in the bathroom environment. A contemporary bathroom design might not only have the travertine on the floor but also on the walls. Often this also involves clever use of space such as recesses within the stonework within shower enclosures or elsewhere, which can be attractively lit and become a feature in their own right.

Another trend, which works well for small bathroom, is using strong dark colours, whether stone or otherwise, particularly for a WC or small ensuite. This has a dramatic impact and has the effect of making the space feel incredibly warm and luxurious.

trends:

TREND: SPA DESIGN
by Helen Green Design

*Leading British interior designer, **Helen Green**, creates British interior design combining timeless elegance with modern contemporary living spaces. Established in 2002, the company encompasses Interior Design, Interior Architecture and bespoke British made furniture and accessories.*

Clients include a wide range of prestigious private and commercial projects including luxury hotels in the UK and overseas such as the Helen Green Suites at The Berkeley Hotel and the Plantation Suites and the new Spa at The Coral Reef Club, Barbados.

Helen Green is based in Milner Street, Chelsea, in the building, which was formerly The Australian Pub, an iconic Chelsea landmark. The building has been transformed into a beautiful showroom and design studios for the team of designers and interior architects, who offer a bespoke and highly personalised service. The showroom displays accessories as well as The Helen Green Furniture Collections inspired by the glamour of the 30s and 40s.

EVOLUTION OF SPA DESIGN

The design of a spa needs to comprise a place that gives a sense of escape from the real world. It needs to be an environment which provides the ultimate in indulgence and relaxation and which encompasses the latest spa technologies, whilst complimenting the building and surroundings.

We understand that guests often arrive at a spa under stress through the pressures of modern life and travel. They want to be able to unlock their senses and instantly feel at ease. The notion of serene escapism and a sense of luxury is key. It is not only about a beautiful interior but also about comfort and being pampered.

Helen Green can not only lead the conceptual design but are also there to think about the many finer elements that really make the difference. A pool and a treatment room are these days not enough; we consider the 'journey' of the guest from the reception, through the

"We provide interior schemes of ultimate style and grace. Sophistication and longevity are our aim."

changing areas and into the spa itself. Relaxation spaces with just the right level of lighting and privacy, couples treatment areas, seating 'booths' and a general flow and synergy throughout are now standard/necessary considerations. A combination of privacy and openness should be experienced through free-flowing spaces and various degrees of transparency and partitions.

HG DESIGN PHILOSOPHY – RESORT AND SPA SPACES

Helen Green recently completed the Spa at the Coral Reef Club, an exquisite destination resort in Barbados, which provides contemporary and elegant spaces.

The four treatment rooms open to a private peaceful outdoor terrace, whilst the magnificent hydro pool with soothing jets and adjoining spa lounge offers a truly peaceful ambience. The walkways flooded with natural light against the porous coral stone and fountains throughout the spa journey are designed to encourage total wellbeing. The treatment pavilion is the perfect retreat for couples looking to indulge in blissful pampering.

Under a thatched roof and adorned with delicate ivory sheer drapery, the spa is open to a stunning private garden and an outdoor ensuite shower facility. The relaxation lounge, located on the upper level, overlooks the ocean. This is a space for relaxation post treatment with an emphasis on comfort and a sense of calmness

In keeping with the local surroundings, a selection of natural materials and fabrics were used throughout to create a fresh and crisp colour palette:

Dark chocolate raffia, soft creamy linens, fine white sand sheers, deep woven wicker, grass cloths and splashes of sage green made for a sophisticated and tranquil colour palate. Practicality and durability always go without saying and therefore the design and material specifications need to be appropriate. We appreciate that people sit on spa loungers with a wet bathing suit and walk through areas with sandy feet. At the Coral Reef Club it was important that the furniture and fabrics could withstand the Caribbean storms!

We provide interior schemes of ultimate style and grace. Sophistication and longevity are our aim.

FUTURE TRENDS

We are now designing towards greater comfort and away from the minimalistic styles which were prevalent in the early part of the decade.

There is less of a need for gimmicks and more demand for superior quality and taste. Our clients are currently looking to gain a sleek yet comfortable look using a lot of natural materials warm to the touch, and are notably opting out of the 'Oriental Look'.

Designs need to incorporate exquisite timeless style yet deliver functionality. They need to meet every requirement of the modern, highly sophisticated traveller.

The challenge of the designer is to recognise which trends are passing phases and which are here to stay. By giving attention to every detail and engaging all senses, Helen Green create spaces that are unique: an essential combination of healing and relaxation.

"A combination of privacy and openness should be experienced through free-flowing spaces and various degrees of transparency and partitions..."

HELEN GREEN DESIGN LIMITED
29 Milner Street
Chelsea
London
SW3 2QD
Tel: 020 7352 3344
Fax: 020 7352 5544
Email: mail@helengreendesign.com
www.helengreendesign.com

trends:

TREND: THE 'INTERIOR' EXPERIENCE
by Kelly Hoppen, MBE

*Having begun her foray into the design world at the age of just 16, **Kelly Hoppen** has made a name for herself as a world renowned British Designer, who has pioneered a simple yet opulent style that is synonymous with the Kelly Hoppen brand. As well as designing apartments, houses and yachts for an international list of private clients, Kelly also works on commercial commissions including hotel, restaurant, office and aircraft interiors. The first winner of the prestigious Andrew Martin International Interior Design Award, Kelly has paved the way for budding interiors designers with collections of paints, fabrics, carpets and more to add to her impressive portfolio. Kelly discusses designing for a range of different applications and how an interior contributes to the overall 'experience'.*

My style is very precise. I like to explore the entire process of creating that meets all my clients' needs – one that is functional and versatile as it is beautiful and nurturing. From a young age I always had an eye on interior and décor. I am best known for bringing East meets West philosophy to interior design focusing implementing the influences and the inspirations that lie behind the style of the Eastern cultures. It gives you a balance between the subtle colors for that great feel and the symmetrical lines to create elegance.

"I like to explore the entire process of creating that meets all my clients' needs- one that is functional and versatile as it is beautiful and nurturing."

Anything in your environment can inspire what you do. You simply need to have an open mind and awaken all your senses to what goes on around you.

My inspiration can also come from having time alone. Often when I'm on holiday I soak up so much from my environment and find inspiration for a specific design.

I think that projects such as ski lodges, hotels, spa's and retreats are a perfect example of how the classic Kelly Hoppen look can be incorporated and given a twist to suit the clients taste and preferences. The Key elements are to combine high quality textures and materials that help to create a luxurious escape from the daily routine. Usually, we keep my classic neutral color theme and signature elements such as cushions and runners are used for character.

In respect of these interior spaces, I have noticed that with ski lodges for example, designers are starting to mix traditional structures with more modern aspects - such as chalet conversions with glass fronted open plan living rooms on the top floor of traditional buildings so that they can have open views of the mountains.

Planning the design of such spaces is very important, First of all, I always begin by presenting a new client with a questionnaire, which gives me time to analyze what it is my clients want and need. This gives me an idea of how they want their clients to feel or how they live if we're designing a house. Then I break it down into several categories and work around each one to plan each area.

"When Designing commercial projects you have to think about the end clients' different experiences in the building, take on a purpose built modern building and create an interior that would provide a glamorous backdrop."

"My solution to commercial projects is to keep it as pure and simple as possible in order to draw the eye."

When Designing commercial projects you have to think about the end clients' different experiences in the building, take on a purpose built modern building and create an interior that would provide a glamorous backdrop. My solution to commercial projects is to keep it as pure and simple as possible in order to draw the eye.

I use organic shapes with modern lines to create an eclectic feel - my own dining table has an organic shape with a driftwood finish and together with the structured dining chairs it creates a really unique look. It is very important that you feel connected to the natural environment in your home or a city apartment

KELLY HOPPEN MBE – LIVING DESIGN

Kelly Hoppen is best known as the interior designer whose calm, elegant aesthetic has permeated our consciousness and achieved an iconic (and much imitated) status.

The celebrated designer who has recently been awarded an MBE for services to design started her business at the age of only 16 ½. Kelly is able to look back at a vast amount of experience having established herself as one of the best know International Interior Designers. Kelly has also successfully implemented her unique approach across a number of business areas, firmly establishing her reputation as designer, retailer, author, educator, innovator and inspiration. Her books have been translated into numerous foreign languages and her work has been on the front covers of magazines worldwide.

Awards - Kelly Hoppen has recently been awarded an MBE – an honour, which she is immensely proud to receive. She was also awarded with the European Women of Achievement Award for Entrepreneurship, 2007 (EWAA) joining an eminent list of those who have collected the EWAA, including, athlete Paula Radcliffe, yachtswoman Ellen MacArthur, explorer Fiona Thorne who has walked to both the North and South Poles, best-selling author Kate Mosse and broadcaster Angela Rippon. Kelly has also won the Grazia Award in the Design & Architecture category.

Being the first designer to receive the Andrew Martin " International Designer of the Year" Award in 1997, Kelly Hoppen's product has also been rewarded with an Elle Decoration Award, a Homes & Garden Award and more over the years. Her tabletop collection for Wedgwood and the KHome range for BHS are nominated for the Elle Decoration Award 2007 and her new book " Home- from concept to reality" has been shortlisted for a RIBA Award.

Retail - Kelly is has just moved her flagship store from Fulham Road to Notting Hill Gate. The new store, which will be called The Yard, opened its doors on 13th April on Chepstow Road in Notting Hill and will house Kelly's eclectic mix of interior pieces, upholstery textiles and KH own brand products.

Books - Kelly Hoppen has published six books, her latest one being " *Kelly Hoppen, Home-From Concept to Reality*". With the help of this book the reader is able to explore the entire process of creating a home that meets all your needs alongside Kelly – one that is as functional and versatile as it is beautiful and nurturing. The book also gives a clear picture of Kelly's design approach at every stage – from the conception and the idea, through to the planning and decision-making, to implementing the work and achieving the reality – she shares her insider secrets and reveals how to get the most out of your living space. Kelly Hoppen's other books are *East Meets West*, *Table Chic*, *In Touch*, *Style* and *Close Up*.

"To design well, you have to be sympathetic to the architectural style and age of the building itself."

so I always incorporate natural products such as wood, stone and natural fabrics in my designs. I love using accessories such as driftwood, coral or fresh-cut flowers to draw in elements of the environment.

I always say that, "to design well, you have to be sympathetic to the architectural style and age of the building itself." Then, of course it depends very much on the building. If you are redecorating an existing property, you might well decide it is too expensive to change certain things. However, if you are designing from the ground up, you need to spend time making sure you get these important elements right. When you look at property, which has aged, don't feel you have to keep the period features for the sake of it. If a building is listed, you have no choice but there is a no rule that says to keep it the same way, there are ways to give something a whole new lease of life.

trends:

TREND: THE INDUSTRY AT LARGE
by George Bond

George Bond is the National Director for the Society of British Interior Designer (SBID) as well as a Fellow of the Royal Society of Arts. George has his own interior design company based in Jesmond, near Newcastle. George Bond's flair for colour and intimate knowledge of texture has been recognised by some of the most discerning and fashionable over the years. With a scholar's grasp of centuries of rich tradition and an alchemist's flair for infinite possibility, George Bond is the acknowledged master of modern interior design, mixing the finest English style with cosmopolitan magnificence. He shot to fame in the late 90s and early 2000's with his unforgettably frank opinions on ITV's Better Homes programme. Since then he has appeared on a number of shows, including Grand Designs, and continues to add his distinctive flair to a number of private and commercial interior design projects worldwide. Here, he discusses the industry and his work as part of SBID.

It's no secret, in the current climate, that the option to move home has been restricted for some, but that loss appears to be the designers' gain, with people now increasingly choosing to create wonderful new interiors for their existing homes. I'm certainly aware that people are now very keen to create statement pieces, in a variety of forms, from bespoke carpets for living rooms to the most state-of-the-art kitchens.

I can't put my finger on it, but the recession seems to have brought out the most creative and imaginative side in everyone. Perhaps the doom and gloom we encounter has triggered something of an antidote to that. People seem to be searching for a release and many seem to have found that with their ideas and plans for their own homes. It's a wonderfully refreshing new challenge, which is reawakening the creative side in designers.

Another refreshing challenge I have recently encountered has been with the launch of the Society of British Interior Design (SBID). The new society has been set up by founding trustees Vanessa Brady and Simon Cavelle through a frustration with belonging to an industry that requires as much knowledge as

> **"People are now very keen to create statement pieces, in a variety of forms, from bespoke carpets for living rooms to the most state-of-the-art kitchens."**

others and yet remains without regulation and direction.

The founding trustees, along with myself and the other board members, have a unique window of opportunity, which enables us to create a national body to address these issues which will ultimately benefit all interior designers and their clients.

The UK is widely regarded as the leading

> **"The UK is widely regarded as the leading centre in the world for interior design, therefore it is imperative that first class support is provided, best practice is encouraged and standards are raised."**

centre in the world for interior design, therefore it is imperative that first class support is provided, best practice is encouraged and standards are raised. The emergence of the SBID and its objectives will not only benefit the practitioners within the industry but also the client – you, the homeowner.

We hope that the SBID will be the industry bearer for British professional interior designers. Our goals for SBID are for it to be constantly shaping and forming to become a platform that will change the perception of the interior design industry in the UK. Our hope is that SBID will be as strong and highly regarded as all other professional independent industry bodies. We want the SBID to suitably reflect the benefit which interior design brings to the UK but most of all we want it to be a recognised kite mark of quality that leaves clients in no doubt as to the quality of the individual or company that they have chosen to work with.

The SBID's logo will be a sign of protection for the consumer, as all members carrying it,

"The UK is widely regarded as the leading centre in the world of Interior Design, therefore it is imperative that first class support is provided."

including designers and suppliers, will be measured to the highest standards achievable through our adaptation of the standards of the European Council of Interior Architects. This means that you can expect the same measured level of qualification from members of the SBID as you would from any European interior designer.

In my role as national director I am now responsible for encouraging and sourcing new members from all aspects of interior design from across all regions. We have some fantastic interior design talent across the country and I aim to encourage these individuals to continue to challenge and educate themselves for the benefit of their clients.

www.georgebond.tv

rends:

TREND: YACHT & JET DESIGN
by the design team at Candy & Candy

Candy and Candy are the award-winning design practice led by **Nick** and **Christian Candy**, providing luxury interior design and project management for the ultra affluent. Both Nick and Chris pride themselves on a tailored, experienced and thorough service in every element of their company. From residential to commercial developments, their unique approach sets a high standard in the world of design. Candy and Candy are leaders in aviation interiors, with fantastic attention to detail and also create exquisite yachts for private clients, tailored to specific needs and with quality and originality at the forefront of their design service.

Here, the design team at Candy and Candy discuss current and future trends in the ultimate luxury in aviation and marine interiors.

We are finding that our clients are demanding an increasing level of bespoke/ one off designs – we therefore aim to push the boundaries of design wherever possible and as a result more likely to set trends as opposed to follow them.

In our experience the aviation and marine industry has focused on a more traditional approach to interior design, with classic and safe colours and conventional designs, using mostly cherry and teak woods teamed with cream carpets and leathers and gold and onyx finishes.

Nick and Christian Candy. Image: Andrew Twort

"Clients are looking for the most unusual and individual boats and jets- size is less important but quality, innovation and style is a priority."

Design themes that we are working on now incorporate more contemporary materials for example dark grey macassor ebony, almond gold, smoked nickel and shaved silk carpets.

There is a whole host of trends and in our experience, they come from the client's 'needs' combined with our design team's innovations:

OUTDOOR SPACES (ON YACHTS)

These have evolved to incorporate more significant sun decks for extensive entertaining but with a new requirement to also incorporate the latest gadgets and technical innovations. For example our design team have recently installed a sun bed which follows the sun, it rotates to ensure optimum sun exposure at all times – leaving no need for the user to keep getting up to change their seating position.

TOYS

A requirement for more fun elements to be incorporated for example scuba diving equipment such as a sea bob - bigger and better toys are now needed, so they need to be housed appropriately, this has created implications for the need for more storage to be seamlessly incorporated into the design.

More dynamic style and individual look Double height ceilings, which give impression of grandeur and maximum impact. Glass Elevators, Leather wrapped floors. An increasing use of carbon fibre and honey combed aluminum are just a few materials we have incorporated to create a more dynamic and stylish look.

We are also finding that previously it was all about 'bigger and better' but now clients are looking for the most unusual and individual boats and jets – size is less important but quality innovation and style is a priority.

Clients want to be individual, expressing their personality within the design of their yacht or jet. They either see their private yacht or jet as a

> *"Outdoor fabrics are becoming broader with much wider colour choices than what was previously available."*

toy or commodity and increasingly more of a statement. Our designers often get carte blanch to create fantasy vessels and aircrafts that push boundaries, challenge convention using new materials that add more drama than they've ever done before. The brief is open. However on the flip side some clients have very basic requirements usually when they use their jet for business.

We are finding that our clients are much younger - with more and more yacht and jet owners being in 30-40's rather than just 50-60's. Their tastes are different and influenced by a host of international styles and cultures – they are more adventurous.

COLOUR AND FABRIC

As mentioned above dark grey macassor ebony, almond gold smoked nickel and shaved silk carpets are more contemporary design choices for yachts and jets now. Specific detailing such as hand embroidery, beading and painting as well as resin-impregnated fabrics are very popular. Outdoor fabrics are becoming broader with much wider colour choices than what was previously available.

We pride ourselves on being at the forefront of originality and quality - our suppliers regularly approach us with new and experimental products, as they are confident we will share their vision and experiment. Our international client base comprises the wealthiest people in the world. They have access to the best products and materials in the world therefore meeting their requirements is often challenging - it is therefore critical that we are constantly researching new design possibilities. We encourage input from our young designers who often think outside of the box and are not constrained by what has been done previously. We also take time to source our items through extensive traveling. Our vast design library at our headquarters in Westminster houses thousands of tried and tested materials from marble samples to carpet swatches to paints and actual household items.

trends:

FORECAST: DESIGNING FOR THE FUTURE
By Sarah Beeny

Sarah Beeny *is a Channel 4 television presenter on the popular Property Snakes and Ladders prime time show. As well as being a well established property mogul Sarah also owns mysinglefriend.com, a social dating website and has just launched Tepilo.com, a property website enabling you to buy or sell your home online without any fees, with tips on design, negotiation and marketing, and all the advice you need along the way. Here, Sarah discusses planning ahead.*

Since the second world war we seem to have had a bit of a problem with the old mixing with the new - as a result the last 60 odd years has seen interiors come and go - and them come and go again.

With a slight blimp in the 1980's, smooth clean lines have been all the rage in one form or another. But I really feel we are finally coming out the other side of filling up skips with gay abandon with last year's version of this year's fashion. Certainly the antique furniture market that is on its knees is desperate to have a revival but more importantly mixing a little of the old with a little of the new, generally ends up often costing less for a timeless look that uses less of the worlds resources.

If you are planning on selling or renting, whilst it

"See if you can find a suitable sized antique wardrobe instead of having fitted furniture made as by the time you have paid a joiner to build and a decorator to paint one it will probably be cheaper and the end result that actually holds its value over time."

may be tricky with leopard skin wallpaper on all your walls and ceilings, there is a great deal between this and magnolia walls with white gloss woodwork. You may find the nicer wallpapers out of affordable reach but I reckon you should always go a few shades bolder with paint that you feel safe with. It may take a little while to hunt down but scour the auctions to see if you can find a suitable sized antique wardrobe instead of having fitted furniture made as by the time you have paid a joiner to build and a decorator to paint one it will probably be cheaper and the end result that actually holds its value over time. Not only that but in terms of design the quality of the work is likely to be far higher and this enables you to bring the best of the old into your 2010 home.

More importantly when you come to sell you will often find you can sell the piece to the buyers separately or take it with you or if the worst comes to the worst you can always sell it again. No skips, no waste and you have the bonus of being able to live with a rather more stylish interior.

"If you are planning on selling or renting, whilst it may be tricky with leopard skin wallpaper on all your walls and ceilings, there is a great deal between this and magnolia walls with white gloss woodwork."

interior design courses

GETTING STARTED: AN INTERIOR DESIGN COURSE GUIDE

It is so important that you trust your designer with the very personal and delicate job of re-designing your home. As a client you know what you look for in a designer; experience, a proven portfolio record and qualifications in the field. It is these requirements that are now, in more demand than ever. Designers hire experience and professionalism into their practices for company growth and the industry bodies nurture their design students, integrating them into the interior design industry.

If you are thinking of taking that next step in a design career, wish to improve your already flourishing skills or simply want to gain that recognisable qualification to allow you to work professionally in the industry, it is important to get accredited with the right University/College.

The Interior Design Yearbook has pulled together a list of some great courses available in the industry. These vary in length of course, location and type of qualification to give you a varied choice and flexible working environment.

AMERICAN INTERCONTINENTAL UNIVERSITY -
LONDON
Courses: Four years Full Time Hons
BA Interior Design
Associate of Arts in
Interior Design (AA)
Bachelor of Fine Arts in Interior
Design (BFA)
**110 Marylebone High Street,
London,
W1U 4RY
Tel: 020 7467 5640**
Email: admissions@aiulondon.ac.uk
Website: **www.aiulondon.ac.uk**

BIRMINGHAM INSTITUTE OF ART AND DESIGN
Courses: Three years Full Time Hons
BA Interior Design Certificate Interior
Design.
**Costa Green,
University of Central England,
Birmingham,
B4 7DX
Tel: 0121 331 5000**
Email: enquiries@students.uce.ac.uk
Website: **www.biad.uce.ac.uk**

CHELSEA COLLEGE OF ART AND DESIGN COURSES: Foundation
Degree (FdA) Interior Design - two
years.
BA Honours Interior and Spatial
Design - three years
Graduate Diploma in Interior Design -
one year
Foundation in design and technical
drawing skills
**16 John Islip Street,
London
SW1P 4JU
Tel: 020 7514 7751**
Email: enquiries@chelsea.arts.ac.uk
shortcourses@chelsea.ac.uk
Website: **www.chelsea.arts.ac.uk**

Edinburgh College of Art
Courses: BA(Hons) Design & Applied
Arts (Interior Design)
**Lauriston Place,
Edinburgh,
EH3 9DF
Tel: 0131 221 6000**
Email: registry@eca.ac.uk
Website: **www.eca.ac.uk**

INCHBALD SCHOOL OF DESIGN
Courses: 10 week Full Time
Certificate Interior Design
One year Full Time Diploma
Architectural Interior Design
Two years Full Time MA Architectural
Interior Design
One year Full Time Post Graduate
Diploma Architectural Interior Design
10 Week Interior Decoration
Certificate
Interior Design and Decoration Week
Three Week Interior Design Drawing
One Day a Week Part Time Interior
Decoration Certificate
Interior Decoration on Saturdays
Online Diploma in Interior Design
**7 Eaton Gate
London
SW1W 9BA
Tel: 020 7730 5508**
Email: interiors@inchbald.co.uk
Website: **www.inchbald.co.uk**

IVY HOUSE DESIGN SCHOOL
Courses: Four week Full Time
Diploma short courses in: Drawing
skills, business skills, and design and
decoration for interior design.
**One Walcot Gate,
Bath,
BA1 5UG
Tel: 01225 421 657**
Email: ivyhousedesign@tiscali.co.uk
www.ivyhousedesignschool.com

KLC SCHOOL OF DESIGN
Courses:
One year Full Time Professional
Diploma Interior Design & Decoration
Blended Learning Professional
Diploma in Interior Design and
Decoration
10 Week Certificate in Interior
Decoration, Part-Time Certificate in
Interior Decoration Short Courses 1
Day, 2 Day, 3 Day, 1 Week and CAD
Open Learning Diploma in Interior
Design and Decoration
Open Learning Design Your Own
Home
Open Learning Diploma in Garden
Design
Open Learning Designing with Plants
**Unit 503,
5th Floor,
The Chambers
Chelsea Harbour
London
SW10 0XF**

Tel: 020 7376 3377
Email: info@klc.co.uk
Website: **www.klc.co.uk**

LONDON METROPOLITAN UNIVERSITY
Courses: Two years Full Time HND
Interior Design
Three years Full Time Hons BA Interior
Architecture & Design
Three years Full Time Hons BA Interior
Design & Technology
**41 Commercial Road,
London,
E1 1LA
Tel: 020 7133 4200**
Email: admissions@londonmet.ac.uk
Website: **www.londonmet.ac.uk**

RHODEC INTERNATIONAL
Courses: Two year Interior Design
Diploma.Dip H/E 2 year BA(Hons) &
BFA - American Intercontinental
University
**35 East Street,
Brighton
BN1 1HL
Tel: 01273 327 476**
Email: contact@rhodec.edu
Website: **www.rhodec.edu**

ST HELENS COLLEGE
Courses: HND in Design for Interiors.
**Brook Street
St Helens Merseyside
WA10 1PZ
Tel: 01744 733 766**
Email: enquire@sthelens.ac.uk
Website: **www.sthelens.ac.uk**

THE GLASGOW SCHOOL OF ART
Courses: Four years Full Time Hons
BA Interior Design
**167 Renfrew Street,
Glasgow,
G3 6RQ
Tel: 0141 353 4512**
Email: info@gsa.ac.uk
Website: **www.gsa.ac.uk**

THE INTERIOR DESIGN SCHOOL
Courses: One year Full time diploma
One year Part-time Evening
Certificate
Two year Part-time Advanced
Certificate
Five week Summer Certificate

Ten week Summer Advanced
Certificate
Saturday Introduction days
22 Lonsdale Road
Queens Park
London
NW6 6RD
Tel: 020 7372 2811
Email: ideas@idschool.co.uk
www.theinteriordesignschool.co.uk

THE LONDON INSTITUTE -
LONDON COLLEGE OF PRINTING.
Courses: Foundation Degree in
Interior Design, Two Years, Full-time.
Elephant & Castle
London
SE1 6SB
Tel: 020 7514 6781
Email: j.james@lcp.linst.ac.uk
Website: **www.linst.ac.uk**

THE MANCHESTER
METROPOLITAN UNIVERSITY
Courses: Three years Full Time Hons
BA Interior Design
All Saints Buildings,
All Saints,
Manchester,
M15 6BH
Tel: 0161 247 2000
Email: enquiries@mmu.ac.uk

Website: **www.mmu.ac.uk**

UNIVERSITY COLLEGE FOR THE
CREATIVE ARTS AT CANTERBURY
Courses: Three years Full Time Hons
BA Interior Design
Three years Full Time Hons BA Interior
Architecture
New Dover Road,
Canterbury,
CT1 3AN
Tel: 01634 888 773
Email: info@ucreative.ac.uk
Website: **www.ucreative.ac.uk**

University College for the Creative
Arts at Farnham
Courses: Three years Full Time Hons
BA Interior Architecture & Design
Falkner Road,
Farnham,
Surrey,
GU9 7DS
Tel: +44 (0) 1252 722441
Email: info@ucreative.ac.uk
www.ucreative.ac.uk/
interiorsfarnham

UNIVERSITY OF CENTRAL
ENGLAND IN BIRMINGHAM
Courses: Three years Full Time Hons

BA Interior Design
Perry Barr Franchise St.
Birmingham
B42 2SU
Tel: 0121 331 5595
Email: info@ucechoices.com
Website: **www.uce.ac.uk**

UNIVERSITY OF THE ARTS
LONDON
Courses: Three years Full Time Hons
BA Interior & Spatial Design
65 Davies Street,
London,
W1K 5DA
Tel: 020 7514 6000 x6197
Email: info@arts.ac.uk
Website: **www.arts.ac.uk**

THE INTERIOR DESIGN INSTITUTE
Course: The Interior Design Course-
12 week diploma
Garrick House
26/27 Southampton Street
Covent Garden
London WC2E 7RS
www.theinteriordesigninstitute.co.uk

For further courses available visit the
BIID website at **www.bida.org** for
other more regional courses.

Mood Boards

· MOOD BOARD ·
Carolyn Trevor

· MOOD BOARD ·
th:2

· MOOD BOARD ·
Anna Dodonova

· MOOD BOARD ·
Sally Storey

MOODS FOR CREATIVITY

Our designers often take inspiration from the smallest details, whether it is an element of nature or a button detail on the coat of a passer-by. Sourcing ideas and bringing together different elements to combine them successfully is an art and a practiced technique by many professionals. Clever use of colours teamed with bold and brave explorations of fabrics and texture types, can result in a beautiful room-set. Here, some of our designers have put together mood boards based on ideas they have either used in recent projects or trends they will be noting in next years designs. From key lighting to combined materials and textures, mood boards help to open up the theme and present an idea of a finished trend in snapshot form.

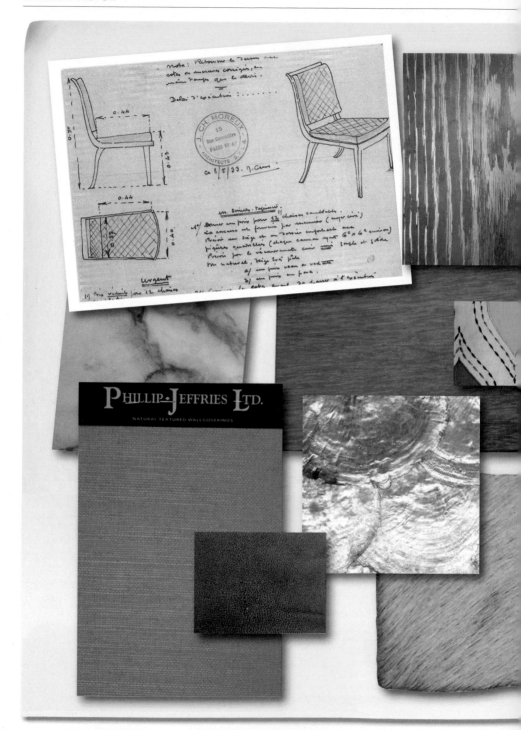

· MOOD BOARD ·
Carolyn Trevor

A MATERIAL WORLD

BY CAROLYN TREVOR

There is much said of timeless design but one need only look at a magazine or interiors article from as recently as five years ago to reveal the lie in this. It is no wonder that things change so quickly when the design industry is always pushing what's new with the relentless cycle of trade shows, exhibitions and press.

On top of this, the march of technology and its impact on all our lives means that ways of occupying space change continually. Increasingly as the shortage of green field sites prevents the spread of new buildings, the designer's role will involve more of 'adapting and modifying' the existing, so making it more appropriate for now. Set against this scenario, we are enjoined to recycle, reuse and consider the environment.

The response for the designer to these requirements often becomes difficult and sometimes impossible to reconcile and probably at no other time has this demand on the designer been greater, as now.

Our clients no longer simply follow the latest fashion or to aspire to a lifestyle. They wish to choose according to their expectations, their desire for comfort and well-being, and their commitment to new environmental and ethical values.

In our work we seek what is appropriate to the client and the site rather than a house style which says more about the designer than the person for whom the design is to serve. A design needs to be appropriate and fit, but IT should never be so inflexible that it does not allow for movement and/or change; it should never look 'done' or' tired'. Most important of all, the client should appear to as well as be very comfortable with their completed project.

Metallics are set to reign supreme in the fashion world and are the perfect look for any home that needs a little injection of life. Simple accessories including vases, pots and framework will update a look instantly, or even little touches like silver napkin rings will bring a dull table setting to life!

This season when entertaining at home, pay great attention to detail and accessorize with **coloured glass**. It's not important to have a complete set of stemware or tumblers. Recycled vintage pieces mixed with brand new glassware is very 'on trend', just be sure to colour match the accent colours of that particular room to add instant energy and wow guests.

DETAILING

BY th:2

Both at home and abroad we find inspiration to style our homes. Each season both the fashion and design worlds bring new trends. For 2010 we've looked at what all industries have to offer and have identified that 'detailing' is a key trend consideration in home furnishings and comforts.

It is important to keep environmental issues at the forefront of our minds when restyling or updating a home. Detailing is definitely an environmentally friendly trend, as it encourages us to update tired looks by recycling and re-vamping, rather than just disposing or replacing old furniture.

Statement chunky china is a big trend for the home next year. Not to be confused with practical china, this look is guaranteed to create a 'wow' factor with a simple concept. Brighten up blank spaces from the bedroom to the dining room with stylised, contemporary designs for a winning look.

COMPANY BACKGROUND

Sister company to the award winning Taylor Howes Designs, th:2 works with investors, estate agents, developers and private clients to create stylish interiors for the buy to let market and more recently, the 'dress to sell' market.

th:2 was set up in 2004 when Karen Howes and Gail Taylor of Taylor Howes Designs realised that there was a gap in the market for an easy to use furnishing service for people buying properties as an investment. By supplying a turn-key, hassle free operation and furnishing properties to an excellent finish, th:2 enables clients to rent out or sell their properties quickly in return for a premium return on investment.

Jazz up tired furniture or fabrics with some 'on-trend' **studding**. All of the hottest fashion accessories for 2010 are decoratively adorned with studded detailing. Simple, slick lines of metal studs or even button studding will add a striking affect to any piece of furniture. Try experimenting on sofas, curtains or lampshades and you'll be creating one of this seasons' hottest trends.

th:2 offers pre-selected interior design and furnishing packages using award winning Taylor Howes techniques (winners of the prestigious 2006 Andrew Martin International Interior Designer of the Year Award) to create their stunning interiors. Skilful direct sourcing from carefully selected European manufacturers allows th:2 to offer a bespoke furnishing package starting from £4000.
www.th2designs.co.uk

• MOOD BOARD •

th:2

FURNISH WITH FASHION IN MIND

BY ANNA DODONOVA

I see two strong trends in interiors for 2010 and both are influenced by the fashion industry and the styles seen on the catwalks. These trends are a welcome change to the overly decorative ostentation seen in the last two years.

The first is a trend for feminine shapes in furniture and accessories. Gentle ovals, curves, delicate ribbon silhouettes and soft sculptural shapes are used to create an elegant effect with seating, mirrors, tables and accessories. Materials such as glass, leather, and painted and lacquered wood play alongside soft colours like white, beige, amethyst, yellow and soft metallics. This is about creating a graceful and chic interior, which is calm and relaxing yet smart. Good examples of this trend are the Bastide chair designed by Andree Putman for Reflex; the delicate ribbon arms of curved lacquered wood meet the comfortable oval seat and chair back and the gently tapered legs add to the style of this chair which is versatile enough to be used in the dining room, dressing room or as an occasional chair. The Neolitico dining table by Reflex repeats the ribbon theme with its delicate glass base and the rounded Murano glass legs of the Gran Canal table, also by Reflex, are subtle, stylish and distinctly feminine.

The second trend is Old Hollywood Glamour. The highly recognisable style and glamour of the forties and fifties encompasses strong silhouettes and a sophistication. This trend uses fashion colours such as red, gold and white and materials such as high gloss lacquer, shiny fabrics, glass and crystals. It is about statement pieces with a real wow factor being central to a scheme and linking fashion with interiors by powering-up understated pieces with eye-catching embellishments. The Casanova table by Reflex with its highly decorative hand-made gold Murano glass base certainly has the wow factor for a glamorous interior.
www.annacasa.net

• MOOD BOARD •
Anna Dodonova

LIGHTING DESIGN
BY SALLY STOREY

First impressions count so it is essential that the right impression is created from the hallway. Often halls are narrow and dull but as the transition space between rooms should not be forgotten.

In this fabulous hallway the decorative chandelier provides the visual reference and helps create a more intimate feeling at the outset. It sets the scene and it's overscaling adds glamour immediately. It is essential to dim so that it remains a decorative effect whilst the rest of the lighting creates the real impact.

Stairs can be an interesting architectural feature. Lighting these with individual stair lights make them feel special. Consider placing a low-level floor washer such as an Oslo on every third step as shown here. Using a 1w LED, it provides the equivalent light of a 20w 12v halogen. These light the treads, not only for safety, but as a feature. A decorative wall light in the alcove adds another layer of light when descending the stairs.

The eye is drawn through this long hallway with the help of uplights to the arches creating focal points along the route. Lighting of these architectural details with narrow beam 1w LED Lucca uplights provide a cost effective and low energy way of adding accents to this hallway. Previously 20w was required to do the same job.

Low glare directional Polestar downlights are added to provide in-fill light and plays with pools of light and shade to add interest. Always remember to dim the hallway as it is a false economy not to as when all the other areas are dim, one doesn't want to go into a bright hall!

The area under stairs is often a forgotten dark area. The gentle curve of the wall is uplit using 1w LED Luccas which also highlights the underside of the stairs.

• MOOD BOARD •
Sally Storey

DESIGN ON LOCATION

The best way to experience a designers' work often takes more than browsing through a catalogue of magazine of showroom features. Experiencing their design methods, their favoured fabrics and the depth and intricateness of their work is something that should be done before handing over the brief. Seeing a designers work in a real room-set is also an excellent source in inspiration for your own projects, as you can really gage the power of colour and texture when all is brought together to create a particular style and ambience. The Interior Design Yearbook has taken a closer look at a selection of showrooms with very different ideas; showing that style knows no bounds.

ARMANI/CASA FLAGSHIP STORE
LONDON

In September 2006, Giorgio Armani opened his London flagship **Armani/Casa** store at 113 New Bond Street, the brand's first standalone store in the UK. The 600 sq m site on New Bond Street reinforces the complete Armani lifestyle message – the store is in close proximity to both the Armani Collezioni and Emporio Armani stores also on New Bond Street.

First launched in 2000 in Milan, Armani/Casa represents Giorgio Armani's vision of the perfect environment: an intimate, individual and sophisticated space in which to relax, unwind and entertain. Giorgio Armani's personal vision of furnishing the home is distinguished by a strong, coherent approach and one that reflects the personality of the designer himself and his preference for pure minimalism, but with cultural references such as the 1930's Art Deco style and Orientalism.

The open-plan London store is split over two levels and has been

designed to create the distinctive, sophisticated atmosphere of Armani/Casa. Products are displayed in both day and night zones which include furniture, accessories, lighting and fabrics in addition to kitchen and bathroom systems. The showroom showcases both a permanent collection of classic furniture as well as temporary lines of seasonal accessories. Also on display are pieces from the Armani/Casa Limited Edition collection; these antiques of tomorrow have been personally signed by Giorgio Armani and include chaise longues, bar units and screens.

The London showroom has recently unveiled pieces from the new 2009-2010 collection. Defined by traditional "Made in Italy" craftsmanship, the collection includes precious woods, leathers and sumptuous fabrics combined with cutting-edge varnishing techniques, such as liquid metal or black nickel. Highlights include an elegant rosewood writing desk, rotating cocktail unit, silver-dipped dining furniture and a striking corner-unit sofa. This is a collection of elegant simplicity and total harmony that reflects the unmistakable style of Giorgio Armani.

Also available to view in-store is Armani/Casa's exclusive new fabric range designed in collaboration with the Venetian fabric house, Rubelli. The collection has been inspired by the 1920's and 1930's and features exquisite jacquards, damasks, velvets and silks. Designs include stylised plant motifs, animal prints, checks and simple plain patterns in a variety of weaves and colours. Furniture in the Armani/Casa range, such as sofas, chairs and beds can now be upholstered in the new collection from Rubelli.

For customers and property developers looking for design consultancy on interiors projects, the New Bond Street store offers a bespoke Interior Design Service from room decoration to complete home re-design. This service will take total responsibility across the full span of a project, from planning to execution.

Armani/Casa
113 New Bond Street,
London
W1S 1DP
Tel: 0207 079 1930
www.armanicasa.com

KATHARINE POOLEY BOUTIQUE

LONDON

Interior Designer **Katharine Pooley**'s boutique is a one-stop destination for gifts and accessories for the home-interior that are truly special. It is full of exotic items sourced from all over the world.

At any one time you might find pieces of antique jade from China, art-deco leather reconditioned chairs, cashmere and fine Italian crystal sitting alongside rare Eastern artifacts and Cambodian monks. Katharine developed exclusive relationships with artisans in Asia whilst living and working in the Far East and many of the pieces will not be found elsewhere in Europe. The shop is testament to her extensive travels and hunter-gatherer instinct for all things beautiful and unique.

The boutique is re-designed every three months and regular buying trips to Europe, America and Asia ensure that there is always something new to discover. There are a wide selection of products to browse including

furniture, tableware, silverware, lighting and artwork. In addition the boutique offers a gift list service catering for all types of occasions from weddings, birthdays, births, christenings and major anniversaries. The boutique recently launched an online boutique meaning products can now be purchased online and will arrive beautifully wrapped, shipped worldwide.

Katharine Pooley Interiors is based two doors down and offers a full interior design and project management service for private and commercial clients with recent commissions including the VIP suites at Heathrow Terminal 5, 3 and 1

160 Walton Street
London
SW3 2JL
Tel: 0207 584 3223
www.katharinepooley.com

MANSERS ANTIQUES & THE HIDDEN TV COMPANY

SHREWSBURY

Mansers Antiques, established in 1944, is a third generation antiques business. Run by Mark & Sonya Manser, it has built a reputation for supplying fine quality furniture and antiques throughout the UK and internationally. In a business passed down from father to son, Mark Manser has lived and breathed antiques all his life and has a profound depth of knowledge and expertise in this field.

Mansers operates out of a stunning, glass fronted, award-winning showroom in Shrewsbury, Shropshire where all are welcome to come in and enjoy the experience of shopping for antiques in a contemporary setting. But it doesn't end there, many of Mansers clients also call upon them for consultancy and design services, such as advising on furniture to complement the style

and period of their homes, sourcing specific pieces, or helping them to determine the provenance of an antique or piece of furniture they may be interested in purchasing elsewhere. Mark Manser says "It's all about trust and building relationships with our customers. Buying antiques is one area where a little knowledge can be a dangerous thing and we aim to help our customers to get the best quality at the right price." Clients include individuals; designers and property developers who want to create a more unique look to their show homes. Now in its 65th year, Mansers has seen many changes in tastes and

shopping habits of its customers and has had to evolve with the times. Recognising that buying antiques could be an intimidating experience, in 2001 they took the bold step of moving from the 1200 sq ft premises where the business had been founded 57 years earlier, into an award winning, contemporary building that was

specially designed for Mansers by architect Paul Harries of Baart Harries Newall .
Another evolution for Mansers was the opening of sister company, The Hidden TV Company. Modern technology in our homes is a fact of life but it can pose challenges for those who don't want their audiovisual equipment to compromise the look of their

home. Using their expertise in fine furniture, Mansers have resolved this by blending craftsmanship and design with state of the art technology to create stylish housing for high tech equipment. With its wide range of British made, handcrafted cabinets, The

Hidden TV Company offers the perfect solution when the latest technology clashes with the decor of your home, or if you only want to see your TV when you are actually watching it. Cabinets can be made in a selection of woods

such as oak, mahogany and walnut; handles and feet can be changed, and cabinets can be colour matched to fit in with existing decor. The design element of the cabinets is perfectly complemented by its functional capabilities, incorporating the latest

plasma and LCD screens, powerful lifting mechanisms, swivel brackets and remote control operation. A bespoke service to create one-off designs is also available, proving especially popular with the designers, royalty and movie stars, which Hidden TV counts amongst its customers.

Mansers Antiques/
The Hidden TV Company
Coleham Head
Shrewsbury
SY3 7BJ
Tel: 01743 351120
www.theantiquedealers.com

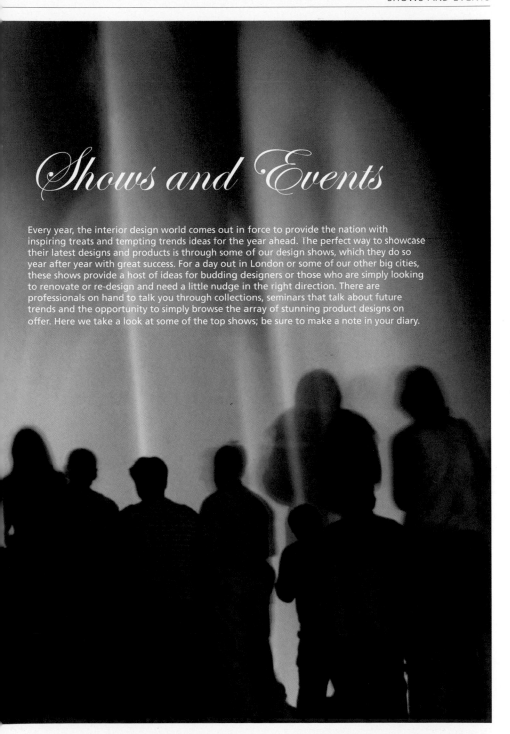

Shows and Events

Every year, the interior design world comes out in force to provide the nation with inspiring treats and tempting trends ideas for the year ahead. The perfect way to showcase their latest designs and products is through some of our design shows, which they do so year after year with great success. For a day out in London or some of our other big cities, these shows provide a host of ideas for budding designers or those who are simply looking to renovate or re-design and need a little nudge in the right direction. There are professionals on hand to talk you through collections, seminars that talk about future trends and the opportunity to simply browse the array of stunning product designs on offer. Here we take a look at some of the top shows; be sure to make a note in your diary.

events

EVENTS: SHOW STOPPERS
A glimpse at the top spots to visit in 2010.

An easy way to gain a great insight into the world of interior design and to pick up some great tips for designing your own home; is to visit some of the shows that go on over the year. Many interior design shows have a key focus on bringing designers to suppliers, providing them with tomorrows new products- today, but, more often than not, these shows will open their doors to the general public for a day during each shows run. By doing this, the exhibition

organisers are providing the public with a glimpse of professional creativity and allowing their exhibitors to showcase their fantastic products to a wider audience. There are a whole host of fantastic shows throughout the year, usually situated in Central London for easy of access. So, if you're in the Capital or fancy a day of design inspiration, why not grab a ticket to one of these hot events and put your creativity to the test.

IDEAL HOME SHOW 2010
20 March – 5 April
EARLS COURT
LONDON
The Ideal Home Show is the original source of ideas and inspiration. Held over approx two weeks, the show incorporates many elements of home living as well as interiors ideas. It is a chance to shop, see and take note of the trends on display. Recognisable Chefs are usually on hand to give tempting demonstrations in Ideal food and the show also steps outside in Ideal Gardens.
www.idealhomeshow.co.uk

LONDON DESIGN WEEK
24, 25 and 26 March 2010. All welcome to event
DESIGN CENTRE CHELSEA HARBOUR
LONDON
London Design Week is one of many opportunities for consumers and trade professionals alike to visit the design centre and its fabulous showrooms. Set over three domes, within 81 showrooms, a dedicated seminar space and the opportunity to hear from many well-known industry designers, London Design Week gives you three whole days to explore and experience the latest trends and techniques in the world of interior design.
www.designcentrechelseaharbour.co.uk

GRAND DESIGNS LIVE 2010
1-9 May 2010
EXCEL
LONDON
Fronted by none other than Channel 4's King of clever concepts, Kevin McCloud, Grand Designs Live runs for nine whole days at the vast EXCEL centre over near London's Docklands. The trip over is well worth it as the show takes a very interactive approach to design. Demonstrations and seminars take place over all nine days within the key areas of the show; Grand Build, Grand Interiors, Grand Kitchens, Grand Bathrooms, Grand Gardens and the Grand Village.
www.granddesignslive.com

RHS CHELSEA FLOWER SHOW
5- 29 May 2010
ROYAL CHELSEA HOSPITAL
GROUNDS
LONDON
The infamous flower show returns
year after year, wowing the crowds
with its ever-impressive displays of
horticultural creativity. There are now
exclusive preview days for RHS
members on 25-26 May on top of
the benefit of discounted tickets. If
you would like to see the colour and
creative garden concepts in the flesh,
visit their website to purchase tickets.
Every year, key industry leaders
display their talents for garden design
and every year it gets better.
www.rhs.org.uk

DECOREX 09
INTERNATIONAL

DECOREX INTERNATIONAL 2010
ROYAL HOSPITAL CHELSEA,
LONDON
The exquisite Decorex exhibition
provides professional interior
designers, retailers, architects and
hotel designers with a beautifully

edited selection of the most
innovative and aspirational suppliers
including fabrics and wallcoverings,
furniture, lighting, floorcoverings,
accessories and bespoke services. As
well as all this, Decorex opens its
doors to consumers for one day
during the fantastic event, providing
you with the same exquisite choices
available to our designers.
To register your interest for the
Decorex 2010 event go to
www.decorex.com
* Dates will be issued soon. The show is
usually towards the end of September of
each year.

FOCUS 10
29 September 2010. All welcome to
event
DESIGN CENTRE
CHELSEA HARBOUR
LONDON
Focus is a fantastic show situated
over at Chelsea Harbour Design
Centre. During the London Design
Festival FOCUS is attended by many a
designer and consumer as they open
their doors to both. The Design
Centre boasts over 81 showrooms
featuring the most well-known
brands in fabrics, lighting accessories
and much more. Teamed with
seminars from industry professionals
and the further showrooms along the
infamous Kings Road in Chelsea,
Focus is one NOT to be missed.
www.designcentrechelseaharbour.co.uk

HOMEBUILDING
& RENOVATING
SHOW

**HOMEBUILDING AND
RENOVATING SHOW 2010**
18-21 March 2010
NEC
BIRMINGHAM
Further dates and locations:
SCOTLAND - SECC, Glasgow, 15 -
16 May 2010
SURREY - Sandown Park, Esher,
Surrey, 26 - 27 June 2010

HARROGATE - Harrogate
International Centre,

5 - 7 November 2010

SOMERSET - Bath & West
Showground, Shepton Mallett, 20 -
21 November 2010

The Homebuilding and Renovating
Show is a hands on event, ideal for
those with 'home build' aspirations
and in need of the products and
services to complete the project. The
benefits of this show include being
set regionally, so there is plenty of
opportunity to visit one or more of
the shows in a variety of locations.
Self-build and renovation experts will
be on hand, with masterclasses and
in-depth seminars shedding new light
on the world of self-build projects.

www.homebuildingshow.co.uk

HEDLEY'S HUMPERS
3 St Leonard's Road
North Acton
London, NW10 6SX
Tel: +44 (0) 20 8965 8733
Fax: +44 (0) 20 8965 0249
London@hedleyshumpers.com
www.hedleyshumpers.com

WHATEVER, WHENEVER, WHEREVER

Hedley's Humpers offers a complete solution to all your transportation, installation and storage requirements.

With over thirty years' experience Hedley's Humpers has established an international reputation of expertise in moving, installing and storing. With offices in London, New York, Paris and the south of France, we are uniquely placed to provide a truly global service to the world of interior design, fine art and antiques.

Our teams are not only experts in the care and transportation of art and antiques; they are also trained in all interior design installation. A dedicated client manager is assigned to every new customer, providing information and advice on each consignment, storage and installation requirement. Genuine passion for quality and customer service ensures a totally unique level of care.

Installation Services
Hedley's offer exclusive teams to fulfil any installation requirements from a single item to full interior design

installations, and window arranging. Our highly trained and specialised teams have over thirty years' experience working with interior designers, international galleries, auction houses, and museums across Europe and America. We are experts in both problem solving and providing customised handling services, which meet each new logistical challenge.

Worldwide Transportation

Hedley's own fleet of vehicles in Europe and America enable us to offer a true door-to-door service, accompanied by professional and experienced drivers. On the road every item is secured in our own specially designed vehicles. Loaded by tail lifts, protected from the extremes of heat and cold within specially designed bodies with padded interiors, every item is also supported by cushioned air ride suspension.

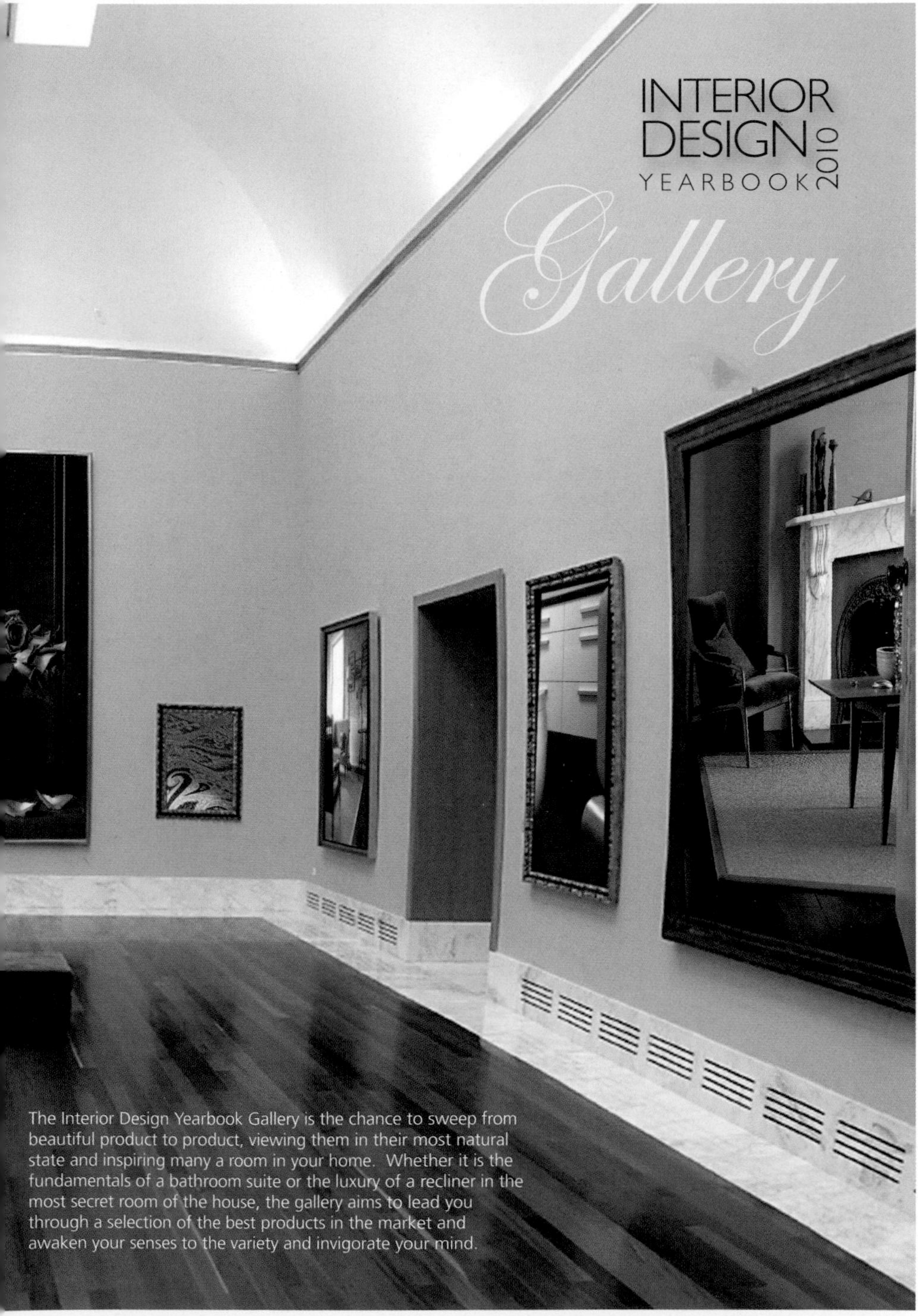

INTERIOR
DESIGN 2010
YEARBOOK

Gallery

The Interior Design Yearbook Gallery is the chance to sweep from beautiful product to product, viewing them in their most natural state and inspiring many a room in your home. Whether it is the fundamentals of a bathroom suite or the luxury of a recliner in the most secret room of the house, the gallery aims to lead you through a selection of the best products in the market and awaken your senses to the variety and invigorate your mind.

Elegance - Rhapsody
www.johnson-tiles.com
01782 575575

Issan Inspirations Co. Ltd
Tel no + +66(0)818635357
Web: www.iisilk.com

Jim Dickens T: 01543 415588 W: www.jimdickens.co.uk E: jimdickens@btconnect.com
For details of stockists please contact us or see website.

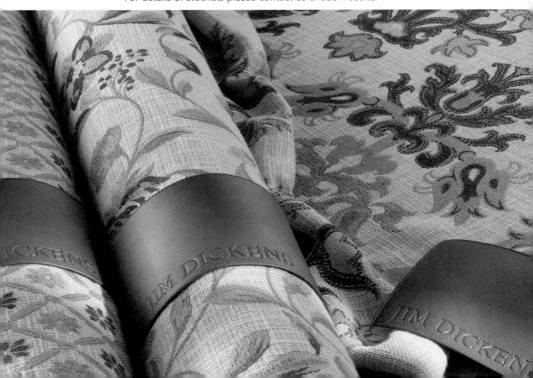

the rubber flooring company

ideal for kitchens and bathrooms
hard-wearing and easy to clean
easy installation for quick,
long-lasting makeovers
wide range of colours and styles in stock for next working day delivery

for free samples or advice at any stage call us on

FREEPHONE 0800 849 6386
or visit us at therubberflooringcompany.co.uk

www.thelittlegreene.com

Dominic and Frances Bromley, the creatives behind Scabetti, specialise in distinctive sculptural lighting such as the award winning Shoal, shown here in Stein's Seafood Restaurant.

Scabetti
t: +44 (0) 1538 371471
e: info@scabetti.co.uk
www.scabetti.co.uk

AN Building & Maintenance is a building
company with a difference: the company
is run by architectural designers.

AN Building & Maintanance Ltd
Tel: +44(0)845 262 3456
Mob: +44(0)7825 279287
Web: www.abnassetti.com

Annabella Nessetti, Architectural Designer.

Vola
Tel: 020 7580 7722
Web: www.vola.com

Dare Studio
Tel | 01273 607192
Web: www.darestudio.co.uk

Fired Earth
Tel: 01295 814 315
Web: www.firedearth.com

Aeon
Tel: 01525 379505
Web: www.aeon.uk.com

The Parsifal
Tel: 0113 201 2240
Web: www.airuno.co.uk

SOURCEBOOK
index:
YOUR A-Z OF **MUST-HAVE** CONTACTS

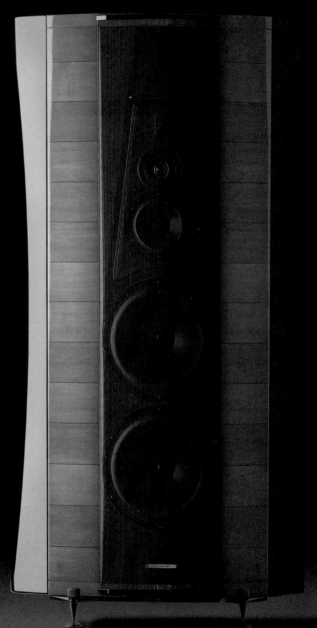

Associations

ART AND ARCHITECTURE ASSOCIATION
70, Cowcross Street, London, EC1M 6EJ
Email: info@artandarchitecture.co.uk
www.artandarchitecture.co.uk

ASCER
Association of Ceramic Tile
Manufacturers of Spain.
www.spaintiles.info

ASSOCIATION OF INTERIOR SPECIALISTS
Olton Bridge
245 Warwick Road, Solihull,
West Midlands, B92 7AH
Tel: 0121 707 0077
Fax: 0121 706 1949
www.ais-interiors.org.uk
Email: info@ais-interiors.org.uk

BRITISH CONTRACT FURNISHING AND DESIGN ASSOCIATION
Project House
25 West Wycombe Road
High Wycombe
Buckinghamshire, HP11 2LQ
Tel: 01494 896790
Fax: 01494 896799
www.thebcfa.com

BRITISH FURNITURE MANUFACTURERS' ASSOCIATION (BFM)
Wycombe House
9 Amersham Hill
High Wycombe
Bucks, HP13 6NR
Tel: 01494 523021
Fax: 01494 474270
www.bfm.org.uk
Email: adam.mason@bfm.org.uk

BRITISH INSTITUTE OF INTERIOR DESIGN (BIID FORMERLY BIDA)
3/18 Chelsea Harbour Design Centre
London, SW10 0XE
Tel: 020 7349 0800
Fax: 020 7349 0500
www.bida.org
Email: enquiries@bida.org

FURNITURE INDUSTRY RESEARCH ASSOCIATION FIRA INTERNATIONAL LTD
Maxwell Road,
Stevenage,
Hertfordshire, SG1 2EW
Tel: +44 (0)1438 777700
Fax: +44 (0)1438 777800
www.fira.co.uk
Email: info@fira.co.uk

INTERNATIONAL FEDERATION OF INTERIOR ARCHITECTS AND DESIGNERS (IFI IDA)
317 Outram Road
#02-57, Concorde Shopping Centre
Singapore, 169075
Tel: +65 63386974
Email: info@ifiworld.org www.ifiworld.org

INTERNATIONAL INTERIOR DESIGN ASSOCIATION
Headquarters 222 Merchandise Mart Plaza,
Suite 567, Chicago, IL 60654-1103
Tel. 001 (312) 467 1950
Fax: 001 (312) 467 0779
www.iida.org
Email: iidahq@iida.org

INTERNATIONAL UNION OF ARCHITECTURE
Tour Maine Montparnasse - B.P. 158
33 Avenue du Maine, 75755 PARIS
cedex 15 - France
Tel: (33.1) 45 24 36 88
Fax: (33.1) 45 24 02 78
Email: uia@uia-architectes.org
www.uia-architectes.org

INTERIORS DESIGNERS INSTITUTE OF BRITISH COLUMBIA
Suite 400 - 601 W. Broadway, Vancouver,
BC Canada, V5Z 4C2
Tel: 604.298.5211
Fax: 604.421.5211
www.idibc.org
Email: info@idibc.org

LIGHTING INDUSTRY FEDERATION
Ground Floor, Westminster Tower,
3 Albert Embankment
London, SE1 7SL
Tel: 0207 793 3020
Fax: 0207 793 3003
www.lif.co.uk
Email: info@lif.co.uk

NATIONAL FIREPLACE ASSOCIATION
PO BOX 583
High Wycombe
Bucks, HP15 6XT
Tel: 0121 288 0050
Fax: 0870 130 6747
www.nfa.org.uk
Email: enquiry@nfa.org.uk

ROYAL INSTITUTE OF BRITISH ARCHITECTS (RIBA)
66, Portland Place,
London, W1B 1AD
Tel +44 (0)20 7307 3700
Fax +44 (0)20 7436 9112
www.ribafind.org
Email: cs@inst.riba.org

SOCIETY OF BRITISH INTERIOR DESIGN (SBID)
10, Cinnamon Row
Plantation Wharf
York Road
London, SW11 3TW
Tel: 0207 738 9383
Email: info@sbid.org
www.sbid.org

THE BATHROOM MANUFACTURERS ASSOCIATION
Federation House, Station Road,
Stoke on Trent, ST4 2RT
Tel: 01782 747123
Fax: 01782 747161
www.bathroom-association.org
Email: info@bathroom-association.org.uk

THE CONTRACT FLOORING ASSOCIATION
4c St Mary's Place, The Lace Market,
Nottingham, NG1 1PH
Tel: 0115 941 1126
Fax: 0115 941 2238
www.cfa.org.uk
Email: info@cfa.org.uk

THE LIGHTING ASSOCIATION
Stafford Park 7, Telford,
Shropshire, TF3 3BQ
Tel: +44 (0) 1952 290905
Fax: +44 (0) 1952 290906
www.lightingassociation.com
Email: enquiries@lightingassociation.com

THE NATIONAL ASSOCIATION OF DECORATIVE FABRIC DISTRIBUTORS
One Windsor Cove, Suite 305
Columbia, South Carolina, 29223
Tel: 001-800-445-8629
Fax: 1-803-765-0860
www.nadfd.com
Email: info@nadfd.com

THE NATIONAL INSTITUTE OF CARPET AND FLOORLAYERS (NICF)
4d St. Mary's Place, The Lace Market
Nottingham, NG1 1PH
Tel: 0115 958 3077
Fax: 0115 941 2238
www.nicfltd.org.uk
Email: info@nicfltd.org.uk

THE TILE ASSOCIATION
Forum Court, 83 Copers Cope Road,
Beckenham
Kent, BR3 1NR
Tel: 020 8663 0946
Fax: 020 8663 0949
www.tiles.org.uk
E-mail info@tiles.org.uk

**THE UNDERFLOOR HEATING
MANUFACTURERS ASSOCIATION**
39 Ethelbert Road, Minnis Bay
Birchington, KENT, CT7 9PX
Tel. and Fax: 01843 842241
www.uhma.org.uk
Email: uhma410@aol.com

Antiques

WWW.ANTIQUES.CO.UK
P O Box 77
Leeds, LS25 9AH
United Kingdom
Tel: 0845 260 2 260
Email: iain@antiques.co.uk
Web: www.antiques.co.uk

Thousands of antiques available at your fingertips throughout the United Kingdom, Search for specific items nearest to your home or office. England is the heart of the Antiques world and we hope that this site will help you find exactly what you are looking for. Happy hunting.

ANTIQUE CHURCH FURNISHINGS
Rivernook Farm, Sunnyside,
Walton On Thames, Surrey, KT12 2ET
www.churchantiques.com
email: info@churchantiques.com
Tel: 01932 252736
Fax: 01932 252736

ANTIQUE LEATHERS
Tel: 01963 370126
Fax: 01963 370126

ART FURNITURE
20 Century Road London, E17 6JB
www.artfurniture.co.uk
email: arts-and-crafts@artfurniture.co.uk
Tel: 020 8527 0676

BELL FINE ART
67b Parchment Street
Winchester, SO23 8AT
www.bellfineart.co.uk
email: bellfineart@btclick.com
Tel: 01962 860439
Fax: 01962 860439

CARVERS & GILDERS LTD
Unit 44 Spaces Business Centre
Ingate Place
London, SW8 3NS
www.carversandgilders.com
email: info@carversandgilders.com
Tel: 0207 498 5070
Fax: 0207 498 1221

CLASSIC BINDINGS LTD
61 Cambridge Street
London
SW1V 4PS
www.classicbindings.net
email: info@classicbindings.net
Tel: 0207 834 5554
Fax: 0207 630 6632

CLASSIC BINDINGS LTD
61 Cambridge Street
London
SW1V 4PS
www.classicbindings.net
email: info@classicbindings.net
Tel: 0207 834 5554
Fax: 0207 630 6632

COHEN & COHEN
Po Box 366
Reigate
RH2 2BB
www.cohenandcohen.co.uk
email: info@cohenandcohen.co.uk
Tel: 01737 242180
Fax: 01737 226236

ELAINE PHILLIPS ANTIQUES LTD
2 Royal Parade
Harrogate
North Yorkshire
HG1 2SZ
www.elainephillipsantiques.co.uk
email: info@elainephillipsantiques.co.uk
Tel: 01423 569745

FELJOY ANTIQUES
Chelsea Galleries. 69-73 Portobello Road,
London
W11 2QB
www.feljoy-antiques.co.uk
email: joy@feljoy-antiques.co.uk
Tel: 02084 458706
Fax: 0208 446 0933

FRITZ FRYER ANTIQUE LIGHTING
23 Station Street
Ross On Wye
HR9 7AG
www.fritzfryer.co.uk
email: enquiries@fritzfryer.co.uk
Tel: 01989 567416
Fax: 01989 566742

G.B. ELIAS ANTIQUES LTD
Elias Antiques Of Dorking
The Dorking Desk Shop
41/42 West Street, Dorking,Surrey
RH4 1BU
www.desk.uk.com
email: dorkingdesks@aol.com
Tel: 01306 883327
Fax: 01306 875363

GILBERT & DALE
The Old Chapel, Church St. Ilchester, Somerset.
BA22 8LN
www.gilbertanddaleantiques.co.uk
email: roy@roygilbert.com
Tel: 01935 840464
Fax: 01935 841599

GEORGIAN ANTIQUES
10 Pattison Street, Leith Links,
Edinburgh, EH6 7HF
Tel: 0131 553 7286
Fax: 0131 553 6299
info@georgianantiques.net
www.georgianantiques.net

Situated in Edinburgh, we are Scotland's leading antique dealer with a five floor converted warehouse in Leith, just ten minutes from the city centre. We carry an extensive range of quality antiques including fine Georgian, Victorian, Edwardian furniture, as well as large mirrors and the more unusual quirky items.
Open: Mon-Fri 8.30am-5.30pm
Sat 10am-2pm

GRAYS
58 Davies Street
& 1-7 Davies Mews
Mayfair
W1K 5AB
www.graysantiques.com
Tel: 02076 297034
Fax: 02074 939344

GUINEVERE WAREHOUSE
Unit 5
92-104 Carnwath Road
London, SW6 3HW
www.guinevere.co.uk
email: sales@guineverewarehouse.co.uk
Tel: 020 7731 5401
Fax: 020 77368267

HALCYON DAYS LTD
14 Brook Street
London
W1S 1BD
www.halcyondays.co.uk
email: info@halcyondays.co.uk
Tel: 020 7629 8811
Fax: 020 7514 5471

HOUSE OF MIRRORS
597 Kings Rd,
SW6 2EL
www.houseofmirrors.co.uk
email: info@housemirrors.co.uk
Tel: 02077 365885
Fax: 02076 109188

HOWE
93 Pimlico Road
Belgravia
London
SW1W 8PH
www.howelondon.com
email: design@howelondon.com
Tel: 02(0) 7730 7987
Fax: 02(0) 7730 0157

JB SILVERWARE
139a New Bond Street
London
W1S 2TN
www.jbsilverware.co.uk
email: elliot@jbsilverware.co.uk
Tel: 0207 6291251
Fax: 0207 4953001

LENNOX CATO ANTIQUES
1 The Square
Church Street
Edenbridge
KENT
www.lennoxcato.com
email: cato@lennoxcato.com
Tel: 01732 865988
Fax: 01732 865988

LENNOX CATO ANTIQUES
1 The Square
Church Street
Edenbridge
KENT
www.lennoxcato.com
email: cato@lennoxcato.com
Tel: 01732 865988
Fax: 01732 865988

LENNOX CATO ANTIQUES
1 The Square
Church Street
Edenbridge, KENT
www.lennoxcato.com
email: cato@lennoxcato.com
Tel: 01732 865988
Fax: 01732 865988

NICHOLAS HASLAM LTD
12-14 Holbein Place
London
SW1W 8NL
www.nicholashaslam.com
Tel: 020 7730 8623
Fax: 020 7730 6679

NOSTALGIA UK LTD
Hollands Mill
61 Shaw Heath
Stockport
SK3 8BH
www.nostalgia-uk.com
email: sales@nostalgia-uk.com
Tel: 0161 4777706
Fax: 0161 4772267

NOSTALGIA UK LTD
Hollands Mill
61 Shaw Heath
Stockport
SK3 8BH
www.nostalgia-uk.com
email: sales@nostalgia-uk.com
Tel: 0161 4777706
Fax: 0161 4772267

O F WILSON LTD
2-4 Queen's Elm Parade
Old Church Street
Chelsea
SW3 6EJ
email: ofw@email.msn.com
Tel: 02073 529554
Fax: 02073 510765

ODEON DESIGN LTD
76-78 St Edward Street
Leek
Staffordshire
ST13 5 DL
odeonantiques.co.uk
email: odeonantiques@hotmail.com
Tel: 01538 378188
Fax: 01538 384235

PERIOD PIANO COMPANY
Park Farm Oast
Hareplain Road
Biddenden, Kent
TN27 8LJ
www.periodpiano.com
email: periodpiano@btopenworld.com
Tel: 01580 291393
Fax: 01580 291393

PERIOD PIANO COMPANY
Park Farm Oast
Hareplain Road
Biddenden, Kent
TN27 8LJ
www.periodpiano.com
email: periodpiano@btopenworld.com
Tel: 01580 291393
Fax: 01580 291393

PETA SMYTH ANTIQUE TEXTILES
42 Moreton Street
London
SW1V 2PB
email: petasmyth@ukonline.co.uk
Tel: 020 7630 9898
Fax: 020 7630 5398

PUGHS ANTIQUES
North Road-Leominster
HR6 0AA
www.pughsantiques.com†
email: sales@pughsantiques.com
Tel: 01568 616646
Fax: 01568 616 144

PUGHS ANTIQUES
North Road-Leominster
HR6 0AA
www.pughsantiques.com†
email: sales@pughsantiques.com
Tel: 01568 616646
Fax: 01568 616 144

PUGHS ANTIQUES
North Road-Leominster
HR6 0AA
www.pughsantiques.com†
email: sales@pughsantiques.com
Tel: 01568 616646
Fax: 01568 616 144

RAMSAY
69 Pimlico Road London
SW1W8NE
email: ramsayprints@btclick.com
Tel: 0207 730 6776
Fax: 0207 730 6775

REINDEER ANTIQUES
81 Kensington Church Street
London
W8 4BG
www.reindeerantiques.co.uk
email: london@reindeerantiques.co.uk
Tel: 02079 373754
Fax: 02079 377199

ROBERT HIRSCHHORN ANTIQUES
London
www.hirschhornantiques.com
email: info@hirschhornantiques.com
Tel: 020 77037443
Fax: 07831 405937

ROBERT HIRSCHHORN ANTIQUES
London
www.hirschhornantiques.com
email: info@hirschhornantiques.com
Tel: 020 77037443
Fax: 07831 405937

ROBERT HIRSCHHORN ANTIQUES
London
www.hirschhornantiques.com
email: info@hirschhornantiques.com
Tel: 020 77037443
Fax: 07831 405937

ROBERT MORLEY & CO LTD
34 Engate Street
Lewisham
London
SE13 7HA
morleypianos.co.uk
email: sales@morleypianos.co.uk
Tel: 0208 318 5838

ROBERT YOUNG ANTIQUES
Tel: 02072 287847
Fax: 02075 850489

SUFFOLK HOUSE ANTIQUES
High Street
Yoxford
Suffolk
IP173EP
www.suffolk-house-antiques.co.uk
email: andrew.singleton@suffolk-house-
antiques.co.uk
Tel: 01728 668122
Fax: 01728 668122

TFW
3 Easton Lane
Winnall
Winchester
SO23 7RU
www.tfw.co.uk
email: sales@tfw.co.uk
Tel: 01962 858820
Fax: 01962 858828

THE CAST IRON RECLAMATION COMPANY
The White House
8a Burgh Heath Road
Epsom, Surrey
KT17 4LJ
perfect-irony.com
email: enquiries@perfect-irony.com
Tel: 02089 775977
Fax: 01372 726845

THE CONRAN SHOP
81 Fulham Road
London
SW3 6RD
www.conranshop.co.uk
Tel: 02075 897401
Fax: 02078 237015

THE HIDDEN TV COMPANY
Coleham Head
Shrewsbury
SY3 7BJ
www.theantiquedealers.com
Tel: 01743 351 120
Fax: 01743 271 047

THE WATER MONOPOLY
16-18 Lonsdale Road
London
NW6 6RD
www.watermonopoly.com
email: enquiries@watermonopoly.com
Tel: 020 7624 2636
Fax: 0207 624 2631

TONY WILLIAMS ANTIQUE MIRRORS
The Old Cottage
13 The Green, Welbourn
Lincoln
LN5 0NJ
www.williamsantiquemirrors.co.uk
email: info@williamsantiquemirrors.co.uk
Tel: 01400 273688
Fax: 07711 207551

WALKER GALLERIES LTD
6 Montpellier Gardens
Harrogate
HG1 2TF
email: wgltd@aol.com
Tel: 01423 567933
Fax: 01423 536664

WALTER MOORES & SON
Po Box 5338
Market Harborough
United Kingdom
LE16 7WG
www.waltermoores.co.uk
email: waltermoores@btinternet.com
Tel: +44(0)7071 226202 or +44(0)77 100 19045
Fax: +44(0)7071 226202

WALTER MOORES & SON
Po Box 5338
Market Harborough
United Kingdom
LE16 7WG
www.waltermoores.co.uk
email: waltermoores@btinternet.com
Tel: +44(0)7071 226202 or +44(0)77 100 19045
Fax: +44(0)7071 226202

WILDWOOD ANTIQUES
Manor Farm, Heyshott
Midhurst
West Sussex
GU29 0DR
www.wildwoodwood.co.uk
Tel: 01730 816880/ 07989815355

WOKA LAMPS VIENNA
Singerstrasse 16
Vienna
A-1010
www.woka.com
Tel: 00 43 1 513 2912
Fax: 00 43 1 513 8505

WWW.ANTIQUES.CO.UK
P.O. Box 77
Leeds
LS25 9AH
www.antiques.co.uk
email: mail@antiques.co.uk
Tel: 0845 260 2 260

WWW.ANTIQUES.CO.UK
P.O. Box 77
Leeds, LS25 9AH
www.antiques.co.uk
email: mail@antiques.co.uk
Tel: 0845 260 2 260

Architectural Features

ANTIQUE BUILDINGS LTD
Dunsfold
Godalming
Surrey, GU8 4NP
antiquebuildings.com
email: info@antiquebuildings.com
Tel: 01483 200477

ANTIQUE CHURCH FURNISHINGS
Rivernook Farm
Sunnyside
Walton On Thames, Surrey
KT12 2ET
www.churchantiques.com
email: info@churchantiques.com
Tel: 01932 252736
Fax: 01932 252736

ASHLEY BAXTER STONEMASONRY
Glebe Cottage
Bishopstrow
Warminster
BA12 9HN
www.ashleybaxter.co.uk
email: enquiries@ashleybaxter.co.uk
Tel: 07887 691008
Fax: 01985 212424

BRIGHTON ROC
Unit 4, Fowlswick Farm, Allington Chippenham
Wiltshire Sn14 6qe United Kingdom
Chippenham
Wiltshire
SN14 6QE
www.brightonroc.co.uk/
email: brighton.roc@btconnect.com
Tel: 01249 782270
Fax: 01249 782270

CLIVE CHRISTIAN
1st Floor, South Dome
Chelsea Harbour Design Centre
London
SW10 OXE
www.clive.com
email: london@clive.com
Tel: 020 73499200

COPPER DEVELOPMENT ASSOCIATION
5 Grovelands Business Centre
Boundary Way
Hemel Hempstead, Herts
HP2 7TE
www.copperinfo.co.uk
email: mail@copperdev.co.uk
Fax: 01442 275716

FUSION GLASS DESIGNS LIMITED
365 Clapham Road
London
SW9 9BT
www.fusionglass.co.uk
email: info@fusionglass.co.uk
Tel: 020 7738 5888
Fax: 020 7738 4888

INGERSOLL RAND SECURITY TECHNOLOGIES
Bescot Crescent
Walsall
West Midlands
WS1 4DL
security.ingersollrand.co.uk
email: info@ingersollrand.co.uk
Tel: 01922 707400
Fax: 0208 6121096

MARIANNE FORREST
3&8 Coach House Cloisters
Hitchin Street
Baldock, Herts
AL8 6QZ
www.marianneforrest.com
Tel: 01462 491992

P-ARCH
Petek Mimarlik Muhendislik
Portakal Yokusu Duvarci Sok
19/2 34300 Ortakoy İStanbul
TURKEY
www.p-arch.com
email: info@p-arch.com
Tel: 0090 212 2366498
Fax: 0090 212 2599588

SAINT-GOBAIN ECOPHON LTD
Tel: 01256 850977
Fax: 01256 851550

SAND & BIRCH DESIGN
Viale Xxi Aprile, 10 04100 Latina (Lt) Italy
4100
www.sandbirch.com
email: info@sandbirch.com
Tel: 0039 (0)773 1762584
Fax: 0039 (0)773 1760684

SOURCE
Victoria Park Business Centre
BA1 3AX
www.sourced.it
Tel: 01225 469200

STAALTECH ALUMINIUM
Leigraafseweg 6
Doesburg
The Netherlands
6983BP
www.staaltech.info
email: ronald@staaltech.info
Tel: 0031 313 419104
Fax: 0031 313 415303

STONE ICONS LTD
The Swan Centre
25 Rosemary Road
London
SW17 0AR
www.stoneicons.com
email: info@stoneicons.com
Tel: 07785 394 587
Fax: 020 8541 5750

THE ROOFLIGHT COMPANY
Wychwood Business Centre
Milton Road
Shipton Under Wychwood
OX7 6XU
www.therooflightcompany.co.uk
email: info@therooflightcompany.co.uk
Tel: 01993 833108
Fax: 01993 831066

TROX UK LTD
Caxton Way
Thetford
Norfolk
IP24 3SQ
www.troxuk.co.uk
email: info@troxuk.co.uk
Tel: 01842 754545
Fax: 01842 763051

ARCHITECTURAL IRONMONGERY

ANTHONY OUTRED ANTIQUES LTD
72 Pimlico Road
London
SW1W 8LS
www.outred.co.uk
email: antiques@outred.co.uk
Tel: 0207 730 7948

BANBURY PLASTIC FITTINGS LTD
Unit 13, Overfield
Thorpe Way
Banbury
OX16 4XR
www.bpfittings.co.uk
email: sales@bpfittings.co.uk
Tel: 01295 264 800
Fax: 01295 264 901

BASSETT & FINDLEY LTD
Talbot Road North,
Wellingborough
Northants
NN8 1QS
www.bassettandfindley.co.uk
email: info@bassettandfindley.ltd.uk
Tel: 01933 224 898
Fax: 01933 227 731

BRASS FOUNDRY CASTINGS LTD
Po Box 226
Bexhill
TN40 9DS
www.brasscastings.co.uk
email: info@brasscastings.co.uk
Tel: 01424 845551
Fax: 01424 848404

CAIRNEY HARDWARE LTD
1 Distillery Lane
EH12 8RE
www.cairney.com
email: gerardv@cairney.com
Tel: 01313 131303
Fax: 01313 31305

CODELOCKS LTD
Castle Industrial Park
Kiln Road
Newbury
RG14 2EZ
www.codelocks.co.uk
email: sales@codelocks.co.uk
Tel: 01635 239645
Fax: 01636 239644

COPPER DEVELOPMENT ASSOCIATION
5 Grovelands Business Centre
Boundary Way
Hemel Hempstead, Herts
HP2 7TE
www.copperinfo.co.uk
email: mail@copperdev.co.uk
Fax: 01442 275716

DOVERHAY FORGE STUDIOS LTD
Porlock
Minehead
Somerset
TA24 8QB
www.doverhay.co.uk
email: jh@doverhay.co.uk
Tel: 01643 862444

DZ DESIGNS
The Old Mill House
Stanwell Moor
Staines
TW19 6BQ
email: dz_designs@btconnect.com
Tel: 01753 682266
Fax: 01753 682203

EUROLINK HARDWARE
Unit 5
Chancel Way
Halesowen
B62 8SE
www.eurolinkhardware.co.uk
email: info@eurolinkhardware.co.uk
Tel: 0121 501 2800
Fax: 0121 434 6989

FARMER BROS & J D BEARDMORE
319-321 Fulham Road
London
SW10 9QL
www.beardmore.co.uk
email: info@beardmore.co.uk
Tel: 020 7351 5444
Fax: 020 7351 5131

FARMER BROS & J D BEARDMORE
319-321 Fulham Road
London
SW10 9QL
www.beardmore.co.uk
email: info@beardmore.co.uk
Tel: 020 7351 5444
Fax: 020 7351 5131

FINESSE DESIGN
Project House
Villa Real
Consett, County Durham
DH8 6BP
www.finessedesign.com
email: sales@finessedesign.com
Tel: 01207 500050
Fax: 01207 599757

FRANCHI LOCKS & TOOLS LTD
278 Holloway Road
London
N7 6NE
www.franchi.co.uk
email: info@franchi.co.uk
Tel: 020 7607 2200
Fax: 020 7700 4050

FULHAM BRASS & IRONMONGERY LIMITED
905 Fulham Rd, London Sw6 5hu
www.fulhambrass.com
Tel: 0207 736 3246
Fax: 0207 736 3362

GIBBS AND DANDY
226 Dallow Road
Luton
LU1 1YB
email: luton@gibbsanddandy.com
Tel: 01582 798798
Fax: 01582 798799

INTERIOR ASSOCIATES
3 Highfield Road
Windsor
SL4 4DN
www.interiorassociates.co.uk
email: sales@interiorassociates.co.uk
Tel: 01753 865339
Fax: 01753 865339

INTERNATIONAL DOOR CONTROLS
www.int-door-controls.com
email: info@int-door-controls.com
Tel: 01384 893333
Fax: 01384 894837

ISAAC LORD LTD
185 Desborough Road
High Wycombe
Bucks
HP11 2QN
www.isaaclord.co.uk
email: info@isaaclord.co.uk
Tel: 01494 835200
Fax: 01494 835254

JOHN PLANCK LTD
3 Southern House / Anthony's Way /Medway
City Estate
Rochester
Kent
ME2 4DN
www.johnplanck.co.uk
email: sales@johnplanck.co.uk
Tel: 01634 720077
Fax: 01634 720111

KARCHER DESIGN
Design - Beschlage
Raiffeisenstreet 32
Bad Rappenau, Germany
74906
www.karcher-design.com
email: mail@karcher-design.com
Tel: 0049 7264 916452
Fax: 0049 7264 916410

LAIDLAW SOLUTIONS LTD
Strawberry Lane
Willenhall
West Midlands
WV13 3RS
www.laidlaw.net
email: shafiq.sharif@laidlaw.net
Tel: 01902 600 400
Fax: 01902 602315

LLOYD WORRALL, MILTON KEYNES
Tel: 01908 643364
Fax: 01908 643643

LOCKS & HANDLES
25 Effie Road
London
SW6 1EK
www.doorhandles.co.uk
email: sales@knobs.co.uk
Tel: 02075 812401
Fax: 02075 894928

MERLIN GLASS
Denmore House
Barn Street
Liskeard
PL14 4BL
www.merlinglass.co.uk
email: info@merlinglass.co.uk
Tel: 01579 342399
Fax: 01579 345110

MORRIS SINGER ART FOUNDERS
9 Swinborne Drive
Springwood Industrial Estate
Braintree
CM7 2YP
www.msaf.co.uk
email: chris@msaf.co.uk
Tel: 01376 343222
Fax: 01376 341793

OPTIMUM BRASSES
Castle Street
Bampton
Nr. Tiverton, Devon
EX16 9NS
www.optimumbrasses.co.uk
email: brass@optimumbrasses.co.uk
Tel: 01398 331515
Fax: 01398 331164

PACKER WOODTURNING LTD
157, Chemical Road
West Wilts Trading Estate
Westbury
BA13 4JN
www.packerwoodturning.com
email:
packerwoodturning@packerwoodturning.com
Tel: 0800 019 6000
Fax: 01373 859702

PHILIP WATTS DESIGN
Unit 11 Byron Industrial Est
Brookfield Rd
Arnold, Nottingham
NG5 7ER
www.philipwattsdesign.com
email: sales@philipwattsdesign.com
Tel: 0115 926 9756
Fax: 0115 920 5395

REDLAKE GROUP
Park Road
Faringdon
Oxfordshire
SN7 7BP
www.redlakegroup.xcom
email: njones@redlakegroup.com
Tel: 01367 241507
Fax: 01367 241705

ROMANYS LTD
104 Arlington Road
Camden Town
London
NW1 7HP
www.romanys.uk.com
Tel: 020 7424 0349
Fax: 020 7428 6465

RONIS-DOM LTD
Unit 1 Junction 2 Industrial Estate
Demuth Way
Oldbury
B69 4LT
www.ronis-dom.co.uk
email: sales@ronis-dom.co.uk
Tel: 0800 988 4348
Fax: 0800 988 4349

SLIMLINE SYSTEMS LIMITED
Woodwards Road
Walsall
WS2 9SL
www.slimline.co.uk
email: sales@slimlinesystems.co.uk
Tel: 01922 748860
Fax: 01922 748869

THE COAT HANGER COMPANY
Awb Ltd
Padholme Road East
Peterborough, Cambs, Uk
PE1 5XL
www.thecoathangercompany.com
email: sales@thecoathangercompany.com
Tel: 01733 555646
Fax: 01733 555887

THE SCREEN GALLERY
The Old Post Office
Abbotts Ann
Andover, Hampshire
SP11 7BG
www.thescreengallery.co.uk
email: info@thescreengallery.co.uk
Tel: 08700 637 547
Fax: 08700 637 548

TURNSTYLE DESIGNS
Baron Way Roundswell Business Park
Barnstaple
Devon
EX31 3TB
www.turnstyledesigns.com
email: sales@turnstyledesigns.com
Tel: 01271 325 325
Fax: 01271 328 248

WESSEX IRONMONGERY LTD
Cedar Unit 4
Dartington Industrial Estate
Dartington Devon
TQ9 6JY
www.wessexironmongery.co.uk
Tel: 01803 866176
Fax: 01803 863697

WILLIAMS IRONMONGERY LTD
11 Princelet Street
Spitalfields
London
E1 6QH
www.williams-ironmongery.co.uk
email: sales@williams-ironmongery.co.uk
Tel: 0207 247 8821
Fax: 0207 247 1638

YANNEDIS
Tel: 020 8550 8833
Fax: 020 8551 0026

AUTOMATED DOORS & GATES

ACCESS CONTROLS
72 Boston Road Leicester
LE4 1HB
www.accesscontrolsolutions.co.uk
email: info@accesscontrolsolutions.co.uk
Tel: 01162 366044
Fax: 01162 366360

ATLAS GROUP
868 Plymouth Road
Slough
Berkshire
SL1 4LP
www.atlasgroup.co.uk
email: info@atlasgroup.co.uk
Tel: 01753 696166
Fax: 01753 696916

IO-HOMECONTROL
47 Rue Maurice Flandin
69003 LYON
www.io-homecontrol.com
email: contact@io-homecontrol.com
Tel: +33 4 72 13 24 01
Fax: +33 4 72 13 23 12

KABA DOOR SYSTEMS LTD
Door Automation
Halesfield 4
Telford, Shropshire
TF7 4AP
www.kabadoorsystems.co.uk
email: info@kdt.kaba.com
Tel: 08700 005252
Fax: 08700 005253

BESPOKE PANELS/SCREENS

3D DISPLAYS LTD
Upper Brents Industrial Estate
ME13 7DZ
email: info@3ddisplays.co.uk
Tel: 01795 532947
Fax: 01795 539934

AUSTIN LUCE & COMPANY LTD
Elm Trees House
Effingham Road
Copthorne
RH10 3HX
www.austinluce.co.uk
email: enquiries@austinluce.co.uk
Tel: 01342 713310
Fax: 01342 718097

BASSETT & FINDLEY LTD
Talbot Road North,
Wellingborough
Northants
NN8 1QS
www.bassettandfindley.co.uk
email: info@bassettandfindley.ltd.uk
Tel: 01933 224 898
Fax: 01933 227 731

DENISE MT BASSO
3 Orchard Studios
Brook Green, Hammersmith
London
W6 7BU
www.bradleybasso.com
email: info@bradleybasso.com
Tel: 0207 6021840
Fax: 0207 6021840

DIANA SPRINGALL
Oast Cottage
2 Park Lane
Kemsing
TN15 6NU
email: dianaspringall@btinternet.com
Tel: 01732 761501
Fax: 01732 761501

DUFAYLITE DEVELOPMENT LTD
Cromwell Road
St Neots
Cambridgeshire
PE19 1QW
www.ultraboard.co.uk
email: enquiries@dufaylite.com
Tel: 01480 215000
Fax: 01480 405526

FAIROAKS TIMBER PRODUCTS
Tel: 01722 716779
Fax: 01722 716761

GLASSCASTS LTD
299 Haggerston Rd, London E8 4en
E8 4EN
www.glasscasts.co.uk
email: jeff@glasscasts.co.uk
Tel: 0207 2758 481
Fax: 0207 275 8481

GLASSECO LTD
Unit 5 ,Highams Farm
Sheepbarn Lane, Warlingham
Surrey
CR6 9PQ
www.glasseco.co.uk
email: info@glasseco.co.uk
Tel: 01959 576897
Fax: 01959 575902

ION GLASS LTD
Po Box 284
Burgess Hill
West Sussex
RH15 0WP
www.ionglass.co.uk
email: sales@ionglass.co.uk
Tel: 0845 658 9988
Fax: 0845 658 9989

JALI HOME DESIGN LIMITED
Albion Works
Church Lane, Barham,
Canterbury
CT4 6QS
www.jali.co.uk
email: sales@jali.co.uk
Tel: 01227 833333
Fax: 01227 831950

JOHN PAUL JACQUES
Unit H
1 Strawberry Vale
Twickenham
TW1 4RY
www.jpjacques.com
email: shoji@jpjacques.com
Tel: 020 8744 1414

KAREN LAWRENCE GLASS
Unit F 272, Riverside Business Centre
Brendon Valley
Wandsworth, London
SW18 4UQ
www.karenlawrenceglass.com
email: karen@karenlawrenceglass.com
Tel: 020 8874 7955

MARK FINZEL DESIGN & PHOTOGRAPHY
www.markfinzel.co.uk
email: mark@markfinzel.co.uk
Tel: 0771 259 0706

MEROFORM
Systemsxl Ltd
4 Marlton Way
Lancaster
LA1 5BW
www.systemsxl.com
email: info@systemsxl.com
Tel: 0845 094 2466
Fax: 0845 094 2470

N E J STEVENSON LTD
Church Lawford Business Centre
Limestone Hall Lane
Church Lawford
CV23 9HD
www.nejstevenson.co.uk
email: neil@nejstevenson.co.uk
Tel: 02476 544662
Fax: 02476 545345

STRETCHED FABRIC SYSTEMS
68a Compton Street, London
EC1V 0BN
www.stretchedfabricsystems.com
email: sales@stretchedfabricsystems.com
Tel: 02072 534608
Fax: 02072 535746

THE SCREEN GALLERY
The Old Post Office
Abbotts Ann
Andover, Hampshire
SP11 7BG
www.thescreengallery.co.uk
email: info@thescreengallery.co.uk
Tel: 08700 637 547
Fax: 08700 637 548

TRENT CONCRETE
Colwick
Nottingham
NG4 2BG
www.trentconcrete.co.uk
Tel: 01159 879747
Fax: 01159 879948

UREDALE GLASS
12 Market Place
Masham
North Yorkshire
HG4 4EF
www.uredale.co.uk
email: info@uredale.co.uk
Tel: 01765 689780
Fax: 01765 689780

BESPOKE STONE FIREPLACES

ASHLEY BAXTER STONEMASONRY
Glebe Cottage
Bishopstrow
Warminster
BA12 9HN
www.ashleybaxter.co.uk
email: enquiries@ashleybaxter.co.uk
Tel: 07887 691008
Fax: 01985 212424

FIREGROUP
5 Stenhouse Mill Wynd
Edinburgh
EH11 3LR
www.firegroup.co.uk
email: sales@firegroup.co.uk
Tel: 0131 444 2262
Fax: 0131 444 1726

HERITAGE STONEWORKS LTD
Unit 2 Southview Ind Est
Off Richard Lane
Tideswell
SK17 8PR
www.heritagestoneworks.co.uk
email: info@heritagestoneworks.co.uk
Tel: 01298 873173
Fax: 01298 873178

MARBLE HILL FIREPLACES
70-72 Richmond Road
Twickenham
TW1 3BE
www.marblehill.co.uk
Tel: 0208 892 1488
Fax: 0208 891 6591

STONE ICONS LTD
The Swan Centre
25 Rosemary Road
London
SW17 0AR
www.stoneicons.com
email: info@stoneicons.com
Tel: 07785 394 587
Fax: 020 8541 5750

CEILINGS

ANTIQUE BUILDINGS LTD
Dunsfold
Godalming
Surrey
GU8 4NP
antiquebuildings.com
email: info@antiquebuildings.com
Tel: 01483 200477

ASSOCIATION OF INTERIOR SPECIALISTS
Olton Bridge
245 Warwick Road
Solihull
B92 7AH
www.ais-interiors.org.uk
email: info@ais-interiors.org.uk
Tel: 0121 707 0077
Fax: 0121 706 1949

FABRIC ARCHITECTURE
Unit B4 Nexus
Hurricane Rd
Brockworth, Glos
GL3 4AG
www.fabricarchitecture.co.uk
email: info@fabarc.co.uk
Tel: 01452 612 800
Fax: 01452 621 200

GO INTERIORS LTD
Units C & D Lea Industrial Estate
Lower Luton Road
Harpenden
AL5 5EQ
www.gointeriors.co.uk
email: customercare@gointeriors.co.uk
Tel: 08700 111167
Fax: 08700 111168

INTERIOR PROPERTY SOLUTIONSLTD
Units 1-3 South Mundells
Welwyn Garden City
Hertfordshire
AL7 1EP
www.ips-interiors.co.uk
email: contact@ips-interiors.co.uk
Tel: 01707 331 078
Fax: 01707 328 828

KNAUF AMF CEILINGS LTD
Thames House
6 Church Street
Twickenham
TW1 3NJ
www.amfceilings.co.uk
email: sales@amfceilings.co.uk
Tel: 020 8892 3216
Fax: 020 8892 6866

KREON
5 St Saviours Wharf
Mill Street
London
SE1 2BF
www.kreon.com
email: salesuk@kreon.com
Tel: +44 20 7740 2112
Fax: +44 20 7740 2923

LASERPOD
Highmoor Park
Highmoor
Henley On Thames
RG9 5DH
www.laserpod.com
email: andy@laserpod.com
Tel: 01491 641 000

SAINT-GOBAIN ECOPHON LTD
Tel: 01256 850977
Fax: 01256 851550

SAS INTERNATIONAL
31 Suttons Business Park
London Road
Reading
RG6 1AZ
www.sasint.co.uk
email: enquiries@sasint.co.uk
Tel: 0118 929 0900
Fax: 0118 929 0901

STEVENSONS OF NORWICH LIMITED
Roundtree Way
Norwich
Norfolk
NR7 8SQ
www.stevensonsofnorwich.com
email: info@stevensonsofnorwich.com
Tel: 01603 400 824
Fax: 01603 405113

STEWARD DESIGN PANELS BV
P.o. Box 96
Gorinchem
Netherlands
4200 AB
www.designpanels.com
email: info@designpanels.com
Tel: 0031 1835 89099
Fax: 0031 1835 89823

STO LTD.
2 Gordon Avenue
Hillington Park
Glasgow, G52 4TG
www.sto.co.uk
email: info.uk@stoeu.com
Tel: 0141 892 8000
Fax: 0141 404 9001

STRETCH CEILINGS UK
Doman Road, Yorktown Industrial Estate,
Camberley, GU15 3DF
Tel: 01276 681000
Fax: 01276 406900
sales@stretchceilings.co.uk,
www.stretchceilings.co.uk

A World leader in Stretch Ceiling
installations, Stretch Ceilings are available
in an extensive range of Colours and
Finishes, requires no painting or
decoration, are hygienic and come with a
12 year Guarantee. The product is 100%
Recyclable and is fire rated to the new
euroclass standard B s2 d0, equivalent in
the UK to a Class 'O' Fire rating.

STRETCHED FABRIC SYSTEMS
68a Compton Street, London
EC1V 0BN
www.stretchedfabricsystems.com
email: sales@stretchedfabricsystems.com
Tel: 02072 534608
Fax: 02072 535746

TROX UK LTD
Caxton Way
Thetford
Norfolk
IP24 3SQ
www.troxuk.co.uk
email: info@troxuk.co.uk
Tel: 01842 754545
Fax: 01842 763051

CONSERVATORIES

DAVID FENNINGS CONSERVATORIES
3a Sunrise Business Park
Higher Shaftesbury Road
Blandford Forum, DT11 8ST
www.davidfenningsconservatories.co.uk
enquiries@davidfenningsconservatories.co.uk
Tel: 01258 459259
Fax: 01258 458129

DAVID SALISBURY
Bennett Road, Isleport Business Park,
Highbridge, Somerset, TA9 4PW
www.davidsalisbury.com
email: sales@davidsalisbury.com
Tel: 0844 800 8808

FOUR SEASONS SUN ROOMS
Lakeside House, Quarry Lane,
Chichester, West Sussex, PO19 8NY
email: info@roomoutside.com
Tel: 01243 538999
Fax: 01243 776313

GLASHAUS
APG Europe Ltd,
14 Marlton Way,
Lancaster, LA15BW
Tel: 0845 094 2466
Fax: 0845 094 2470
Email: info@glas-haus.co.uk
Web: www.glas-haus.co.uk

Looking for a modern conservatory,
which oozes quality, class & style?

Our GlasHaus conservatories are
constructed from ultra high performance,
self-cleaning, safety glass with solar
protection! We can provide integrated
photo voltaic cells in the roof producing
green energy, as well as LED lighting and
other features we're certain you'd want!

Interested to find out more? With no
obligation to buy, call us now for latest
offers!

J R WILLOUGHBY
www.jrwilloughby.co.uk
Tel: 0845 22 22 640

KLOEBER UK LTD
Klm Building
Earith Business Park
Meadow Drove
PE28 3QF
www.kloeber.co.uk
email: info@kloeber.co.uk
Tel: 01487 740044
Fax: 01487 740404

MALBROOK CONSERVATORIES
2 Crescent Stables
Upper Richmond Road
London
SW15 2TN
www.malbrook.co.uk
email: info@malbrook.co.uk
Tel: 02087 805522
Fax: 02087 803344

S:CRAFT
Newdown Farm
Micheldever
Winchester, Hampshire
SO21 3BT
www.s-craft.co.uk
email: sales@s-craft.co.uk
Tel: 01962 794530
Fax: 01962 794 531

TENSARC
95 Stirling Enterprise Park
Stirling
FK7 7RP
www.tensarc.co.uk
email: info@tensarc.co.uk
Tel: 01786 450083

TOWN & COUNTRY - FINE GLASS BUILDINGS
61 Lambeth Walk
London, SE11 6DX
www.townandcountryuk.com
email: london@townandcountryuk.com
Tel: 020 7091 0621
Fax: 020 7091 0622

VINCENT SHEPPARD
Industriepark 5
Spiere - Belgium, 8587
www.vincentsheppard.com
email: uk@vincentsheppard.com
Tel: 0032 5646 1111
Fax: 0032 56461112

WILLIAM LUSTY (UK) LTD
Hoo Lane, Chipping Campden,
Glos. GL55 6AU
www.lloyd-loom.co.uk
email: geoffreylusty@aol.com
Tel: 01386 840379
Fax: 01386 841322

COVING

DAVUKA GRP LTD
Tel: 020 8660 2854
Fax: 020 8645 2556
Email: info@davuka.co.uk
Web: www.davuka.co.uk

Suppliers of fine quality decorative
mouldings, nationwide.
Comprehensive range of interior
cornice, skirting, corbels, columns,
dado, architrave, ceiling roses etc, all
as fitted in top international hotels
and developments. See our website
for inspirational ideas and designs or
phone for catalogue and/or samples.

DECORATIVE LAMINATE

A. C. TOON LTD
Units 2-4 Warwick Street Ind. Estate
Storforth Lane
Chesterfield
S40 2TT
www.actoon.co.uk
email: sales@actoon.co.uk
Tel: 01246 223900
Fax: 01246 223901

AAZTEC CUBICLES
Tel: 01423 326400
Fax: 01423 325115

FORMICA LIMITED
1 Silver Fox Way
Cobalt Business Park
Newcastle Upon Tyne
NE27 0QJ
www.formica.com
email: info@formica.co.uk
Tel: 0191 259 3100
Fax: 0191 259 2648

NCS COLOUR CENTRE
1 Ancastle Green
Henley On Thames
Oxfordshire, United Kingdom
RG9 1TS
www.ncscolour.co.uk
Tel: 0149 141 1717
Fax: 0149 141 1231

TBS FABRICATIONS LTD
Martens Road
Northbank Industrial Park
Irlam, Manchester
M44 5AX
www.tbs-fabrications.com
email: info@tbs-fabrications.com
Tel: 0161 775 1871
Fax: 0161 775 8929

DOOR & WINDOW
IRONMONGERY

CAIRNEY HARDWARE LTD
Distillery Lane
H12 8RE
www.cairney.com
email: gerardv@cairney.com
Tel: 01313 131303
Fax: 01313 31305

CLEMENT STEEL WINDOWS LTD
Clement House
Weydown Road Industrial Estate
Haslemere
GU27 1HR
www.clementsteelwindows.com
email: info@clementwg.co.uk
Tel: 01428 643393
Fax: 01428 644436

CODELOCKS LTD
Castle Industrial Park
Kiln Road
Newbury
RG14 2EZ
www.codelocks.co.uk
email: sales@codelocks.co.uk
Tel: 01635 239645
Fax: 01636 239644

DICKINSON'S PERIOD HOUSE SHOPS
41 Corve Street, Ludlow SY8 2PG
5 Wyle Cop, Shrewsbury SY1 1UX
6 Market Place, Warwick CV34 4SD
www.periodhouseshops.com &
www.periodlightingshop.com
email: periodhouseshop@yahoo.co.uk
Tel: 01584 877276
Fax: 01584 875411

DRUMMOND'S
78 Royal Hospital Raod
Chelsea
London
SW3 4HN
www.drummonds-uk.com
email: info@drummonds-uk.com
Tel: 0207 376 4499
Fax: 0207 376 4488

EUROLINK HARDWARE
Unit 5
Chancel Way
Halesowen
B62 8SE
www.eurolinkhardware.co.uk
email: info@eurolinkhardware.co.uk
Tel: 0121 501 2800
Fax: 0121 434 6989

FARMER BROS & J D BEARDMORE
319-321 Fulham Road
London
SW10 9QL
www.beardmore.co.uk
email: info@beardmore.co.uk
Tel: 020 7351 5444
Fax: 020 7351 5131

FINESSE DESIGN
Project House
Villa Real
Consett, County Durham
DH8 6BP
www.finessedesign.com
email: sales@finessedesign.com
Tel: 01207 500050
Fax: 01207 599757

FRANCHI LOCKS & TOOLS LTD
278 Holloway Road
London
N7 6NE
www.franchi.co.uk
email: info@franchi.co.uk
Tel: 020 7607 2200
Fax: 020 7700 4050

FRANCO-FILE
Po Box 31, Tiverton, Devon
EX16 4YU
franco-file.co.uk
email: info@franco-file.co.uk
Tel: 01884 253556
Fax: 01884 251367

**FULHAM BRASS & IRONMONGERY
LIMITED**
905 Fulham Rd, London Sw6 5hu
www.fulhambrass.com
Tel: 0207 736 3246
Fax: 0207 736 3362

HAF (HANDLES AND FITTINGS)
Handles And Fittings Ltd
Haf House
Mead Lane, Hertford,
SG13 7AP
www.hafinternational.com
Tel: 01992 505 655
Fax: 01992 505 705

**INGERSOLL RAND SECURITY
TECHNOLOGIES**
Bescot Crescent
Walsall
West Midlands
WS1 4DL
security.ingersollrand.co.uk
email: info@ingersollrand.co.uk
Tel: 01922 707400
Fax: 0208 6121096

INTERNATIONAL DOOR CONTROLS
www.int-door-controls.com
email: info@int-door-controls.com
Tel: 01384 893333
Fax: 01384 894837

JIM LAWRENCE
The Ironworks
Lady Lane Industrial Estate
Hadleigh
IP7 6BQ
www.jim-lawrence.co.uk
email: sales@jim-lawrence.co.uk
Tel: 01473 828176
Fax: 01473 824074

JOHN PLANCK LTD
3 Southern House
Anthony's Way
Medway City Estate
Rochester
Kent
ME2 4DN
www.johnplanck.co.uk
email: sales@johnplanck.co.uk
Tel: 01634 720077
Fax: 01634 720111

KARCHER DESIGN
Design - Beschlage
Raiffeisenstreet 32
Bad Rappenau
Germany
74906
www.karcher-design.com
email: mail@karcher-design.com
Tel: 0049 7264 916452
Fax: 0049 7264 916410

LAIDLAW SOLUTIONS LTD
Strawberry Lane
Willenhall
West Midlands
WV13 3RS
www.laidlaw.net
email: shafiq.sharif@laidlaw.net
Tel: 01902 600 400
Fax: 01902 602315

LLOYD WORRALL, MILTON KEYNES
Tel: 01908 643364
Fax: 01908 643643

LOCKS & HANDLES
25 Effie Road
London
SW6 1EK
www.doorhandles.co.uk
email: sales@knobs.co.uk
Tel: 02075 812401
Fax: 02075 894928

NANZ
20 Vandam Street
Fifth Floor
New York
Usa
10013
www.nanz.com
Tel: 001 212 367 7000

PACKER WOODTURNING LTD
157
Chemical Road
West Wilts Trading Estate
Westbury
BA13 4JN
www.packerwoodturning.com
packerwoodturning@packerwoodturning.com
Tel: 0800 019 6000
Fax: 01373 859702

PREFIT
14 Sovereign Park, Coronation Road,
London, NW10 7QP
Tel: +44 (0) 20 8961 4777
Fax: +44 (0) 20 8961 4747
Web: www.prefit-fittings.com
Prefit is a division of J. Preedy & Sons Limited

PREFIT are renowned for their
innovative architectural Ironmongery
which is specified for a diverse range
of applications in securing Glass. The
product portfolio includes Manual and
Automated Pivoting and sliding Doors,
Structural Balaustraude and point
fixings, Shower Screens and Hinges,
Handles and Locksets. All Prefit
products are design led to ensure they
enhance yet remain functional.

PHILIP WATTS DESIGN
Unit 11 Byron Industrial Est
Brookfield Rd
Arnold, Nottingham
NG5 7ER
www.philipwattsdesign.com
email: sales@philipwattsdesign.com
Tel: 0115 926 9756
Fax: 0115 920 5395

STAALTECH ALUMINIUM
Leigraafseweg 6
Doesburg
The Netherlands
6983BP
www.staaltech.info
email: ronald@staaltech.info
Tel: 0031 313 419104
Fax: 0031 313 415303

TURNSTYLE DESIGNS
Baron Way Roundswell Business Park
Barnstaple
Devon
EX31 3TB
www.turnstyledesigns.com
email: sales@turnstyledesigns.com
Tel: 01271 325 325
Fax: 01271 328 248

WILLIAMS IRONMONGERY LTD
11 Princelet Street
Spitalfields
London, E1 6QH
www.williams-ironmongery.co.uk
email: sales@williams-ironmongery.co.uk
Tel: 0207 247 8821
Fax: 0207 247 1638

YANNEDIS
Tel: 020 8550 8833
Fax: 020 8551 0026

ELECTRICAL ACCESSORIES

BANBURY PLASTIC FITTINGS LTD
Unit 13, Overfield
Thorpe Way
Banbury
OX16 4XR
www.bpfittings.co.uk
email: sales@bpfittings.co.uk
Tel: 01295 264 800
Fax: 01295 264 901

BDC
Bdc Head Office
550 White Hart Lane
London
N17 7RQ
www.bdc.co.uk
email: sales@bdc.co.uk
Tel: 0844 811 0040
Fax: 0844 811 0041

BISSELL
The Boatyard
105 Straight Road
Old Windsor
SL4 2SE
www.bissell.com
email: gary.clowes@bissell.com
Tel: 0870 2250109
Fax: 017538 67684

BISSELL
The Boatyard
105 Straight Road
Old Windsor
SL4 2SE
www.bissell.com
email: gary.clowes@bissell.com
Tel: 0870 2250109
Fax: 017538 67684

BISSELL
The Boatyard
105 Straight Road
Old Windsor
SL4 2SE
www.bissell.com
email: gary.clowes@bissell.com
Tel: 0870 2250109
Fax: 017538 67684

BRILLIANT FIRES
Thwaites Close
Shadsworth Business Park
Blackburn
BB1 2QQ
www.brilliantfires.co.uk
email: info@brilliantfires.co.uk
Tel: 01254 682384
Fax: 01254 672647

CMD LTD, POWERPLAN
Brockholes Way
Claughton-On-Brock
Preston
PR3 0PZ
www.powerplan.co.uk
email: enquiries@powerplan.co.uk
Tel: 01995 640844
Fax: 01995 640798

DANLERS LTD
Danlers Business Centre
Vincients Road
Chippenham
SN14 6NQ
www.danlers.co.uk
email: sales@danlers.co.uk
Tel: 01249 443377
Fax: 01249 443388

DICKINSON'S PERIOD HOUSE SHOPS
141 Corve Street, Ludlow Sy8 2pg
65 Wyle Cop, Shrewsbury Sy1 1ux
66 Market Place, Warwick Cv34 4sd
www.periodhouseshops.com &
www.periodlightingshop.com
email: periodhouseshop@yahoo.co.uk
Tel: 01584 877276
Fax: 01584 875411

FLAMERITE FIRES
Greenhough Road
Lichfield
Staffs
WS13 7AU
www.flameritefires.com
email: info@flameritefires.com
Tel: 01543 251 122
Fax: 01543 251 133

FULHAM BRASS & IRONMONGERY LIMITED
905 Fulham Rd, London Sw6 5hu
www.fulhambrass.com
Tel: 0207 736 3246
Fax: 0207 736 3362

LEGRAND ELECTRIC LTD
Great King Street North
Birmingham
B19 2LF
Tel: 0870 608 9000

LLOYTRON PLC
Laltex House, Leigh Commerce Park
Greenfold Way
Leigh, Lancashire
WN7 3XH
www.lloytron.com
email: lloytron@laltex.com
Tel: 01942 687040
Fax: 01942 687070

MUSIC IN EVERY ROOM LTD
16 The Sidings
Guiseley
Leeds
LS20 8BX
www.musicineveryroom.co.uk
email: sales@musicineveryroom.co.uk
Tel: 0845 094 1857
Fax: 01943 872768

S:CRAFT
Newdown Farm
Micheldever
Winchester, Hampshire
SO21 3BT
www.s-craft.co.uk
email: sales@s-craft.co.uk
Tel: 01962 794530
Fax: 01962 794 531

TURNSTYLE DESIGNS
Baron Way Roundswell Business Park
Barnstaple
Devon
EX31 3TB
www.turnstyledesigns.com
email: sales@turnstyledesigns.com
Tel: 01271 325 325
Fax: 01271 328 248

WANDSWORTH GROUP
Albert Drive
Woking
Surrey
GU21 5SE
www.wandsworthgroup.com
email: info@wandsworthgroup.com
Tel: 01483 713400
Fax: 01483 740384

FALSE CEILINGS
KNAUF AMF CEILINGS LTD
Thames House
6 Church Street
Twickenham
TW1 3NJ
www.amfceilings.co.uk
email: sales@amfceilings.co.uk
Tel: 020 8892 3216
Fax: 020 8892 6866

MEROFORM
Systemsxl Ltd
14 Marlton Way
Lancaster
LA1 5BW
www.systemsxl.com
email: info@systemsxl.com
Tel: 0845 094 2466
Fax: 0845 094 2470

TENSARC
95 Stirling Enterprise Park
Stirling
FK7 7RP
www.tensarc.co.uk
email: info@tensarc.co.uk
Tel: 01786 450083

FIREPLACES & FIRE SURROUNDS
ACRES FARM CLUB FENDERS
Acres Farm
Bradfield
Nr Reading
RG7 6JH
www.acresfarm.co.uk
email: enquiries@acresfarm.co.uk
Tel: 01189 744305
Fax: 01189 744012

ASHLEY BAXTER STONEMASONRY
Glebe Cottage
Bishopstrow
Warminster
BA12 9HN
www.ashleybaxter.co.uk
email: enquiries@ashleybaxter.co.uk
Tel: 07887 691008
Fax: 01985 212424

BE MODERN
Western Approach
South Shields
Tyne & Wear
NE33 5QZ
www.bemodern.com
email: enquiries@bemodern.com
Tel: 0191 455 3571
Fax: 0191 456 5556

BFM EUROPE LTD
Gordon Banks Drive
Trentham Lakes
Stoke-On-Trent
ST4 4TJ
www.bfm-europe.com
email: info@bfm-europe.com
Tel: 01782 339000
Fax: 01782 339009

BRILLIANT FIRES
Thwaites Close
Shadsworth Business Park
Blackburn
BB1 2QQ
www.brilliantfires.co.uk
email: info@brilliantfires.co.uk
Tel: 01254 682384
Fax: 01254 672647

CAMINOS STOVES, LANDY VENT LTD
Foster House
2 Redditch Rd
Studley, Warwickshire
B80 7AX
www.caminosstoves.co.uk
email: sales@caminosstoves.co.uk
Tel: 01527 857814
Fax: 01527 854101

CAPITAL FIREPLACES LTD
Units 12-17 Henlow Trading Estate
Henlow
Bedfordshire
SG16 6DS
www.capitalfireplaces.co.uk
email: alex.shaw@capitalfireplaces.co.uk
Tel: 01462 813138
Fax: 08009 804847

CLASSIC MANTELS
Unit B2, Ford Airfield Industrial Estate
Ford
Arundel, West Sussex
BN18 0HY
www.classicmantels.co.uk
email: classicmantels@yahoo.co.uk
Tel: 01903 717770
Fax: 01903 716100

DOVERHAY FORGE STUDIOS LTD
Porlock
Minehead
Somerset
TA24 8QB
www.doverhay.co.uk
email: jh@doverhay.co.uk
Tel: 01643 862444

FIREGROUP
5 Stenhouse Mill Wynd
Edinburgh
EH11 3LR
www.firegroup.co.uk
email: sales@firegroup.co.uk
Tel: 0131 444 2262
Fax: 0131 444 1726

ENGLISH FIREPLACES
Unit 6 The Brows, Farnham Rd,
Liss, Hants, GU33 6JG
Tel: 01730 897600
Fax: 01730 897609
E: info@englishfireplaces.co.uk
W: www.englishfireplaces.co.uk

We make beautiful hand carved fire
surrounds from marble and limestone.
Stock designs range from the
contemporary to authentic period
reproductions. In addition we have a
speedy highly cost effective bespoke
service. We supply throughout the UK
supported by a network of experienced
qualified installers.

FLAMERITE FIRES
Greenhough Road
Lichfield
Staffs, WS13 7AU
www.flameritefires.com
email: info@flameritefires.com
Tel: 01543 251 122
Fax: 01543 251 133

FLAMEWAVE FIRES
P.o.box 611
Folkestone, CT18 7WY
www.flamewavefires.co.uk
email: info@flamewavefires.co.uk
Tel: 0845 257 5028
Fax: 0845 257 5038

GRANTS MARBLE MANUFACTORY LTD
And Scagliola Workshop
Bradley Mill
Newton Abbot, TQ12 1LZ
www.grantsmarble.com
email: mark@grantsmarble.co.uk
Tel: 01626 331699
Fax: 01626 331699

HERITAGE STONEWORKS LTD
Unit 2 Southview Ind Est
Off Richard Lane
Tideswell, SK17 8PR
www.heritagestoneworks.co.uk
email: info@heritagestoneworks.co.uk
Tel: 01298 873173
Fax: 01298 873178

MAGIGLO LTD
Lysander Close, Broadstairs,
Kent, CT10 2YJ
www.magiglo.co.uk
email: sales@magiglo.co.uk
Tel: 01843 602863
Fax: 01843 86 0108

For your nearest stockist of Montpellier's award winning fireplaces or a copy of our brochure please call 01452 714 800 or log on to www.montpellier.co.uk

MONTPELLIER
NATURAL STONE FOR EVERY HOME

MARBLE HILL FIREPLACES
70-72 Richmond Road
Twickenham TW1 3BE
www.marblehill.co.uk
Tel: 0208 892 1488
Fax: 0208 891 6591

MINSTERSTONE LTD
Pondhayes Farm
Dinnington
Hinton St George TA17 8SU
www.minsterstone.com
email: sales@minsterstone.ltd.uk
Tel: 01460 52277
Fax: 01460 57865

MORLEY STOVE COMPANY LTD
Marsh Lane
Ware
Herts SG12 9QB
www.morley-stoves.co.uk
email: info@morley-stoves.co.uk
Tel: 01920 468001
Fax: 01920 463893

NOSTALGIA UK LTD
Hollands Mill
61 Shaw Heath
Stockport SK3 8BH
www.nostalgia-uk.com
email: sales@nostalgia-uk.com
Tel: 0161 4777706
Fax: 0161 4772267

PICTURE HOUSE CABINETS
Po Box 421
Surrey
KT14 6YR
www.picturehouse.eu
email: info@picturehouse.eu
Tel: 01932 345 184
Fax: 01932 402128

REAL FLAME
80 New Kings Road, Fulham, SW6 4LT
Tel: 020 7731 5025
E-mail: sales@realflame.co.uk
Web: www.realflame.co.uk

Over 30 years ago Real Flame pioneered the development of the decorative gas fire in the UK. Since then we have been installing "England's Finest Fireplaces" for our architect, designer and builder clients in some of the most important buildings in the country as well as for our private domestic clients. Whatever your needs for a fire, we can help you achieve the effect you're looking for. Please visit our website to see for yourself, or better still our showroom in London to see the wide variety of solutions we have available.

SMART FIRE LTD
Lyon House
160-166 Borough High St, SE1 1JR
www.ecosmartfire.com
email: uk(at)ecosmartfire.com
Tel: 020 7173 5000
Fax: 020 7173 5001

SMITH'S ENVIRONMENTAL PRODUCTS
Units 1-2 Blackall Industrial Estate
South Woodham Ferriers
Chelmsford, Essex, CM3 5UW
www.smiths-env.com
email: info@smiths-env.com
Tel: 01245 324900
Fax: 01245 324422

SPIRIT FIRES LIMITED
4 Beaumont Square
Aycliffe Industrial Park
Newton Aycliffe, Co Durham, DL5 6SW
www.spiritfires.co.uk
Tel: 01325 327221
Fax: 01325 327929

GLASS & GLAZING

BALCONY SYSTEMS LTD
Unit 5 Forest Row Business Pk
Station Road
Forest Row
RH18 5DW
www.balconette.co.uk
email: enquiries@balconette.co.uk
Tel: 01342 410 411
Fax: 01342 410412

CATRIN JONES ARCHITECTURAL GLASS
www.catrinjones.co.uk
email: catrin@catrinjones.co.uk
Tel: 01792 469256
Fax: 08701 302830

CLAUDIA PHIPPS ARCHITECTURAL GLASS
18. Horn Street
Nunney
Frome
BA114NP
www.claudiaphipps.co.uk
email: info@claudiaphipps.co.uk
Tel: 01373 836367

DAEDALIAN GLASS LTD
The Old Smithy, Cold Row, Carr Lane
Stalmine
Poulton - Le - Fylde
FY6 9DW
www.daedalian-glass.co.uk
email: chris@daedalian-glass.co.uk
Tel: 01253 702531
Fax: 01253 702532

DAVID FENNINGS CONSERVATORIES
3a Sunrise Business Park
Higher Shaftesbury Road
Blandford Forum
DT11 8ST
www.davidfenningsconservatories.co.uk
enquiries@davidfenningsconservatories.co.uk
Tel: 01258 459259
Fax: 01258 458129

DENISE MT BASSO
3 Orchard Studios
Brook Green, Hammersmith
London
W6 7BU
www.bradleybasso.com
email: info@bradleybasso.com
Tel: 0207 6021840
Fax: 0207 6021840

FOUR SEASONS SUN ROOMS
Lakeside House
Quarry Lane
Chichester, West Sussex
PO19 8NY
email: info@roomoutside.com
Tel: 01243 538999
Fax: 01243 776313

FUSION GLASS DESIGNS LIMITED
365 Clapham Road
London
SW9 9BT
www.fusionglass.co.uk
email: info@fusionglass.co.uk
Tel: 020 7738 5888
Fax: 020 7738 4888

INTERGRATED GLASS FORMING
Tel: 01454 880892
Fax: 01454 880892

JP GLASS & DECOR LTD
Units 1-6 Eastcote Ind Estate
Eastcote
Middlesex
HA4 9XG
www.jpglass.com
email: sales@jpglass.com
Tel: 02084 292999
Fax: 02088 684314

KLOEBER UK LTD
Klm Building
Earith Business Park
Meadow Drove
PE28 3QF
www.kloeber.co.uk
email: info@kloeber.co.uk
Tel: 01487 740044
Fax: 01487 740404

daedalian
glass design

FabriLAM Laminated Doors

Introducing the new range of doors from Daedalian Glass.

Tough yet stylish, each door has a luxury voil fabric laminated between 2 pieces of safety glass. All our doors are wipe clean, made to measure and each one available in a range of styles, frameless or framed to suit. Also available are a range of lead crystal handles, as shown, and hinges to fit any location. Delivery nationwide.

01253 702531
www.daedalian-glass.co.uk

MALBROOK CONSERVATORIES
2 Crescent Stables
Upper Richmond Road
London
SW15 2TN
www.malbrook.co.uk
email: info@malbrook.co.uk
Tel: 02087 805522
Fax: 02087 803344

MEROFORM
Systemsxl Ltd
14 Marlton Way
Lancaster
LA1 5BW
www.systemsxl.com
email: info@systemsxl.com
Tel: 0845 094 2466
Fax: 0845 094 2470

RUPERT SCOTT LTD
The Glass Studio
Broadlands Enterprise Park
St Davids
SA62 6BR
www.rupertscott.com
email: glass@rupertscott.com
Tel: 0845 450 7684
Fax: 0845 017 7685

SAPER GLASS INDUSTRIES LTD
Thames House
Longreach Road
Barking, Essex
IG11 0JR
www.saperglass.co.uk
email: tech.sales@saperglass.co.uk
Tel: 020 8594 4949
Fax: 020 8594 5252

SASHA WARD GLASS
19 Salisbury Road
Marlborough
Wiltshire
SN8 4AD
email: sasha@artward.org.uk
Tel: 01672 515638
Fax: 01672 516738

SCHOTT UK LTD
Drummond Road
Stafford
United Kingdom
ST16 3EL
www.schott.com/uk
email: info.uk@schott.com
Tel: 01785 223166

SOLAR GARDÆ
Ball Mill Top Business Park
Grimley
Worcestershire
WR2 6LS
www.solargard.co.uk
email: solargard@touchdownpr.com
Tel: +44 (0)1905 640 400
Fax: +44 (0)1905 640 500

STAALTECH ALUMINIUM
Leigraafseweg 6
Doesburg
The Netherlands
6983BP
www.staaltech.info
email: ronald@staaltech.info
Tel: 0031 313 419104
Fax: 0031 313 415303

STAINED GLASS STUDIO
The Meadows Off Blanche Lane
South Mimms
Herts
EN6 3PD
stainedglassstudio.co.uk
email: matthew@stainedglassstudio.co.uk
Tel: 01707 66 11 77
Fax: 01707 66 11 77

VITRICS
14 Rue Gambetta
Mesnil-Le-Roi
78600
www.vitrics.com
Tel: 0870 777 1101

LEADED LIGHTS & WINDOWS

ANDREW MOOR ASSOCIATES
14 Chamberlain Street
London
NW1 8XB
www.andrewmoor.co.uk
email: andrew@andrewmoor.co.uk
Tel: 02075 868181
Fax: 02075 868484

BRADLEY BASSO
3 Orchard Studios
Brook Green, Hammersmith
London
W6 7BU
www.bradleybasso.com
email: info@bradleybasso.com
Tel: 0207 602 1840

CLEMENT STEEL WINDOWS LTD
Clement House
Weydown Road Industrial Estate
Haslemere
GU27 1HR
www.clementsteelwindows.com
email: info@clementwg.co.uk
Tel: 01428 643393
Fax: 01428 644436

DENISE MT BASSO
3 Orchard Studios
Brook Green, Hammersmith
London
W6 7BU
www.bradleybasso.com
email: info@bradleybasso.com
Tel: 0207 6021840
Fax: 0207 6021840

LEAD & LIGHT
35a Hartland Road
NW1 8DB
Tel: 02074 850997
Fax: 02072 842660

MERRIN JOINERY
Unit 9 Cunliffe Drive
Kettering
Northamptonshire
NN16 8LD
www.merrinjoinery.com
email: enquiries@merrinjoinery.com
Tel: 01536 514442
Fax: 01536 514442

PRISMS GLASS DESIGN
Unit 31 Kingsgate Workshops
114 Kingsgate Road
NW6 2JG
www.prismsglass.com
email: prisms.glass@virgin.net
Tel: 02076 243240
Fax: 02076 243240

SASHA WARD GLASS
19 Salisbury Road
Marlborough
Wiltshire
SN8 4AD
email: sasha@artward.org.uk
Tel: 01672 515638
Fax: 01672 516738

STAINED GLASS STUDIO
The Meadows Off Blanche Lane
South Mimms
Herts
EN6 3PD
stainedglassstudio.co.uk
email: matthew@stainedglassstudio.co.uk
Tel: 01707 66 11 77
Fax: 01707 66 11 77

TONY SANDLES GLASS LTD
Unit 6, Park Farm, Park Road, Great
Chesterford, Essex
CB10 1RN
www.sandles-glass.co.uk
email: tony@sandles-glass.co.uk
Tel: 01799 531516
Fax: 01799 531516

LIFTS

PICKERINGS LIFTS
Globe Elevator Works
Po Box 19, Stockton On Tees
Cleveland
TS20 2AD
www.pickerings.co.uk
email: info@pickerings.co.uk
Tel: 01642 607161
Fax: 01642 677638

PARTITIONS

AAZTEC CUBICLES
Tel: 01423 326400
Fax: 01423 325115

ALBION DESIGN & FABRICATION LTD
4-16 Gosforth Close
Middlefield Industrail Estate
Sandy
SG191RB
www.albion-manufacturing.com
email: info@albion-manufacturing.com
Tel: 01767 692313
Fax: 01767 683157

ASSOCIATION OF INTERIOR SPECIALISTS
Olton Bridge
245 Warwick Road
Solihull
B92 7AH
www.ais-interiors.org.uk
email: info@ais-interiors.org.uk
Tel: 0121 707 0077
Fax: 0121 706 1949

BRITISH GYPSUM
Head Office
East Leake
Loughborough
LE12 6HX
www.british-gypsum.com
email: bgtechnical.enquiries@bpb.com
Tel: 01159 451000
Fax: 01159 451901

BROCKHOUSE
Aztec House
137 Molesey Avenue
West Molesey
KT8 2RY
www.brockhouse.net
email: sales@brockhouse.net
Tel: 01905 330055
Fax: 01905 330234

GO INTERIORS LTD
Units C & D Lea Industrial Estate
Lower Luton Road
Harpenden
AL5 5EQ
www.gointeriors.co.uk
email: customercare@gointeriors.co.uk
Tel: 08700 111167
Fax: 08700 111168

INTERIOR PROPERTY SOLUTIONSLTD
Units 1-3 South Mundells
Welwyn Garden City
Hertfordshire
AL7 1EP
www.ips-interiors.co.uk
email: contact@ips-interiors.co.uk
Tel: 01707 331 078
Fax: 01707 328 828

KABA DOOR SYSTEMS LTD
Door Automation
Halesfield 4
Telford, Shropshire
TF7 4AP
www.kabadoorsystems.co.uk
email: info@kdt.kaba.com
Tel: 08700 005252
Fax: 08700 005253

OPTIMA PRODUCTS LTD
Courtyard House
Westend Road
High Wycombe, Buckinghamshire
HP11 2QB
www.optimasystems.com
email: marketing@optima-group.co.uk
Tel: 01494 492 725
Fax: 01494 492 726

PROCOL LTD
New Hall
Market Place
Melksham
SN12 6EX
www.procol.ltd.uk
email: nick@procol.ltd.uk
Tel: 01225 701701
Fax: 01225 701702

SODEM SYSTEM UK LIMITED
Units 2 - 4 Maylan Court
Corby
NN17 4DR
www.sodemsystem.com
email: sales@sodem.co.uk
Tel: 01536 408686
Fax: 01536 408687

STORAGE CONCEPTS LTD
Pate Road , Leicester Road Industrial Estate ,
Melton Mowbray , Leicestershire
LE13 0RG
www.storageconcepts.co.uk
Tel: 01664 410414
Fax: 01664 569969

THE SCREEN GALLERY
The Old Post Office
Abbotts Ann
 Andover, Hampshire
SP11 7BG
www.thescreengallery.co.uk
email: info@thescreengallery.co.uk
Tel: 08700 637 547
Fax: 08700 637 548

TRADEMARK INTERIORS LTD
8 Marchmont Gate
Boundary Way
Hemel Hempstead, Herts
HP27BF
www.tmark.co.uk
email: barrycollins@tmark.co.uk
Tel: 01442 260022
Fax: 01442 232244

PLASTERWORK & MOULDINGS

GRANTS MARBLE MANUFACTORY LTD
And Scagliola Workshop
Bradley Mill
Newton Abbot
TQ12 1LZ
www.grantsmarble.com
email: mark@grantsmarble.co.uk
Tel: 01626 331699
Fax: 01626 331699

LOCKER & RILEY (FIBROUS PLASTERING) LTD
42-50 Bancrofts Road
South Woodham Ferrers
Chelmsford
CM3 5UQ
www.lockerandriley.com
Tel: 01245 322022
Fax: 01245 322033

REVIVAL DECORATIVE MOULDINGS
Pennyfarthing Barn
Water End
Maulden, Bedfordshire
MK45 2BD
www.revivalplaster.co.uk
email: salesr@revivalplaster.co.uk
Tel: 01525 862717

STEVENSONS OF NORWICH LIMITED
Roundtree Way
Norwich
Norfolk
NR7 8SQ
www.stevensonsofnorwich.com
email: info@stevensonsofnorwich.com
Tel: 01603 400 824
Fax: 01603 405113

THE SCAGLIOLA COMPANY
Chapeltown Business Centre
231 Chapeltown Road
Leeds
LS7 3DX
www.scagliolaco.com
email: info@scagliolaco.com
Tel: 01132 626811
Fax: 0113 2626811

STAIRCASES & HANDRAILS

GRADUS LIMITED
Park Green
Macclesfield
Cheshire
SK11 7LZ
www.gradusworld.com
email: sales@gradusworld.com
Tel: 01625 428 922
Fax: 01625 433 949

HADDONCRAFT FORGE
The Forge House
East Haddon
Northampton
NN6 8DB
www.haddoncraft.co.uk
email: info@haddoncraft.co.uk
Tel: 01604 772 027
Fax: 01604 770 027

INTERIOR ASSOCIATES
3 Highfield Road
Windsor
SL4 4DN
www.interiorassociates.co.uk
email: sales@interiorassociates.co.uk
Tel: 01753 865339
Fax: 01753 865339

KENNGOTT STAIRS LTD
New Inn Farm
Dawson Lane
Leyland
PR25 5DB
email: keith.barrett@kenngott.de
Tel: 01772 423441

KENSINGTON GROUP
23-25 Ribocon Way
Luton
LU4 9UR
www.balustrade-systems.com
email: sales@kensingtonforge.co.uk
Tel: 01582 563794
Fax: 01582 491925

KENSINGTON GROUP
23-25 Ribocon Way
Luton, LU4 9UR
www.balustrade-systems.com
email: sales@kensingtonforge.co.uk
Tel: 01582 563794
Fax: 01582 491925

LAIDLAW SOLUTIONS LTD
Strawberry Lane
Willenhall
West Midlands, WV13 3RS
www.laidlaw.net
email: shafiq.sharif@laidlaw.net
Tel: 01902 600 400
Fax: 01902 602315

MERRIN JOINERY
Unit 9 Cunliffe Drive
Kettering
Northamptonshire, NN16 8LD
www.merrinjoinery.com
email: enquiries@merrinjoinery.com
Tel: 01536 514442
Fax: 01536 514442

POLAIR LTD
17 Purdeys Way
Purdeys Industrial Estate
Rochford. Essex, SS4 1ND
www.polairltd.co.uk
Tel: 01702 544141
Fax: 01702 544263

MATT LIVSEY HAMMOND

MATT LIVSEY HAMMOND
Designer and producer of fine bespoke metal balustrading and architectural metalwork, Matt Livsey Hammond has established an impressive portfolio of work undertaken for a wide range of interior designers, architects and private clients. With over 16 years of experience, Matt Livsey Hammond specialises in filigree work, curving staircase balustrades and interior gates. Matt Livsey Hammond provides a complete service from design and construction to fitting and finishing. However an advisory and design-only service is also available. Further information and examples are available on our website at
www.mattlivseyhammond.co.uk
or contact us at
matt@mattlivseyhammond.co.uk

SG SYSTEM PRODUCTS LTD
Unit 22
Wharfedale Road
Ipswich
IP1 4JP
www.handrailsuk.co.uk
email: sales@sgsystems.co.uk
Tel: 01473 240055
Fax: 01473 461616

SG SYSTEM PRODUCTS LTD
Unit 22
Wharfedale Road
Ipswich
IP1 4JP
www.handrailsuk.co.uk
email: sales@sgsystems.co.uk
Tel: 01473 240055
Fax: 01473 461616

SPIRAL CONSTRUCTION LTD
Tel: 01326 574497
Fax: 01326 574760

SPM INTERNATIONAL LTD
Unit 4 Houndhill Park
Bolton Road
Wath Upon Dearne
S63 7JY
www.spm-international.com
email: stephen_woodhead@hotmail.com
Tel: 01709 871111
Fax: 01709 871122

SPM INTERNATIONAL LTD
Unit 4 Houndhill Park
Bolton Road
Wath Upon Dearne
S63 7JY
www.spm-international.com
email: stephen_woodhead@hotmail.com
Tel: 01709 871111
Fax: 01709 871122

STAIRLIFTS

PICKERINGS LIFTS
Globe Elevator Works
Po Box 19, Stockton On Tees
Cleveland
TS20 2AD
www.pickerings.co.uk
email: info@pickerings.co.uk
Tel: 01642 607161
Fax: 01642 677638

STONE FINISHES

DIAPOL GRANITE LTD
Kasesalu 4
Saue
76505 - ESTONIA
www.diapol.co.uk
email: jason@diapol.co.uk
Tel: 020 8099 7828
Fax: 020 7012 1297

DREAMWALL
18 Glebe Road Scartho
Grimsby
North East Lincolnshire
DN33 2HL
www.dreamwall.co.uk
email: info@dreamwall.co.uk
Tel: 01472 750552
Fax: 01472 750552

ISLAND STONE

Island Stone specialises in manufacturing unique natural stone tiles and cladding tiles. Rustic Cladding is made up of 8 individual wedges of precision-cut stone to create a 3D woven design.

For your nearest stockist please call
Tel: +44 0800 083 9351
www.islandstone.co.uk

FAIRHAVEN AND WOODS LTD
Northfield Farm Stoneyard
Lode Road, Bottisham
Cambridge, CB25 9DN
www.fairhavengroup.co.uk
email: office@fairhavengroup.co.uk
Tel: 01223 812555
Fax: 01223 812554

H & L MARBLE LTD
Unit 2 Abbey Wharf
Mount Pleasant
Wembley, HA0 1NR
www.hlmarble.co.uk
email: sales@hlmarble.co.uk
Tel: 02089 035811
Fax: 02089 033930

KIRKSTONE
Skelwith Bridge
Ambleside
Cumbria, LA22 9NN
www.kirkstone.com
email: info:kirkstone.com
Tel: 01539 433296
Fax: 015394 34006

M. J. WRIGHT & SONS LTD.
Units 104 - 106, Northwick Business Centre
Blockley, Moreton-In-Marsh
Gloucestershire, GL56 9RF
www.wrightsofcampden.co.uk
email: office@mjwrights.fsnet.co.uk
Tel: (01386) 700497
Fax: (01386) 701144

MARBLE HEATING COMPANY
Po Box 51292, London, SE17 3AA
www.marbleheating.co.uk
email: sales@marbleheating.co.uk
Tel: 0845 230 0877
Fax: 0845 230 0878

MARBLE CITY LIMITED
22 Smugglers Way, London, SW18 1EG
Tel: 0208 8711191
Fax: 0208 8749276
Email: sales@marble-city.co.uk
Web: www.marble-city.co.uk

Marble City are a bespoke natural and composite stone company, specialising in the template, manufacture and installation of worktops, cladding and tiling for both residential and commercial work.

Natural stone flooring
Marble & granite worktops
Bespoke bathrooms

Call us on 01452 714 800 or visit www.montpellier.co.uk

MONTPELLIER
NATURAL STONE FOR EVERY HOME

SHANGHAI LAUTUS MARBLE CO
3 Yeda Road, Songjiang, Shanghai, China 201608
www.lautus-marble.com
email: info@lautus-marble.com
Tel: 0086 21 5031 7155
Fax: 0086 21 5032 5955

STONE PRODUCTIONS LTD
Tel: 02088 719257
Fax: 02088 719259

THE SCAGLIOLA COMPANY
Chapeltown Business Centre
231 Chapeltown Road
Leeds
LS7 3DX
www.scagliolaco.com
email: info@scagliolaco.com
Tel: 01132 626811
Fax: 0113 2626811

TOUCHSTONE WORKTOPS LTD
Unit 2 Chase Rd. Trading Est.
51 Chase Rd.
London
NW10 6LG
www.touchstoneworktops.com
email: sales@touchstoneworktops.com
Tel: 020 8963 7450
Fax: 020 8963 7455

TRENT CONCRETE
Colwick
Nottingham
NG4 2BG
www.trentconcrete.co.uk
Tel: 01159 879747
Fax: 01159 879948

STOVES

The Ceramic Stove Company

THE CERAMIC STOVE COMPANY
4 Earl Street
Oxford
OX2 0JA
Tel/Fax: +44 (0)1865 245077
Email: info@ceramicstove.com
Web: www.ceramicstove.com

The Ceramic Stove Company continues to offer a diverse range of high-quality, high-efficiency, heat-retaining woodburning ceramic stoves and ovens from manufacturers who are concerned about style, efficiency and the environment in equal measure.

WINDOWS, DOORS & SHUTTERS

BALCONY SYSTEMS LTD
Unit 5 Forest Row Business Pk
Station Road
Forest Row
RH18 5DW
www.balconette.co.uk
email: enquiries@balconette.co.uk
Tel: 01342 410 411
Fax: 01342 410412

BASSETT & FINDLEY LTD
Talbot Road North,
Wellingborough
Northants
NN8 1QS
www.bassettandfindley.co.uk
email: info@bassettandfindley.ltd.uk
Tel: 01933 224 898
Fax: 01933 227 731

BLIND FASHION
Unit 12
Jubilee Way
Grange Moor, Wakefield, WF4 4TD
www.blindfashion.com
email: sales@blindfashion.co.uk
Tel: 01 924 844610
Fax: 01924 844618

BRADBURY SECURITY
Dunlop Way
Queensway Industrial Estate
Scunthorpe
DN16 3RN
www.bradburyuk.com
email: sales@bradburyuk.com
Tel: 01724 271 999
Fax: 01724 271 888

CRITTALL WINDOWS LIMITED
Francis House, Freebournes Road,
Witham, Essex, CM8 3UN
Tel 01376 530800
Fax 01376 530801
E-mail: hq@crittall-windows.co.uk
Website: www.crittall-windows.com

Crittall designed and manufactured the first standard steel windows in the 1920's. Today's units replicate that same classic elegant slimline styling whilst offering superb thermal performance that meets the latest requirements of Part L of the Building Regulations. With hot dipped galvanising and a Duralife polyester powder coat finish, maintenance is kept a minimum.

CLAUDIA PHIPPS ARCHITECTURAL GLASS
18. Horn Street
Nunney
Frome
BA114NP
www.claudiaphipps.co.uk
email: info@claudiaphipps.co.uk
Tel: 01373 836367

CLEMENT STEEL WINDOWS LTD
Clement House
Weydown Road Industrial Estate
Haslemere
GU27 1HR
www.clementsteelwindows.com
email: info@clementwg.co.uk
Tel: 01428 643393
Fax: 01428 644436

DAVID FENNINGS CONSERVATORIES
3a Sunrise Business Park
Higher Shaftesbury Road
Blandford Forum
DT11 8ST
www.davidfenningsconservatories.co.uk
enquiries@davidfenningsconservatories.co.uk
Tel: 01258 459259
Fax: 01258 458129

DAVID SALISBURY
Bennett Road
Isleport Business Park
Highbridge, Somerset
TA9 4PW
www.davidsalisbury.com
email: sales@davidsalisbury.com
Tel: 0844 800 8808

DECORATIVE LIVING
The Studio
CHISWICK LONDON W4
www.decorativeliving.co.uk
email: info@decorativeliving.co.uk
Tel: 020 89950037

DISAPPEARING DOOR CO
3 Southern House / Anthony's Way /Medway City Estate
Rochester
Kent
ME2 4DN
www.disappearingdoors.co.uk
email: sales@disappearingdoors.co.uk
Tel: 08450 720 102
Fax: 01634 720 866

DRAKS INTERIOR DOOR SYSTEMS LIMITED
Unit 221 -225 Heyford Park
Upper Heyford
Oxon
OX25 5HA
www.draksonline.co.uk
email: info@draksonline.co.uk
Tel: 01869 232989
Fax: 01869 232979

FAIROAKS TIMBER PRODUCTS
Tel: 01722 716779
Fax: 01722 716761

HAF (HANDLES AND FITTINGS)
Handles And Fittings Ltd
Haf House
Mead Lane , Hertford
SG13 7AP
www.hafinternational.com
Tel: 01992 505 655
Fax: 01992 505 705

INGERSOLL RAND SECURITY TECHNOLOGIES
Bescot Crescent
Walsall
West Midlands
WS1 4DL
security.ingersollrand.co.uk
email: info@ingersollrand.co.uk
Tel: 01922 707400
Fax: 0208 6121096

INTERIOR ASSOCIATES
3 Highfield Road
Windsor
SL4 4DN
www.interiorassociates.co.uk
email: sales@interiorassociates.co.uk
Tel: 01753 865339
Fax: 01753 865339

KABA DOOR SYSTEMS LTD
Door Automation
Halesfield 4
Telford, Shropshire
TF7 4AP
www.kabadoorsystems.co.uk
email: info@kdt.kaba.com
Tel: 08700 005252
Fax: 08700 005253

KLOEBER UK LTD
Klm Building
Earith Business Park
Meadow Drove
PE28 3QF
www.kloeber.co.uk
email: info@kloeber.co.uk
Tel: 01487 740044
Fax: 01487 740404

LEADERFLUSH SHAPLAND
Milnhay Road
Langley Mill
Nottingham
NG16 4AZ
www.leaderflushshapland.co.uk
email: enquiries@leaderflushshapland.co.uk
Tel: 01773 530500
Fax: 01773 530040

MALBROOK CONSERVATORIES
2 Crescent Stables
Upper Richmond Road
London
SW15 2TN
www.malbrook.co.uk
email: info@malbrook.co.uk
Tel: 02087 805522
Fax: 02087 803344

MERRIN JOINERY
Unit 9 Cunliffe Drive
Kettering
Northamptonshire
NN16 8LD
www.merrinjoinery.com
email: enquiries@merrinjoinery.com
Tel: 01536 514442
Fax: 01536 514442

MIVAN LTD
Newpark
Greystone Road
Antrim
BT41 2QN
www.mivan.com
email: hq@mivan.com
Tel: 02894 481000
Fax: 02894 466338

PURLFROST LTD
180 Park Avenue, London, NW10 7XH
Tel: 020 8961 7337
info@purlfrost.com
www.purlfrost.com

"Your windows onto the world"

When you need privacy but don't want
heavily dressed windows, the subtle
quality of Purlfrost window film offers a
light and contemporary alternative.
Purlfrost film is a self-adhesive vinyl that
when applied gives the appearance of
etched glass and at a fraction of the cost.
Purlfrost have a fantastic range of
designs, which can be cut out of the film
to suit your exact window
measurements. This facility is ideal for
house numbers to go above a front door.

PLANTATION SHUTTERS
Unit 4 St George's Court
131 Putney Bridge Road
London, SW15 2PA
www.plantation-shutters.co.uk
email: sales@plantation-shutters.co.uk
Tel: 0208 871 9222
Fax: 020 8871 0041

PREMDOR
Birthwaite Business Park
Huddersfield Road
Darton, Barnsley, S75 5JS
www.premdor.co.uk
email: ukmarketing@premdor.com
Tel: 0844 209 000 8
Fax: 01226 388808

RONIS-DOM LTD
Unit 1 Junction 2 Industrial Estate
Demuth Way
Oldbury, B69 4LT
www.ronis-dom.co.uk
email: sales@ronis-dom.co.uk
Tel: 0800 988 4348
Fax: 0800 988 4349

S:CRAFT
Newdown Farm
Micheldever
Winchester, Hampshire, SO21 3BT
www.s-craft.co.uk
email: sales@s-craft.co.uk
Tel: 01962 794530
Fax: 01962 794 531

SHUTTER FRONTIER LTD
2 Rosemary Farmhouse, Rosemary Lane,
Flimwell, East Sussex, TN5 7PT
www.shutterfrontier.co.uk
email: jane@shutterfrontier.co.uk
Tel: 01580 879761 / 07708 229 295

VENTROLLA
Central Office, Crimple Court
Hornbeam Business Park
Harrogate
HG2 8PB
www.ventrolla.co.uk
email: info@ventrolla.co.uk
Tel: 0800 0277 454
Fax: 01423 859321

WINE CELLARS

SPIRAL CELLARS LTD
Tel: 0845 241 2768
E-mail: info@spiralcellars.com
Web: www.spiralcellars.com

Have your own real wine cellar …
Differentiate your home from others by
installing a Spiral Cellar. It is a modular
concrete construction that can be
located beneath any ground floor
room, requires no power to run and
provides the optimum environment for
wine storage. Available in 5 sizes,
storing from 650-1900 bottles.
Installation takes no more than 5
working days by Spiral Cellars teams.

Bathrooms

2020 TECHNOLOGIES
10b Eagley House, Deakins Business Park
The Hall Coppice
Egerton, Bolton
BL7 9RP
www.2020technologies.com
email: uksales@2020.net
Tel: 01204 304 040
Fax: 01204 304 422

BRITISH BATHROOM CENTRE
Oxgate House
Oxgate Lane
London
NW2 7HU
www.bathcentre.com
email: sales@bathcentre.com
Tel: 020 8453 7000
Fax: 020 8830 8056

CAESARSTONE
Gorrels Way
Trans-Pennine Industrial Estate
WF3 3LY
www.caesarstone.uk.com
email: info@ebor.co.uk
Tel: 01706 863 600

DOMOVARI GMBH
Bruchfeld 87
47809 Krefeld
www.domovari.de
Tel: 0049 2151 15509 0
Fax: 0049 2151 15509 16

ELLBEE LTD
Grangefield Industrial Estate
Pudsey
West Yorkshire
LS28 6LF
www.ellbee.co.uk
email: sales@ellbee.co.uk
Tel: 0113 257 9711
Fax: 0113 236 2891

HYDRA-SPA
Unit P Little Moor Lane
Loughborough
Leceistershire
LE11 1SF
www.hydraspa.co.uk
email: info@premservices.co.uk
Tel: 01509 611092
Fax: 01509 266835

KEUCO (UK) LTD
Amersham House
Mill Street
Berkhamsted, Herts
HP4 2DT
www.keuco.de
email: klaus@keuco.co.uk
Tel: 01442 865220
Fax: 01442 865260

LIVINGHOUSE
59-61
Fisherton Street
Salisbury, SP27SU
www.livinghouse.co.uk
email: sales@livinghouse.co.uk
Tel: 01722 415000
Fax: 01722 414816

MARMORIN
225 Bilton Road
London
Poland 64-234 PrzemęT
UB6 7HQ
www.marmorin.pl/
email: artur.wnekowski@marmorin.pl
Tel: +44(0)7734530951
Fax: +44(0)2089978185

MASTERPIECES LTD
St Oswalds Road
Gloucester, GL1 2SG
www.masterpieces.ltd.uk
Tel: 01452 423261
Fax: 01452 310968

ORIGINAL BATHROOMS LIMITED
143-145 Kew Road,
Richmond, Surrey, TW9 2PN
Tel: 020 8940 7554
sales@original-bathrooms.co.uk
www.original-bathrooms.co.uk

PLANIT FUSION
Inca House, Eureka Scinece Park
Trinity Road
Ashford, Kent, TN25 4AB
www.2020-fusion.com
email: fusionsales@2020.net
Tel: 01233 649 700
Fax: 01233 627 855

ORIGINAL BATHROOMS LIMITED
143-145 Kew Road,
Richmond, Surrey, TW9 2PN
Tel: 020 8940 7554
sales@original-bathrooms.co.uk
www.original-bathrooms.co.uk

Original Bathrooms is a long-
established family business and we
care passionately about the products
we sell. We offer an exciting range of
traditional and contemporary
bathroom products and accessories,
many of which are exclusive to us.
Our in-house bathroom design service
is backed up by first-class knowledge,
experience and service.

ROMANYS LTD
104 Arlington Road
Camden Town
London
NW1 7HP
www.romanys.uk.com
Tel: 020 7424 0349
Fax: 020 7428 6465

SAMUEL HEATH
Tel: 0121 766 4200
Web: www.samuel-heath.com

SHANGHAI LAUTUS MARBLE CO
3 Yeda Road, Songjiang, Shanghai, China
201608
www.lautus-marble.com
email: info@lautus-marble.com
Tel: 0086 21 5031 7155
Fax: 0086 21 5032 5955

STIFFKEY BATHROOMS
89 Upper St.giles Street
Norwich
Norfolk
NR2 1AB
www.stiffkeybathrooms.com
email: info@stiffkeybathrooms.com
Tel: 01603 627850
Fax: 01603 619775

STONE PRODUCTIONS LTD
Tel: 02088 719257
Fax: 02088 719259

TAYLOR ETC
Beaufort Road
Plasmarl
Swansea
SA6 8JG
www.taylorsetc.co.uk
email: info@taylortiles.co.uk
Tel: 01792 797712
Fax: 01792 791103

THE WATER MONOPOLY
16-18 Lonsdale Road
London
NW6 6RD
www.watermonopoly.com
email: enquiries@watermonopoly.com
Tel: 020 7624 2636
Fax: 0207 624 2631

THOMAS CRAPPER & COMPANY LTD
The Stable Yard, Alscot Park,
Stratford On Avon,
Warwickshire.
CV37 8BL
www.thomas-crapper.com
email: wc@thomas-crapper.com
Tel: 01789 450522
Fax: 01789 450523

TUBISM
Tel: 01283 761 477
Fax: 01283 763 852

It's just a shower, isn't it?

You could say that. Or you could say it's a Samuel Heath 'Fairfield' shower. You could point out that it's been meticulously formed from the purest European brass; then hand polished and chrome-plated in up to 34 individual processes. You could say it's manufactured entirely in the UK and it's passed over 500 hours of salt spray and humidity testing. You could say it'll last a lifetime. Or, of course, you could insist that it's just a shower.

Discover more about what goes into the most impressive range of classic and contemporary designs at www.samuel-heath.com or call 0121 766 4200

SAMUEL HEATH
for a life less ordinary

TAPS • SHOWERS • ACCESSORIE

ACCESSORIES

ANCIENNE AMBIANCE LUXURY CANDLES
www.ancienneambiance.com
email: info@ancienneambiance.com
Tel: 0870 199 8958
Fax: 020 7373 8583

ANCIENNE AMBIANCE LUXURY CANDLES
www.ancienneambiance.com
email: info@ancienneambiance.com
Tel: 0870 199 8958
Fax: 020 7373 8583

BANBURY PLASTIC FITTINGS LTD
Unit 13, Overfield
Thorpe Way
Banbury
OX16 4XR
www.bpfittings.co.uk
email: sales@bpfittings.co.uk
Tel. 01295 264 800
Fax: 01295 264 901

BEAUDESERT
The Square
Tisbury
Wiltshire
SP3 6JP
www.beaudesert.co.uk
email: showroom@beaudesert.co.uk
Tel: 0845 838 8720
Fax: 01747 871016

BRISTAN
Birch Coppice Business Park
Dordon
Tamworth
B78 1SG
www.bristan.com
email: enquire@bristan.com
Tel: 0844 701 6274
Fax: 0808 1611002

BURGBAD AG
Burgkama Gmbh
Harborough Road
Brixworth, Northamptonshire
NN6 9BH
www.burgbad.com
email: john.drake@burgbad.com
Tel: 0049 2974 96170
Fax: 0049 2974 9617277

CAIRNEY HARDWARE LTD
1 Distillery Lane
EH12 8RE
www.cairney.com
email: gerardv@cairney.com
Tel: 01313 131303
Fax: 01313 31305

CHARTLEY LTD
Attn Lisa Landells
Opal Business Centre
Opal Way, Stone, Staffs
ST15 0SS
www.chartley.com
email: sales@chartley.com
Tel: 01785 811836
Fax: 01785 811837

GINGERLILLY
www.gingerlilly.co.uk
Tel: 0870 1161 368
Fax: 0870 1161 369

HIB LTD
Castle House
21/23 Station Road
New Barnet, Herts
EN5 1PH
www.hib.co.uk
email: sales@hib.co.uk
Tel: 020 8441 0352
Fax: 020 8441 0219

IB RUBINETTERIE
Via Dei Pianotti 3
25068
www.ibrubinetterie.it
email: info@ibrubinetterie.it
Tel: 0039 0308 02101
Fax: 0039 0308 03097

ISAGI LIMITED
The Laurels
34 Sheepfold Lane
Amersham, Bucks
HP7 9EJ
www.isagi.co.uk
email. sales@isagi.co.uk
Tel: 01494 729345
Fax: 01494 729345

JEFFREYS INTERIORS
8 North West Circus Place
Edinburgh
EH3 6ST
www.jeffreys-interiors.co.uk
email: sales@jeffreys-interiors.co.uk
Tel: 0131 247 8010
Fax: 0845 882 2656

JOHN PLANCK LTD
3 Southern House / Anthony's Way /Medway City Estate
Rochester
Kent
ME2 4DN
www.johnplanck.co.uk
email: sales@johnplanck.co.uk
Tel: 01634 720077
Fax: 01634 720111

JUDY HOLME LIMITED
The Watermark
9-15 Ribbleton Lane
Preston
PR1 5EZ
www.judyholme.com
email: sales@judyholme.com
Tel: 0845 389 3131
Fax: 0845 389 3121

KEUCO (UK) LTD
Amersham House
Mill Street
Berkhamsted, Herts
HP4 2DT
www.keuco.de
email: klaus@keuco.co.uk
Tel: 01442 865220
Fax: 01442 865260

KIT MOOI
email: info@kitmooi.com
Tel: 07944691119

LELIEVRE
108-110 Design Centre
Chelsea Harbour
London
SW10 0XE
www.lelievre.eu
email: enquiries@lelievre.eu
Tel: 020 7352 4798
Fax: 020 7352 9569

LLOYD WORRALL, MILTON KEYNES
Tel: 01908 643364
Fax: 01908 643643

LOCKS & HANDLES
25 Effie Road
London
SW6 1EK
www.doorhandles.co.uk
email: sales@knobs.co.uk
Tel: 02075 812401
Fax: 02075 894928

MARMORIN
225 Bilton Road
London
Poland 64-234 PrzemęT
UB6 7HQ
www.marmorin.pl/
email: artur.wnekowski@marmorin.pl
Tel: +44(0)7734530951
Fax: +44(0)2089978185

MARYLYN LARKIN
6 Queens Court
230 West End Lane
London
NW61UT
email: marylyn.larkin@blueyonder.co.uk
Tel: 02074 353001
Fax: 02074 353001

MIRRORMEDIA LTD
15 Southmill Trading Centre
Southmill Road
Bishop's Stortford
CM23 3DY
www.mirrormedia.com
email: sales@mirrormedia.com
Tel: 0870 386 6333
Fax: 0870 386 6111

NANZ
20 Vandam Street, Fifth Floor
New York
Usa
10013
www.nanz.com
Tel: 001 212 367 7000

NICHOLAS HASLAM LTD
12-14 Holbein Place
London
SW1W 8NL
www.nicholashaslam.com
Tel: 020 7730 8623
Fax: 020 7730 6679

PLUMO LTD
The Chocolate Factory
Unit C004, 5 Clarendon Road
London
N22 6XJ
www.plumo.com
email: office@plumo.com
Tel: 0208 8899945
Fax: 0208 8887402

PRICE & COMPANY (REGENCY) LIMITED
North Street
Portslade
East Sussex
BN41 1ES
www.price-regency.co.uk
email: enquiries@price-regency.co.uk
Tel: 01273 439 527
Fax: 01273 421888

PROPRESS
Unit 3, Pavillions
2 East Road
South Wimbledon
SW19 1UW
www.propress.co.uk
email: info@propress.co.uk
Tel: 020 8417 0660
Fax: 020 8544 9468

RAMSAY
69 Pimlico Road London
SW1W8NE
email: ramsayprints@btclick.com
Tel: 0207 730 6776
Fax: 0207 730 6775

RASMUS
12-13 Royal Parade
Harrogate
North Yorkshire
HG1 2SZ
www.rasmusdesign.co.uk
email: info@rasmusdesign.co.uk
Tel: 01423 560050
Fax: 01423 875087

ROMAN LTD
Whitworth Avenue
Aycliffe Industrial Park
County Durham
DL5 6YN
www.roman-showers.com
email: info@roman-showers.com
Tel: 01325 311 318
Fax: 01325 319889

SPINA DESIGN
12 Kingsgate Place
London
NW6 4TA
www.spinadesign.co.uk
email: info@spinadesign.co.uk
Tel: 0207 328 5274
Fax: 0207 624 2078

STEPEVI
274 King's Road
London
SW3 5AW
email: info@stepevi.com
Tel: 020 7376 7574
Fax: 020 7376 7577

STIFFKEY BATHROOMS
89 Upper St.giles Street
Norwich
Norfolk
NR2 1AB
www.stiffkeybathrooms.com
email: info@stiffkeybathrooms.com
Tel: 01603 627850
Fax: 01603 619775

SYLGLAS
Denso House, Chapel Road, London
SE27 0TR
www.sylglas.com
email: mail@sylglas.com
Tel: 020 8670 7511
Fax: 0208 761 2456

TFW
3 Easton Lane
Winnall
Winchester
SO23 7RU
www.tfw.co.uk
email: sales@tfw.co.uk
Tel: 01962 858820
Fax: 01962 858828

THE CECIL BEATON FABRIC COLLECTION
The Square
Tisbury
Wiltshire
SP3 6JP
www.cecilbeatonfabrics.com
email: beaton@beaudesert.co.uk
Tel: 0845 838 8720
Fax: 01747 871016

THE LINEN PRESS LTD
Hartley Fold
Hartley
Kirkby Stephen
CA17 4JH
www.thelinenpress.co.uk
email: sales@thelinenpress.co.uk
Tel: 01768 372777
Fax: 01768 372794

THE WATER MONOPOLY
16-18 Lonsdale Road
London
NW6 6RD
www.watermonopoly.com
email: enquiries@watermonopoly.com
Tel: 020 7624 2636
Fax: 0207 624 2631

TRIFLOW CONCEPTS
Unit 1, Gateway Xiii
Ferry Lane
Rainham
RM13 9JY
www.triflowconcepts.com
email: marketing@triflowconcepts.com
Tel: 01708 526361
Fax: 01708 550220

TROYNORTH
High Ardley,
Hexham
NE46 2LG
email: mail@troynorth.com
Tel: 01434 607 366
Fax: 01434 608 415

VISMARAVETRO
12 Handsworth Crescent
Eastern Green
Coventry
CV3 7GE
www.jnjbathrooms.co.uk
email: sales@jnjbathrooms.co.uk
Tel: 02476 468850
Fax: 02476 468830

WELSPUN UK LTD (CHRISTY)
Po Box 19
Newton Street
Hyde
SK14 4NR
www.christy-home.com
Tel: 01613 681961

WILLIAMS IRONMONGERY LTD
11 Princelet Street
Spitalfields
London
E1 6QH
www.williams-ironmongery.co.uk
email: sales@williams-ironmongery.co.uk
Tel: 0207 247 8821
Fax: 0207 247 1638

YANNEDIS
Tel: 020 8550 8833
Fax: 020 8551 0026

BATHROOM FURNITURE

BESPOKE GLASS BASINS
33 Clifford Way
Maidstone
Kent
ME16 8GD
www.bespokeglassbasins.com
email: info@bespokeglassbasins.com
Tel: 01622 662316

BRITISH BATHROOM CENTRE
Oxgate House
Oxgate Lane
London
NW2 7HU
www.bathcentre.com
email: sales@bathcentre.com
Tel: 020 8453 7000
Fax: 020 8830 8056

BURGBAD AG
Burgkama Gmbh
Harborough Road
Brixworth, Northamptonshire
NN6 9BH
www.burgbad.com
email: john.drake@burgbad.com
Tel: 0049 2974 96170
Fax: 0049 2974 9617277

DAVAL FURNITURE
Spa Fields Industrial Estate
New Street
Slaithwaite , Huddesfield
HD7 5BB
Tel: 01484 848500
Fax: 01484 848 520

DREAM DESIGN
A35 Lyndhurst Road
Christchurch
Dorset
BH23 7DU
www.dream-design.co.uk
email: sales@dream-design.co.uk
Tel: 01425 279525
Fax: 01425 273550

HIB LTD
Castle House
21/23 Station Road
New Barnet, Herts
EN5 1PH
www.hib.co.uk
email: sales@hib.co.uk
Tel: 020 8441 0352
Fax: 020 8441 0219

HUDSON REED
Widow Hill Rd
Heasandford Industrial Estate
Burnley Lancs
BB10 2BE
www.hudsonreed.co.uk
email: info@ultra-group.co.uk
Tel: 01282 418 000
Fax: 01282 428915

J ËNÍ J BATHROOMS
12 Handsworth Crescent
Eastern Green
Coventry
CV5 7GE
www.jnjbathrooms.co.uk
email: sales@jnjbathrooms.co.uk
Tel: 024 7646 8850
Fax: 024 7646 8830

LIVINGHOUSE
59-61
Fisherton Street
Salisbury
SP27SU
www.livinghouse.co.uk
email: sales@livinghouse.co.uk
Tel: 01722 415000
Fax: 01722 414816

MM2 LTD
Orchard House
Church Road
Ramsden Bellhouse, Billericay
CM11 1RH
www.mm2ltd.com
email: sales@mm2ltd.com
Tel: 01268 712801
Fax: 01268 712803

MONTROSE FURNITURE LTD
Paycocke Road
Basildon
Essex
SS14 3NW
www.montrosefurniture.co.uk
email: enquiries@montrosefurniture.co.uk
Tel: 01268 476800
Fax: 01268 476808

PARAPANÆ
Thistle House
Gildersome Spur
Morley
LS27 7JZ
www.parapan.co.uk
email: info@parapan.co.uk
Tel: 0113 201 2240
Fax: 0113 253 0717

PHILIP WATTS DESIGN
Unit 11 Byron Industrial Est
Brookfield Rd
Arnold, Nottingham
NG5 7ER
www.philipwattsdesign.com
email: sales@philipwattsdesign.com
Tel: 0115 926 9756
Fax: 0115 920 5395

PUJI
20 Ashfield Parade
South Gate
London
N14 5EJ
email: www.puji.com
Tel: 0208 886 3000
Fax: 0208 886 3012

R.I.M TILE AND MOSAIC BOUTIQUE
Unit 311 Design Centre Chelsea Harbour
London
SW10 0XE
www.rim.ru
email: info@rimdesign.co.uk
Tel: 020 7376 5820

SCOPE BATHROOM INTERIORS
40 Colquhoun Ave
Hillington
Glasgow
G52 4BN
email: sales@scope-bathrooms.co.uk
Tel: 0141 882 8282

SPLASH DISTRIBUTION
email: info@splashdistribution.co.uk
Tel: 01444 473355

STIFFKEY BATHROOMS
89 Upper St.giles Street
Norwich
Norfolk
NR2 1AB
www.stiffkeybathrooms.com
email: info@stiffkeybathrooms.com
Tel: 01603 627850
Fax: 01603 619775

TFW
3 Easton Lane
Winnall
Winchester
SO23 7RU
www.tfw.co.uk
email: sales@tfw.co.uk
Tel: 01962 858820
Fax: 01962 858828

THE SYMPHONY GROUP PLC
Pen Hill Estate
Park Spring Road
Grimethorpe
S72 7EZ
www.symphony-group.co.uk
email: enquiries@symphony-group.co.uk
Tel: 01226 446000
Fax: 01226 711185

TUTTOBAGNO
76 Blackpool Road
FY67QQQ
www.tuttobagno.com
email: graham.shaw@gmail.com
Tel: 01253 885980
Fax: 01253 886074

VISMARAVETRO
12 Handsworth Crescent
Eastern Green
Coventry
CV3 7GE
www.jnjbathrooms.co.uk
email: sales@jnjbathrooms.co.uk
Tel: 02476 468850
Fax: 02476 468830

BATHROOM SUITES

BESPOKE GLASS BASINS
33 Clifford Way
Maidstone
Kent
ME16 8GD
www.bespokeglassbasins.com
email: info@bespokeglassbasins.com
Tel: 01622 662316

BURGBAD AG
Burgkama Gmbh
Harborough Road
Brixworth, Northamptonshire
NN6 9BH
www.burgbad.com
email: john.drake@burgbad.com
Tel: 0049 2974 96170
Fax: 0049 2974 9617277

CLEARWATER REVIVAL (WORLDWIDE) LTD
Enterprise House
Ironworks Park
Bowling Back Lane, Bradford
BD4 8SX
www.clearwater-revival.co.uk
email: enquiries@clearwater-revival.com
Tel: 01274 738140
Fax: 01274 732461

C.P. HART
Unit 40, Charles Park, Claire Causeway,
Crossways Business Park,
Dartford, Kent, DA2 6QA
Tel: 0845 600 1950
Fax: 01322 422 101
E-mail: info@cphart.co.uk
Web: www.cphart.co.uk

Leading luxury bathroom supplier, C.P.
Hart, is renowned for being first-to-
market the latest designs exclusively
sourced from around the world and
superbly displayed.
The C.P.Hart website ensures all
bathroom products can be sourced in
one location with DWG files and
technical information erasing the need
to trawl through supplier websites.
The company's design division offers site
visits and meetings to produce 3D visuals
and 2D architectural drawings.

CONSULTO COLLECTION LTD
Unit B 33-36 Victoria Road
Victoria Industrial Estate
Burgess Hill, West Sussex, RH15 9LR
www.consultocollection.com
email: info@consultocollection.com
Tel: 01444 241296
Fax: 01444 247234

DOMOVARI GMBH
Bruchfeld 87
47809 Krefeld
www.domovari.de
Tel: 0049 2151 15509 0
Fax: 0049 2151 15509 16

DRUMMOND'S
78 Royal Hospital Raod
Chelsea
London, SW3 4HN
www.drummonds-uk.com
email: info@drummonds-uk.com
Tel: 0207 376 4499
Fax: 0207 376 4488

GIBBS AND DANDY
226 Dallow Road
Luton
LU1 1YB
email: luton@gibbsanddandy.com
Tel: 01582 798798
Fax: 01582 798799

HYDRA-SPA
Unit P Little Moor Lane
Loughborough
Leceistershire
LE11 1SF
www.hydraspa.co.uk
email: info@premservices.co.uk
Tel: 01509 611092
Fax: 01509 266835

RAK CERAMICS UK LTD
Paris House, Frenchmans Road, Petersfield, Hampshire, GU32 3AW.
T: 01730 237850
E: info@rakceramics.co.uk
W: www.rakceramics.co.uk

RAK Ceramics offers a full range of stylish and quality bathrooms along with stunning taps to provide ultimate value for money. Our innovative new Infinity range showcases a beautifully simple design blending originality with functionality and all our sanitaryware is backed by a 20-year guarantee. Our range of ceramic and porcelain wall and floor tiles adds the ultimate finish to any bathroom project.

SCOPE BATHROOM INTERIORS
40 Colquhoun Ave,
Hillington,
Glasgow, G52 4BN
email: sales@scope-bathrooms.co.uk
Tel: 0141 882 8282

SPLASH DISTRIBUTION
email: info@splashdistribution.co.uk
Tel: 01444 473355

TUTTOBAGNO
76 Blackpool Road,
FY67QQQ
www.tuttobagno.com
email: graham.shaw@gmail.com
Tel: 01253 885980
Fax: 01253 886074

TWYFORD BATHROOMS
Lawton Road,
Alsager,
Stoke-On-Trent,
ST7 2DF
www.twyfordbathrooms.com
email: twyford.sales@twyfordbathrooms.com
Tel: 01270 879777
Fax: 01270 873864

HEATED BATHROOM MIRRORS

HIB LTD
Castle House
21/23 Station Road
New Barnet, Herts
EN5 1PH
www.hib.co.uk
email: sales@hib.co.uk
Tel: 020 8441 0352
Fax: 020 8441 0219

R&D MARKETING (demista™) LTD
Land House
Anyards Road
Cobham
Surrey, KT11 2LW
Tel: 01932 866600
Fax: 01932 866 688
E-mail: rd@demista.co.uk
Web: www.demista.co.uk

demista™ Heated Mirror Pads ensure your bathroom mirror remains steam free and crystal clear even in the most steamy bathroom. Manufactured in the UK in standard sizes, **demista™** is internationally approved and carries a 10-year warranty. The pads are fitted world-wide in houses, apartments, caravans, hotels, etc.

SPEEDHEAT
Iona House
Stratford Rd
Wicken , Milton Keynes, MK19†6DF
www.speedheat.co.uk
email: info@speedheat.co.uk
Tel: 01908 562 211
Fax: 01908 562 205

THE HEATED MIRROR COMPANY LTD
Sherston
Wiltshire, SN17 0LW
www.heated-mirrors.co.uk
email: heated.mirror@virgin.net
Tel: 01666 840003
Fax: 01666 840856

LUXURY FITTINGS

AQATA LIMITED
Brookfield, Harrowbrrok Industrial Estate,
Hinckley , Leicestershire, LE10 3DU
www.aqata.co.uk
email: sales@aqata.co.uk
Tel: 01455 896500
Fax: 01455 896501

BESPOKE GLASS BASINS
33 Clifford Way, Maidstone,
Kent, ME16 8GD
www.bespokeglassbasins.com
email: info@bespokeglassbasins.com
Tel: 01622 662316

CONSULTO COLLECTION LTD
Unit B 33-36 Victoria Road
Victoria Industrial Estate
Burgess Hill, West Sussex, RH15 9LR
www.consultocollection.com
email: info@consultocollection.com
Tel: 01444 241296
Fax: 01444 247234

CZECH & SPEAKE
244-254 Cambridge Heath Road,
London, E2 9DA
T: 020 8983 7400
F: 020 8981 7232
www.czechandspeake.com

Czech & Speake are renowned for sophisticated and beautifully executed ranges of sanitaryware, handcrafted furniture, fittings, distinctive accessories and aromatic collections for the ultimate luxurious bathing experience. Our Edwardian, Cubist and DCA/FSD collections will be superb additions in both contemporary and traditional interior settings, domestic or commercial.

DORNBRACHT
Unit 8
Fletchworth Gate
Coventry, CV5 6SP
www.dornbracht.com
email: sales@dornbracht.com
Tel: 02476 717129
Fax: 02476 718907

GROHE LTD
Blays House
Wick Road
Englefield Green, Egham, TW20 0HJ
www.grohe.co.uk
email: info-uk@grohe.com
Tel: 0871 200 3414
Fax: 0871 200 3415

HAF (HANDLES AND FITTINGS)
Handles And Fittings Ltd
Haf House
Mead Lane , Hertford, SG13 7AP
www.hafinternational.com
Tel: 01992 505 655
Fax: 01992 505 705

MAJESTIC SHOWER COMPANY LTD
1 North Place
Edinburgh Way
Harlow, CM21 9HX
www.majesticshowers.com
email: info@majesticshowers.com
Tel: 01279 443644
Fax: 01279 635074

SHANGHAI LAUTUS MARBLE CO
3 Yeda Road, Songjiang, Shanghai, China
201608
www.lautus-marble.com
email: info@lautus-marble.com
Tel: 0086 21 5031 7155
Fax: 0086 21 5032 5955

STEPHEN EINHORN
210 Upper Street
London
N1 1RL
www.stepheneinhorn.co.uk
email: info@stepheneinhorn.co.uk
Tel: 020 7359 4977
Fax: 020 7354 0953

TARNSJO GARVERI AB
Garverivagen 6
740 45 TARNSJO
www.tarnsjogarveri.se
email: info@tarnsjogarveri.se
Tel: 0046 29270 750
Fax: 0046 29270 769

TUBISM
Tel: 01283 761 477
Fax: 01283 763 852

TUTTOBAGNO
76 Blackpool Road
FY67QQQ
www.tuttobagno.com
email: graham.shaw@gmail.com
Tel: 01253 885980
Fax: 01253 886074

SHOWER SCREENS & CUBICLES

AQATA LIMITED
Brookfield
Harrowbrrok Industrial Estate
Hinckley , Leicestershire
LE10 3DU
www.aqata.co.uk
email: sales@aqata.co.uk
Tel: 01455 896500
Fax: 01455 896501

CORAM SHOWERS
Stanmore Industrial Estate
Bridgnorth
Shropshire
WV15 5HP
www.coram.co.uk
email: sales@coram.co.uk
Tel: 01746 766466
Fax: 01746 764140

ELLBEE LTD
Grangefield Industrial Estate
Pudsey
West Yorkshire
LS28 6LF
www.ellbee.co.uk
email: sales@ellbee.co.uk
Tel: 0113 257 9711
Fax: 0113 236 2891

H PPE UK
Unit 5, Greenfield Road
Greenfield Farm Industrial Estate
Congleton
CW12 4TR
www.hueppe.com
email: hueppeuk@hueppe.com
Tel: 01260 276188
Fax: 01260 280889

HYDRA-SPA
Unit P Little Moor Lane
Loughborough
Leceistershire
LE11 1SF
www.hydraspa.co.uk
email: info@premservices.co.uk
Tel: 01509 611092
Fax: 01509 266835

J ËNÍ J BATHROOMS
12 Handsworth Crescent
Eastern Green
Coventry
CV5 7GE
www.jnjbathrooms.co.uk
email: sales@jnjbathrooms.co.uk
Tel: 024 7646 8850
Fax: 024 7646 8830

JP GLASS & DECOR LTD
Units 1-6 Eastcote Ind Estate
Eastcote
Middlesex
HA4 9XG
www.jpglass.com
email: sales@jpglass.com
Tel: 02084 292999
Fax: 02088 684314

KERMI UK LTD
7 Brunel Road
Corby
Northants
NN17 4JW
www.kermi.co.uk
email: marketing@kermi.co.uk
Tel: 01536 400 004
Fax: 01536 446 614

MAJESTIC SHOWER COMPANY LTD
1 North Place
Edinburgh Way
Harlow
CM21 9HX
www.majesticshowers.com
email: info@majesticshowers.com
Tel: 01279 443644
Fax: 01279 635074

METROPOLITAN SHOWER COMPANY
Boston Street
Nelson
Lancashire
BB9 0JA
www.metropolitanshowers.co.uk
email: sales@metropolitanshowers.co.uk
Tel: 0845 2579050
Fax: 0845 2579060

ROMAN LTD
Whitworth Avenue
Aycliffe Industrial Park
County Durham
DL5 6YN
www.roman-showers.com
email: info@roman-showers.com
Tel: 01325 311 318
Fax: 01325 319889

SANIFLO LTD
Howard House
The Runway
South Ruislip
HA4 6SE
www.saniflo.co.uk
email: sales@saniflo.co.uk
Tel: 020 8842 0033
Fax: 020 8842 1671

SAPER GLASS INDUSTRIES LTD
Thames House
Longreach Road
Barking, Essex
IG11 0JR
www.saperglass.co.uk
email: tech.sales@saperglass.co.uk
Tel: 020 8594 4949
Fax: 020 8594 5252

TBS FABRICATIONS LTD
Martens Road
Northbank Industrial Park
Irlam, Manchester
M44 5AX
www.tbs-fabrications.com
email: info@tbs-fabrications.com
Tel: 0161 775 1871
Fax: 0161 775 8929

TWYFORD BATHROOMS
Lawton Road
Alsager
Stoke-On-Trent
ST7 2DF
www.twyfordbathrooms.com
email: twyford.sales@twyfordbathrooms.com
Tel: 01270 879777
Fax: 01270 873864

VISMARAVETRO
12 Handsworth Crescent
Eastern Green
Coventry
CV3 7GE
www.jnjbathrooms.co.uk
email: sales@jnjbathrooms.co.uk
Tel: 02476 468850
Fax: 02476 468830

SHOWERS

AQATA LIMITED
Brookfield
Harrowbrrok Industrial Estate
Hinckley , Leicestershire
LE10 3DU
www.aqata.co.uk
email: sales@aqata.co.uk
Tel: 01455 896500
Fax: 01455 896501

BRISTAN
Birch Coppice Business Park
Dordon
Tamworth
B78 1SG
www.bristan.com
email: enquire@bristan.com
Tel: 0844 701 6274
Fax: 0808 1611002

CHARTLEY LTD
Attn Lisa Landells
Opal Business Centre
Opal Way, Stone, Staffs
ST15 0SS
www.chartley.com
email: sales@chartley.com
Tel: 01785 811836
Fax: 01785 811837

CORAM SHOWERS
Stanmore Industrial Estate
Bridgnorth
Shropshire
WV15 5HP
www.coram.co.uk
email: sales@coram.co.uk
Tel: 01746 766466
Fax: 01746 764140

DOMOVARI GMBH
Bruchfeld 87
47809 Krefeld
www.domovari.de
Tel: 0049 2151 15509 0
Fax: 0049 2151 15509 16

DORNBRACHT
Unit 8
Fletchworth Gate
Coventry, CV5 6SP
www.dornbracht.com
email: sales@dornbracht.com
Tel: 02476 717129
Fax: 02476 718907

DOUGLAS DELABIE
7 Henderson House
Hithercroft Road
Wallingford, Oxfordshire, OX10 9DG
www.douglasdelabie.co.uk
email: sales@douglasdelabie.co.uk
Tel: 01491 824449
Fax: 01491 825727

ELLBEE LTD
Grangefield Industrial Estate
Pudsey
West Yorkshire, LS28 6LF
www.ellbee.co.uk
email: sales@ellbee.co.uk
Tel: 0113 257 9711
Fax: 0113 236 2891

FANSKI GROUP INC
M&E Industrial Zone, Yuhuan County, Zhejiang
Provice, 317600 Pr China, 317600
www.fanski.com
email: fanski@fanski.com
Tel: 86 576 87276781
Fax: 86 576 87276797

GROHE LTD
Blays House, Wick Road,
Englefield Green, Egham, TW20 0HJ
www.grohe.co.uk
email: info-uk@grohe.com
Tel: 0871 200 3414
Fax: 0871 200 3415

HANSGROHE
Units D1 and D2
Sandown Park Trading Estate
Royal Mills, Esher, Surrey, KT10 8BL
Tel: 01372 465655
Fax: 01372 470670
E-mail: enquiries@hansgrohe.co.uk
Web: www.hansgrohe.co.uk

Hansgrohe is a leading international manufacturer of bathroom products with an unsurpassed reputation for innovation, design and showering pleasure at the highest level. Products include a wide range of showers, bathroom fittings and matching accessories to suit every bathroom project whether small or large and for all design preferences.

MATKI PLC
Churchward Road
Yate
Bristol
BS37 5PL
Tel: 01454 322888
Fax: 01454 315284
Email: helpline@matki.co.uk
www.matki.co.uk

Contemporary style, technical innovation and top quality engineering are the hallmarks of the Matki Showering collection. The new EauZone Plus collection offers total freedom to choose the size and panel combination best suited for your shower installation. Particular attention has been paid to the finer details with beautifully crafted parts, a non-slip hinge and superb finish.

HUDSON REED
Widow Hill Rd
Heasandford Industrial Estate
Burnley Lancs, BB10 2BE
www.hudsonreed.co.uk
email: info@ultra-group.co.uk
Tel: 01282 418 000
Fax: 01282 428915

IB RUBINETTERIE
Via Dei Pianotti 3, 25068
www.ibrubinetterie.it
email: info@ibrubinetterie.it
Tel: 0039 0308 02101
Fax: 0039 0308 03097

MAJESTIC SHOWER COMPANY LTD
1 North Place
Edinburgh Way
Harlow, CM21 9HX
www.majesticshowers.com
email: info@majesticshowers.com
Tel: 01279 443644
Fax: 01279 635074

MARMOX UK LTD
Unit 3, Forward Way
Laker Road
Rochester, ME1 3QX
www.marmox.co.uk
email: sales@marmox.co.uk
Tel: 01634 862277
Fax: 01634 864223

SMR BATHROOMS
Unit Q, Fishers Grove
Farlington
Portsmouth, PO6 1RN
www.smrbathrooms.co.uk
email: general-enquiry@smrbathrooms.co.uk
Tel: 08452 255045
Fax: 08452 255046

SAMUEL HEATH
Tel: 0121 766 4200
Web: www.samuel-heath.com

Samuel Heath taps, showers and accessories are crafted from the finest solid brass combining traditional craftsmanship with the latest in design and technology. Design innovation and quality have remained our core values since the company was founded in 1820. Whether for contemporary or classic design; experience a lifetime of appreciation.

WETROOM INNOVATIONS
Unit L9 Riverside Business Park
Buxton Road
Bakewell, DE45 1GS
www.wetroominnovations.com
email: wetroominnovations@hotmail.com
Tel: 01629 815500
Fax: 01629 815500

TAPS & BRASSWARE
ABODE
Unit L Zenith Park
Whaley Road
Barnsley, S75 1HT
www.abode.eu
email: info@abode.eu
Tel: 01226 283434
Fax: 01226 282434

ABODE
Unit L Zenith Park, Whaley Road,
Barnsley, S75 1HT
www.abode.eu
email: info@abode.eu
Tel: 01226 283434
Fax: 01226 282434

BLANCO
1 Victor Way, Colney Street,
St.albans , Herts, AL2 2FL
www.blanco.co.uk.
email: salesdesk@blanco.co.uk
Tel: 0844 912 0100

BRISTAN
Birch Coppice Business Park
Dordon, Tamworth, B78 1SG
www.bristan.com
email: enquire@bristan.com
Tel: 0844 701 6274
Fax: 0808 1611002

CZECH & SPEAKE
244-254 Cambridge Heath Road,
London, E2 9DA
T: 020 8983 7400
F: 020 8981 7232
www.czechandspeake.com

Czech & Speake produce luxurious and
superbly crafted fittings, available in a
range of premium finishes including
chrome, platinum and durabrass. Our
classic tailored Edwardian and Cubist,
bath, shower and vanity fittings have
recently been complemented with DCA,
our first contemporary collection
designed in conjunction with award
winning architect David Chipperfield.

CAPLE
Fourth Way
Avonmouth
Bristol BS11 8DW
www.caple.co.uk
Tel: 0117 938 1900
Fax: 0800 373 163

CARRON PHOENIX
Carron Works
Stenhouse Road
Carron , Falkirk, FK2 8DW
www.carron.com
email: sales@carron.com
Tel: 01324 638 321
Fax: 01324 620 978

CHARTLEY LTD
Attn Lisa Landells
Opal Business Centre
Opal Way, Stone, Staffs, ST15 0SS
www.chartley.com
email: sales@chartley.com
Tel: 01785 811836
Fax: 01785 811837

CONSULTO COLLECTION LTD
Unit B 33-36 Victoria Road
Victoria Industrial Estate
Burgess Hill, West Sussex, RH15 9LR
www.consultocollection.com
email: info@consultocollection.com
Tel: 01444 241296
Fax: 01444 247234

DORNBRACHT
Unit 8, Fletchworth Gate,
Coventry, CV5 6SP
www.dornbracht.com
email: sales@dornbracht.com
Tel: 02476 717129
Fax: 02476 718907

DOUGLAS DELABIE
7 Henderson House
Hithercroft Road
Wallingford, Oxfordshire
OX10 9DG
www.douglasdelabie.co.uk
email: sales@douglasdelabie.co.uk
Tel: 01491 824449
Fax: 01491 825727

FANSKI GROUP INC
M&E Industrial Zone, Yuhuan County, Zhejiang
Provice, 317600 Pr China
317600
www.fanski.com
email: fanski@fanski.com
Tel: 86 576 87276781
Fax: 86 576 87276797

GROHE LTD
Blays House
Wick Road
Englefield Green, Egham
TW20 0HJ
www.grohe.co.uk
email: info-uk@grohe.com
Tel: 0871 200 3414
Fax: 0871 200 3415

HUDSON REED
Widow Hill Rd
Heasandford Industrial Estate
Burnley Lancs
BB10 2BE
www.hudsonreed.co.uk
email: info@ultra-group.co.uk
Tel: 01282 418 000
Fax: 01282 428915

IB RUBINETTERIE
Via Dei Pianotti 3
25068
www.ibrubinetterie.it
email: info@ibrubinetterie.it
Tel: 0039 0308 02101
Fax: 0039 0308 03097

J ËNÍ J BATHROOMS
12 Handsworth Crescent
Eastern Green
Coventry
CV5 7GE
www.jnjbathrooms.co.uk
email: sales@jnjbathrooms.co.uk
Tel: 024 7646 8850
Fax: 024 7646 8830

KEUCO (UK) LTD
Amersham House
Mill Street
Berkhamsted, Herts
HP4 2DT
www.keuco.de
email: klaus@keuco.co.uk
Tel: 01442 865220
Fax: 01442 865260

MM2 LTD
Orchard House
Church Road
Ramsden Bellhouse, Billericay
CM11 1RH
www.mm2ltd.com
email: sales@mm2ltd.com
Tel: 01268 712801
Fax: 01268 712803

PYRAMIS UK LTD
Unit 20-22,Haddenham Business Park,
Haddenham,
Bucks, HP178LJ
www.pyramisgroup.com
email: julianpyramis@talktalk.net
Tel: 01844 295882
Fax: 01844 291892

RAK CERAMICS UK LTD
Paris House,
Frenchmans Road,
Petersfield, Hampshire, GU32 3AW.
Tel: 01730 237850
Email: info@rakceramics.co.uk
Web: www.rakceramics.co.uk

STEPHEN EINHORN
210 Upper Street, London, N1 1RL
www.stepheneinhorn.co.uk
email: info@stepheneinhorn.co.uk
Tel: 020 7359 4977
Fax: 020 7354 0953

SURESTOP LTD
Unit 3, Century Park
Starley Way, Bickenhill, B37 7HF
www.surestop.co.uk
email: sales @surestop.co.uk
Tel: 0845 643 1800
Fax: 0845 643 1801

THOMAS CRAPPER & COMPANY LTD
The Stable Yard, Alscot Park,
Stratford On Avon,
Warwickshire.
CV37 8BL
www.thomas-crapper.com
email: wc@thomas-crapper.com
Tel: 01789 450522
Fax: 01789 450523

SAMUEL HEATH
Tel: 0121 766 4200
Web: www.samuel-heath.com

Samuel Heath taps, showers and
accessories are crafted from the finest
solid brass combining traditional
craftsmanship with the latest in design
and technology. Design innovation and
quality have remained our core values
since the company was founded in
1820. Whether for contemporary or
classic design; experience a lifetime of
appreciation.

WATERFRONT BATHROOMS
Old Worcester Buildings
Birmingham Road
Redditch
B97 6DY
Tel: 01527 584244
www.waterfrontbathrooms.com
info@waterfrontbathrooms.com

Waterfront sets the benchmark in
both stylish and elegant design
combined with exceptional quality of
engineering and value for money. The
last 15 years have seen the portfolio
flourish. With aspirational additions
incorporating world-renowned
designers, all of Waterfront's products
are complemented and supported by
customer service excellence and
industry-leading warranties.

TRIFLOW CONCEPTS
Unit 1, Gateway Xiii,
Ferry Lane, Rainham, RM13 9JY
www.triflowconcepts.com
email: marketing@triflowconcepts.com
Tel: 01708 526361
Fax: 01708 550220

TWYFORD BATHROOMS
Lawton Road, Alsager,
Stoke-On-Trent, ST7 2DF
www.twyfordbathrooms.com
email: twyford.sales@twyfordbathrooms.com
Tel: 01270 879777
Fax: 01270 873864

WC SEATS
FAMILY SEAT LTD
www.familyseat.com
email: sales@familyseat.com
Tel: 0845 833 0448
Fax: 0845 833 0449

THOMAS CRAPPER & COMPANY LTD
The Stable Yard, Alscot Park,
Stratford On Avon, Warwickshire, CV37 8BL
www.thomas-crapper.com
email: wc@thomas-crapper.com
Tel: 01789 450522
Fax: 01789 450523

WETROOMS
AQUAVISION WATERPROOF TELEVISIONS
Ibroc House, Essex Road,
Hoddesdon, EN11 0QS
www.aquavision.co.uk
email: info@aquavision.co.uk
Tel: 01992 708333
Fax: 01992 708308

BRITISH BATHROOM CENTRE
Oxgate House
Oxgate Lane
London
NW2 7HU
www.bathcentre.com
email: sales@bathcentre.com
Tel: 020 8453 7000
Fax: 020 8830 8056

CCL SPECIALIST SUPPLIES LTD
Highview Business Park
The Barracks
Hook,   Hampshire
RG27 9NL
www.wetroom-solutions.co.uk
email: info@tile-safe.co.uk
Tel: 01256 763 100
Fax: 01256 765 100

CORAM SHOWERS
Stanmore Industrial Estate
Bridgnorth
Shropshire
WV15 5HP
www.coram.co.uk
email: sales@coram.co.uk
Tel: 01746 766466
Fax: 01746 764140

EBECO UK LTD
Unit N
Kingsfield Business Centre
Redhill , Surrey
RH1 4DP
www.ebeco.com
email: uksales@ebeco.com
Tel: 01737 761767
Fax: 01737 507907

KERMI UK LTD
7 Brunel Road
Corby
Northants
NN17 4JW
www.kermi.co.uk
email: marketing@kermi.co.uk
Tel: 01536 400 004
Fax: 01536 446 614

LIVINGHOUSE
59-61
Fisherton Street
Salisbury
SP27SU
www.livinghouse.co.uk
email: sales@livinghouse.co.uk
Tel: 01722 415000
Fax: 01722 414816

MARLBOROUGH TILES
www.marlboroughtiles.com
Tel: 01672 512422
Fax: 01672 515791

MARMOX UK LTD
Unit 3, Forward Way, Laker Road,
Rochester, ME1 3QX
www.marmox.co.uk
email: sales@marmox.co.uk
Tel: 01634 862277
Fax: 01634 864223

ROMAN LTD
Whitworth Avenue
Aycliffe Industrial Park
County Durham, DL5 6YN
www.roman-showers.com
email: info@roman-showers.com
Tel: 01325 311 318
Fax: 01325 319889

On the Level, UK manufacturer of patented
wetroom shower trays, offers a complete
package containing everything you need
to create a stylish and contemporary
wetroom. The package includes the easy-
to-install Birch Ply shower tray, drain gully,
waterproofing kit a wide choice of steel or
polished chrome floor gratings and glass
shower screens. Everything you need to
achieve the perfect wetroom.

For stockists contact On The Level:
Tel: 01525 373202
E-mail: sales@onthelevel.co.uk
Web: www.onthelevel.co.uk

SCOPE BATHROOM INTERIORS
40 Colquhoun Ave
Hillington
Glasgow, G52 4BN
email: sales@scope-bathrooms.co.uk
Tel: 0141 882 8282

STONE PRODUCTIONS LTD
Tel: 02088 719257
Fax: 02088 719259

THE MOSAIC STUDIO
54 Darlinghurst Grove
Leigh On Sea
Essex
SS9 3LG
www.themosaicstudio.com
email: fiona@themosaicstudio.demon.co.uk
Tel: 01702 712111
Fax: 01702 712111

TUBISM
Tel: 01283 761 477
Fax: 01283 763 852

WETROOM INNOVATIONS
Unit L9 Riverside Business Park
Buxton Road
Bakewell
DE45 1GS
www.wetroominnovations.com
email: wetroominnovations@hotmail.com
Tel: 01629 815500
Fax: 01629 815500

Bedrooms

ALEXANDER MILES
68 Welbeck Street
London
W1G 0AS
www.alexandermiles.co.uk
email: office@alexandermiles.co.uk
Tel: 0207 486 4545
Fax: 0207 935 2684

COTSWOLD BESPOKE KITCHENS
Riverside House,
Bridgend Works,Stonehouse,
Gloucestershire
GL10 2BA
www.bespokekitchendesign.co.uk
email: info@bespokekitchendesign.co.uk
Tel: 01453 791222
Fax: 01453 825254

CURTIS INTERIORS
4 Berking Avenue
Leeds
LS9 9LF
www.curtisinteriors.co.uk
email: info@curtisinteriors.co.uk
Tel: 0845 47 49 032
Fax: 0113 235 0225

KOZEESLEEP
Tel: 01924 526789

MASTERPIECES LTD
St Oswalds Road
Gloucester
GL1 2SG
www.masterpieces.ltd.uk
Tel: 01452 423261
Fax: 01452 310968

NORDIC STYLE
109 Lots Road
London
SW10 0RN
www.nordicstyle.com
email: sales@nordicstyle.com
Tel: 0207 351 1755
Fax: 0207 351 4966

BEDS & MATTRESSES

ABACA ORGANIC
Tycroes Business Park
Ammanford
Wales,
SA18 3RD
Tel: 01269 598 491
Fax: 01269 598 492

ABBEY QUILTING LTD
Selinas Lane
Dagenham
RM8 1ES
www.abbey-quilting.co.uk
email: enquiries@abbey-quilting.co.uk
Tel: 02085 922233
Fax: 02085 933787

BEAUDESERT
The Square
Tisbury
Wiltshire
SP3 6JP
www.beaudesert.co.uk
email: showroom@beaudesert.co.uk
Tel: 0845 838 8720
Fax: 01747 871016

BED BAZAAR
The Old Railway Station
Station Road
Framlingham
IP139EE
www.bedbazaar.co.uk
email: sales@bedbazaar.co.uk
Tel: 01728 723756
Fax: 01728 724626

BRETZ
Alexander-Bretz-Street 2
55116 Gensingen
Germany
55116
www.bretz.com
email: cultsofa@bretz.de
Tel: 0049 672 78 950
Fax: 0049 676 21 030

CUMFILUX.BEDS LTD
Tel: 01384 455515
Fax: 01384 246179

EPOC BEDS
6 Whittle Road,
Hadleigh Road Industrial Estate,
Ipswich, Suffolk, IP2 0UH
Tel: 01473 226614
E-mail: info@epocbeds.co.uk
Web: www.epocbeds.co.uk

EPOC Beds specialise in making hand
crafted mattresses and divan beds to the
very highest calibre and in the traditional
manner. Over fifty years of experience is
bought to bear in each and every
bespoke product. Each item is made to
order and we take great pride in our
workmanship.

EPOC BEDS
6 Whittle Road,
Hadleigh Road Industrial Estate,
Ipswich, Suffolk, IP2 0UH
Tel: 01473 226614
E-mail: info@epocbeds.co.uk
Web: www.epocbeds.co.uk

EPOC Beds specialise in making hand
crafted mattresses and divan beds to
the very highest calibre and in the
traditional manner. A member of the
same bedding group as Mattison
Contract Beds, EPOC now offer a
bespoke contract range; a perfect
choice for the hotel interior designer.

ERSKINE FURNITURE
Bishopton
Renfrewshire, PA7 5PU
www.erskinefurniture.co.uk
email: erskine.furniture@erskine.co.uk
Tel: 0141 812 7979
Fax: 0141 812 8254

FEATHER & BLACK
Terminus Road
Chichester, BN13 2RU
www.featherandblack.com
email: sales@featherandblack.com
Tel: 01243 380 600
Fax: 01243 790 589

FRANK HUDSON LTD
Rosebery Avenue
Pinions
High Wycombe, Bucks
HP13 7AH
www.frankhudson
email: keith@frankhudson.com
Tel: 01494 522 011
Fax: 01494 436 158

JYSK
Melford Road
Hazel Grove
Stockport
SK3 0JD
www.jysk.co.uk
email: dgoo@jysk.com
Tel: 0845 389 3089

Hästens
Fulfilling dreams
since 1852

Made entirely from natural materials, feel the difference that only Hästens can give you. Discover which of our extensive range of craftsmen built beds is perfect for you. See and experience the bed of your dreams at one of our three exclusive stores.

Hästens Kings Road, 579-581 Kings Road, London W1H 2HN.
Tel: 020 7384 2020

Hästens West End, 99 Crawford Street, London W1H 2HN. **Tel: 020 7723 2925**

Walton Bed Studio, Auckland House, New Zealand Avenue, Walton-on-Thames KT12 1PL. **Tel: 01932 260 034**

www.hastenswestend.com

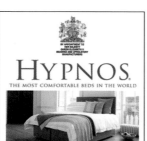

HYPNOS
THE MOST COMFORTABLE BEDS IN THE WORLD

HYPNOS LIMITED
Station Road, Princes Risborough, Buckinghamshire., HP27 9DN
Tel: +44 (0) 1844 348200
Fax: +44 (0) 1844 346112
Email: sleep@hypnosbeds.com
www.hypnosbeds.com

Hypnos has been making luxury handmade beds for over 100 years, and has a reputation for making the most comfortable beds in the world. Each and every Hypnos bed is individually made by master craftsmen, guaranteeing years of sumptuous and comfortable sleep. A Royal Warrant from Her Majesty Queen Elizabeth II reinforces Hypnos's reputation for service excellence and the very best of British quality.

KOMFI UK
Fao Phillip Whittell
Units 60/70 Bmk Industrial Estate
Wakefield Road, Liversedge
WF15 6BS
www.komfi.com
email: sales@komfi.com
Tel: 0800 6524445
Fax: 01924 408541

KOZEESLEEP
Tel: 01924 526789

LIVING IT UP
Tel: 0116 2695 960

NATURAL HOME PRODUCTS LTD
5 Station Court
Station Lane
Hethersett
NORFOLK
www.naturalhome-products.com
email: sales@naturalhome-products.com
Tel: 01508 491 117

PROJEKTER INDUSTRIAL DESIGN
Springwall 4
47051 Duisburg
Germany
www.projekter.de
email: contact@playzzle.de
Tel: 0049 203 728 1827

PUJI
20 Ashfield Parade
South Gate
London
N14 5EJ
email: www.puji.com
Tel: 0208 886 3000
Fax: 0208 886 3012

+TEMPUR®
PRESSURE RELIEVING MATTRESSES AND PILLOWS

TEMPUR UK LTD
Caxton Point, Printing House Lane, Hayes, Middlesex, UB3 1AP
Tel: 0800 616 135
Email: info@tempur.co.uk
Web: www.tempur.co.uk

TEMPUR® is a temperature sensitive pressure-relieving material that moulds to your shape, providing unrivalled support and comfort. Originally developed by NASA, the pressure-relieving properties of TEMPUR are clinically proven to alleviate pain and improve sleep quality. TEMPUR is used and recommended by more than 75,000 professional medical customers worldwide.

SICO EUROPE LTD
The Link Park
Lympne Industrial Estate
Lympne, Kent
CT21 4LR
www.sico-europe.com
email: sales@sico-europe.com
Tel: 01303 234000
Fax: 01303 234001

SILVERMOON STYLES LTD
14 Holmwood Court
Keymer Road
Hassocks
BN6 8AS
www.silvermoonstyles.com
email: info@silvermoonstyles.com
Tel: 01273 844413
Fax: 01273 844413

THE FRENCH BEDROOM COMPANY
www.frenchbedroomcompany.co.uk
Tel: 08456 448022

BED LINEN
ABBEY QUILTING LTD
Selinas Lane
Dagenham
RM8 1ES
www.abbey-quilting.co.uk
email: enquiries@abbey-quilting.co.uk
Tel: 02085 922233
Fax: 02085 933787

BBD INTERIORS
Unit 18c Euro Business Park
Little Island
Cork
IRELAND
www.bbd.ie
email: info@bbd.ie
Tel: 00353 21435 1999
Fax: 00353 21435 1998

BEDECK
189 Lurgan Roaad, Magheralin, County Down, Northern Ireland, Bt67 0qs
www.bedeckhome.com
Tel: 028 3831 3000
Fax: 028 3831 3 001

BURKE BY DESIGN WHOLESALE LTD
18c Euro Business Park
Little Island
Cork
IRELAND
www.bbd.ie
email: info@bbd.ie
Tel: 00353 21 435 1999
Fax: 00353 21 435 1998

DESIGN HOUSE EUROPE
Design House
Balme Road
Cleckheaton
BD19 4EW
www.prontex.co.uk
email: louisemarren@designhouseeurope.com
Tel: 01274 863747
Fax: 01274 863748

DORMA
Fosse Way
Syston
Leicestershire
LE7 1NF
www.dorma.co.uk
email: enquiries@dorma.co.uk
Tel: 0116 2644408
Fax: 0116 2644490

FEATHER & BLACK
Terminus Road
Chichester
BN13 2RU
www.featherandblack.com
email: sales@featherandblack.com
Tel: 01243 380 600
Fax: 01243 790 589

FRANCESCO CALVIDINI COLLEZIONE
123 Wolsey House
46 High Street
Esher
KT10 9RB
www.calvidini.it
email: showroom@calvidini.com
Tel: 07515 36 35 34
Fax: 08704 86 94 92

GINGERLILLY
www.gingerlily.co.uk
Tel: 0870 1161 368
Fax: 0870 1161 369

HAINSWORTH INTERIOR FABRICS
Spring Valley Mills
Stanningley
Pudsey, West Yorkshire
LS28 6DW
www.hainsworth.co.uk
email: interiors@hainsworth.co.uk
Tel: 0113 395 5695
Fax: 0113 3955686

LUXURY LIVING LONDON LIMITED
103 Wandsworth Bridge Road
London
SW6 2TE
www.luxuryliving.uk.com
email: showroom@luxuryliving.uk.com
Tel: 0207 384 9722
Fax: 020 7384 9721

NATURAL HOME PRODUCTS LTD
5 Station Court
Station Lane
Hethersett
NORFOLK
www.naturalhome-products.com
email: sales@naturalhome-products.com
Tel: 01508 491 117

NATUREWARM LTD
27 Water Lane
South Witham
Grantham
NG33 5PH
www.naturewarm.co.uk
email: sales@naturewarm.co.uk
Tel: 01572 768362
Fax: 01572 767146

SUSIE WATSON DESIGN
125 Northcote Rd
Battersea
London
SW11 6PS
www.susiewatsondesigns.co.uk
Tel: 0207 228 0787

THE LINEN PRESS LTD
Hartley Fold
Hartley
Kirkby Stephen
CA17 4JH
www.thelinenpress.co.uk
email: sales@thelinenpress.co.uk
Tel: 01768 372777
Fax: 01768 372794

THE WHITE COMPANY
Unit 30 Perivale Industrial Park,
Horsenden Lane South, Greenford,
Middlesex, UB6 7RJ
Tel: 0845 678 8149
Fax: 0845 678 8151
Email: B2B@thewhitecompany.com
Web: www.thewhitecompany.com

The White Company specialises in
offering stylish, affordable, designer
quality items for the home, principally
in white. Gorgeous bedlinen remains
at the heart of the range but you'll
also find everything from fantastic
lighting and beautiful cushions to
delicious home scents and toiletries.

YVES DELORME
54 Duke of York Square, Chelsea
London SW3 4LY
Tel: 020 7730 3435
6 Royal Parade, Chislehurst,
Kent BR7 6NR
Tel: 020 8467 3347

Luxurious and elegant bed linen and
towelling, offering glorious choices of
plain colour percales, cotton sateens,
jacquards or exquisite prints. Yves
Delorme also makes beautiful
accessories such as bed throws,
cushions, scented candles and sprays.

Telephone **01296 394 980** for details.
www.yvesdelorme.com

VOLGA LINEN
Unit 1 Eastlands Industrial Estate
Leiston
Suffolk
IP16 4LL
www.volgalinen.co.uk
email: info@volgalinen.co.uk
Tel: 01728 635 020
Fax: 01728 635 021

WELSPUN UK LTD (CHRISTY)
Po Box 19
Newton Street
Hyde
SK14 4NR
www.christy-home.com
Tel: 01613 681961

BEDROOM ACCESSORIES

BEDECK
189 Lurgan Roaad, Magheralin, County Down,
Northern Ireland, Bt67 Oqs
www.bedeckhome.com
Tel: 028 3831 3000
Fax: 028 3831 3 001

DEBORAH ROLT RUGS
www.deborahroltrugs.co.uk
email: anne@deborahroltrugs.co.uk
Tel: 020 8780 5288

DENTRO HOME
Calle Cobalto 152, 1-A
L'h De Llobregat
Barcelona
8907
www.dentrohome.com
email: info@dentrohome.com
Tel: 0034 93 337 8300

GINGERLILLY
www.gingerlily.co.uk
Tel: 0870 1161 368
Fax: 0870 1161 369

J-ME
Unit 1.15
Oxo Tower Wharf
London
SE1 9PH
www.j-me.co.uk
email: info@j-me.co.uk
Tel: 020 7928 8828
Fax: 020 7928 8846

MARYLYN LARKIN
6 Queens Court
230 West End Lane
London
NW61UT
email: marylyn.larkin@blueyonder.co.uk
Tel: 02074 353001
Fax: 02074 353001

SHUTTER FRONTIER LTD
2 Rosemary Farmhouse, Rosemary Lane,
Flimwell, East Sussex, Tn5 7pt
TN5 7PT
www.shutterfrontier.co.uk
email: jane@shutterfrontier.co.uk
Tel: 01580 879761 / 07708 229 295

WELSPUN UK LTD (CHRISTY)
Po Box 19
Newton Street
Hyde
SK14 4NR
www.christy-home.com
Tel: 01613 681961

BEDROOM FURNITURE

BA COMPONENTS
Derryloran Ind Estate
Cookstown
Co Tyrone
BT80 9LU
www.bellabyba.com
email: enquiries@bellabyba.co.uk
Tel: 028 8676 4 600
Fax: 028 8676 4404

BED BAZAAR
The Old Railway Station
Station Road
Framlingham
IP139EE
www.bedbazaar.co.uk
email: sales@bedbazaar.co.uk
Tel: 01728 723756
Fax: 01728 724626

BENTLEY DESIGNS (UK) LTD
Unit 1, Tera 40
Auriol Drive
Greenford
UB6 0TP
www.bentleydesigns.com†
email: emma@bentleydesigns.com
Tel: 020 8833 7500
Fax: 020 8578 2696

BLUE BONE IMPORTS LIMITED
River Mill 2
Park Road
Dukinfield
SK16 5PD
www.bluebone.co.uk
email: manchester@bluebone.co.uk
Tel: 0161 330 8959
Fax: 0161 330 8949

CHAPLINS FURNITURE LTD
477-507 Uxbridge Rd
Hatch End
Middlesex
HA5 4JS
www.chaplins.co.uk
email: sales@chaplins.co.uk
Tel: 020 84211779
Fax: 020 84213872

CHARLES PAGE FURNITURE & INTERIOR DESIGN
61 Fairfax Road
Swiss Cottage
London
NW6 4EE
www.charlespage.co.uk
email: info@charlespage.co.uk
Tel: 02073 289851
Fax: 02073 287240

CURTIS INTERIORS
4 Berking Avenue
Leeds
LS9 9LF
www.curtisinteriors.co.uk
email: info@curtisinteriors.co.uk
Tel: 0845 47 49 032
Fax: 0113 235 0225

DAVAL FURNITURE
Spa Fields Industrial Estate
New Street
Slaithwaite , Huddesfield
HD7 5BB
Tel: 01484 848500
Fax: 01484 848 520

DENTRO HOME
Calle Cobalto 152, 1-A
L'h De Llobregat
Barcelona
8907
www.dentrohome.com
email: info@dentrohome.com
Tel: 0034 93 337 8300

ERSKINE FURNITURE
Bishopton
Renfrewshire
PA7 5PU
www.erskinefurniture.co.uk
email: erskine.furniture@erskine.co.uk
Tel: 0141 812 7979
Fax: 0141 812 8254

ETHNICRAFT
Scheldeweg 5
Boom
Belgium
2850
www.ethnicraft.com
email: alf@ethnicraft.com
Tel: 00323 443 0126
Fax: 00323 443 0127

FEATHER & BLACK
Terminus Road
Chichester
BN13 2RU
www.featherandblack.com
email: sales@featherandblack.com
Tel: 01243 380 600
Fax: 01243 790 589

FLEXA
Bjornkjaervej 16
Hornsyld
Denmark
8783
www.flexa.dk
email: flexa@flexa.dk
Tel: +45 7668 8055
Fax: +45 7668 8069

FRANK HUDSON LTD
Rosebery Avenue
Pinions
High Wycombe, Bucks
HP13 7AH
www.frankhudson
email: keith@frankhudson.com
Tel: 01494 522 011
Fax: 01494 436 158

GILLMORESPACE LTD
22 Torbay Business Park
Woodview Road
Paignton
TQ4 7HP
www.gillmorespace.com
email: info@gillmorespace.com
Tel: 0845 373 2763
Fax: 0845 373 2764

HULSTA FURNITURE U K LTD
5th Floor
2 Conduit Street
London
W1S 2XB
www.hulsta.co.uk
email: sales@huelsta.co.uk
Tel: 02073 188000
Fax: 02074 092417

LA MAISON
107-108 Shoreditch High Street,
London, E1 6JN
Tel: 0207 729 9646
Fax: 0207 729 6399
info@lamaisonlondon.com
www.lamaisonlondon.com

La Maison create finely crafted, hand carved reproduction furniture and offer a fully bespoke service. All our furniture is completed with a choice of tailor made finishes carried out by skilled craftsmen in-house. Our 'Signature Range' focuses on making a statement, from our emboldened Rococo flourishes to the exquisitely carved details of Louis XVI style. Our bespoke service is creative carte blanche. What can we make for you?

LAWRENCE WALSH FURNITURE
7 St Clare Business Park, Holly Road,
Hampton Hill, Middlesex, TW12 1PZ
Tel: 020 8941 8181
Email: info@lawrencewalsh.co.uk
Web: www.lawrencewalsh.co.uk

Lawrence Walsh furniture for bedrooms, walk-in closets and libraries. We have an extensive range of furniture from Traditional hand painted through to Veneers and Contemporary lacquer. The range is both creative and exciting and is made to an exacting standard which is the hallmark of Lawrence Walsh quality. Call for the new brochure.

LAWRENCE WALSH LTD
7 St Clare Business Park, Holly Road,
Hampton Hill, TW12 1PZ
www.lawrencewalsh.co.uk
email: info@lawrencewalsh.co.uk
Tel: 02089 418181
Fax: 02089 418101

LIVING IT UP
Tel: 0116 2695 960

MARTIN MOORE & COMPANY
Altrincham, Old Amersham,
Esher, Halifax And Fulham
www.martinmoore.com
Tel: 0161 928 2643

PARAPANÆ
Thistle House
Gildersome Spur
Morley, LS27 7JZ
www.parapan.co.uk
email: info@parapan.co.uk
Tel: 0113 201 2240
Fax: 0113 253 0717

PAVILLION RATTAN
The Ulvers Building
Budby Road
Notts, NG20 - 9JP
www.pavilionrattan.co.uk
email: sales@pavilionrattan.co.uk
Tel: 01623 847030
Fax: 0870 706 2159

PTT DESIGN LTD
Bleachers Yard
Radford Road
Nottingham
NG7 7EF
www.pttdesign.com
email: info@pttdesign.com
Tel: 01159 420014
Fax: 01159 422155

PUJI
20 Ashfield Parade
South Gate
London
N14 5EJ
email: www.puji.com
Tel: 0208 886 3000
Fax: 0208 886 3012

SJ UNITS
Unit 5, Leopold Ctr, Smethurst Lane,
Pemberton, Wigan,
WN5 8EG
www.sjunits.co.uk†
email: info@sjunits.co.uk
Tel: 01942 621 361
Fax: 01942 621362

STEENS FURNITURE
Unit 5 Berrywood Business Village
Hedge End
Southampton, SO30 2UN
www.steens.dk
email: sales@steens.dk
Tel: 01489 778890
Fax: 01489 796408

SYLVAWOOD FURNITURE
The Old Workshops
Longbridge Deverill
Wiltshire
BA12 7DP
www.sylvawoodfurniture.co.uk
email: sales@sylvawoodfurniture.co.uk
Tel: 01985 840012
Fax: 01985 840781

THE COAT HANGER COMPANY
Awb Ltd
Padholme Road East
Peterborough, Cambs, Uk
PE1 5XL
www.thecoathangercompany.com
email: sales@thecoathangercompany.com
Tel: 01733 555646
Fax: 01733 555887

THE FRENCH BEDROOM COMPANY
www.frenchbedroomcompany.co.uk
Tel: 08456 448022

THE SYMPHONY GROUP PLC
Pen Hill Estate
Park Spring Road
Grimethorpe
S72 7EZ
www.symphony-group.co.uk
email: enquiries@symphony-group.co.uk
Tel: 01226 446000
Fax: 01226 711185

WILLIAM LUSTY (UK) LTD
Hoo Lane, Chipping Campden, Glos.
GL55 6AU
www.lloyd-loom.co.uk
email: geoffreylusty@aol.com
Tel: 01386 840379
Fax: 01386 841322

WILLIS & GAMBIER
Kingston Park
Flaxley Road
Peterborough
PE2 9EN
www.wguk.com
Tel: 0845 606 7004

YP FUNITURE LTD
Corringham Road Industrial Estate
Gainsborough
Lincs
DN21 1QB
Tel: 01664 434 188

YTM FURNITURE
Grove Road
Pontefract
West Yorkshire
WF8 1EE
www.ytmfurniture.com
email: sales@ytmfurniture.com
Tel: 01977 703271
Fax: 01977 701882

INTERIOR DESIGN TODAY

THE TRADE ONLY MAGAZINE FOR INTERIOR DESIGN PROFESSIONALS   NOV/DEC 2009 £5.95

PRODUCT DESIGNS
LIGHTING
BATHROOMS

100% DESIGN
THE COMPANIES AT THE TOP OF
OUR LIST ARE REVEALED IN LIGHT
OF THE RECENT SHOW

DECOREX
CHELSEA WAS
CHARMED BY THE
STUNNING CREATIVITY
ON DISPLAY

A HISTORY OF
GOOD DESIGN
BRINTON'S STEPS BACK IN TIME TO
REVEAL OUR MOST POWERFUL
DESIGN INFLUENCES

IDTMAGAZINE.CO.UK

it's a personal experience   VADO

Decorative Accessories

AUTHENTIC MODELS
24 Lintot Sq.
Fairbank Rd
Southwater, West Sussex
RH13 9LA
www.authenticmodels.com
email: info@am-uk.eu
Tel: 01403 734 999
Fax: 01403 734888

COMITTI OF LONDON
The Clock And Barometer Strore
Four Wantz Corner
Ongar, Essex
CM5 0AH
www.comitti.com
Tel: 01277 367670
Fax: 01277 369805

CONNECTIONS INTERIORS LTD
286 -288 Leigh Road
Leigh-On-Sea
Essex
SS9 1BW
www.connectionsinteriors.co.uk
email: sales@connectionsinteriors.co.uk
Tel: 01702 470 939
Fax: 01702 480 238

DESIGN WRIGHT
Lf3.4, The Leathermarket
11/13 Weston St
London
SE1 3ER
www.designwright.co.uk
email: studio@designwright.co.uk
Tel: 020 7357 7788

GOLFAR & HUGHES
2/8 Design Centre, Chelsea Harbour, London
SW10 0XE
www.golfarandhughes.com
email: caroline@golfarandhughes.com
Tel: 020 7351 3700
Fax: 020 7351 3701

GRAYS
58 Davies Street
& 1-7 Davies Mews
Mayfair
W1K 5AB
www.graysantiques.com
Tel: 02076 297034
Fax: 02074 939344

HALCYON DAYS LTD
14 Brook Street
London
W1S 1BD
www.halcyondays.co.uk
email: info@halcyondays.co.uk
Tel: 020 7629 8811
Fax: 020 7514 5471

HERALDIC PORCELAIN
Po Box 54829
London
SW1V 3YD
www.heraldicporcelain.com
email: crests@heraldicporcelain.co.uk
Tel: 0207 8281055
Fax: 0207 8281055

INEX SERVICE LTD
152 Franciscan Road
London, SW17 8HH
www.inexgroup.com
email: sales@inexgroup.com
Tel: 020 868 22604
Fax: 020 868 22641

J-ME
Unit 1.15
Oxo Tower Wharf
London, SE1 9PH
www.j-me.co.uk
email: info@j-me.co.uk
Tel: 020 7928 8828
Fax: 020 7928 8846

MOOOI
Minervum 7003
4817 ZL BREDA
www.moooi.com
email: info@moooi.com
Tel: 0031 765784444
Fax: 0031 765710621

PERIOD PIANO COMPANY
Park Farm Oast
Hareplain Road
Biddenden, Kent
TN27 8LJ
www.periodpiano.com
email: periodpiano@btopenworld.com
Tel: 01580 291393
Fax: 01580 291393

Mbomyo °

MBOMYO
Adalland 6
108 Reykjavik
Iceland
Tel: +354-690-5704
E-mail: Volker@mbomyo.com
Web: www.mbomyo.com

Mbomyo design & produces products.

Ceta, a planter based on the different
vibe plants give depending on the
angle they are appreciated.

Hand made. Available in different sizes
& on Marble, Quartz, Onix, Granite.

PLUMO LTD
The Chocolate Factory
Unit C004, 5 Clarendon Road
London
N22 6XJ
www.plumo.com
email: office@plumo.com
Tel: 0208 8899945
Fax: 0208 8887402

RALPH LAUREN HOME
1 New Bond Street
London
W1S 3RL
www.ralphlaurenhome.com
Tel: 020 7535 4557

SANT STUDIO
64 Thoroughfare
Woodbridge
Suffolk
IP12 1AL
www.santstudio.co.uk
email: georginadavid@btinternet.com
Tel: 07791 576786
Fax: 02075 867742

TENTERDEN (PEWTER) COLLECTION, THE
108-110 High Street
Tenterden
Kent
TN30 6HT
email: tenterdenhouseinteriors@hotmail.com
Tel: 01580 764481
Fax: 01580 765531

THE LITTLE GREENE PAINT COMPANY
Wood Street
Openshaw
Manchester
M11 2FB
www.thelittlegreene.com
email: mail@thelittlegreene.com
Tel: 0161 230 0880
Fax: 0161 223 3208

BESPOKE ART & INSTALLATIONS

55MAX
6 Lonsdale Road
Queens Park
London
NW6 6RD
www.55max.com
email: info@55max.com
Tel: 020 7625 3774
Fax: 020 7625 3776

ANDREW MOOR ASSOCIATES
14 Chamberlain Street
London
NW1 8XB
www.andrewmoor.co.uk
email: andrew@andrewmoor.co.uk
Tel: 02075 868181
Fax: 02075 868484

ART SEARCH LTD
83 Kingswood Avenue
London
NW6 6LR
www.artsearchlimited.co.uk
email: info@artsearchlimited.co.uk
Tel: 02089 699844

ARTDESIGN
Cheltenham
Gloucestershire
www.artdesign.org.uk/fineart.html
email: gallery@artdesign.org.uk
Tel: 01242 514224

ARTISTIC-LICENCE
57 Harrow Road
Wollaton Park
Nottingham
NG8 1FL
www.artistic-licence.com
email: studio@artistic-licence.com
Tel: 01159 724 777

ARTIZAN EDITIONS
Ground Floor East, Industrial House
Conway Street
Hove
BN3 3LW
www.arizaneditions.co.uk
email: info@artizaneditions.co.uk
Tel: 01273 773959

BRADLEY BASSO
8 Orchard Studios
Brook Green, Hammersmith
London
W6 7BU
www.bradleybasso.com
email: info@bradleybasso.com
Tel: 0207 602 1840

CARINA HASLAM ART
2 Reyners Green
Little Kingshill, Great Missenden
Bucks
HP16 0EQ
www.carinahaslamart.com
email: art@carinahaslamart.com
Tel: 01494866914 or 0797 3322397

CATRIN JONES ARCHITECTURAL GLASS
www.catrinjones.co.uk
email: catrin@catrinjones.co.uk
Tel: 01792 469256
Fax: 08701 302830

CLASSIC BINDINGS LTD
61 Cambridge Street
London
SW1V 4PS
www.classicbindings.net
email: info@classicbindings.net
Tel: 0207 834 5554
Fax: 0207 630 6632

CUT IT OUT LTD
9 Marine Court
St Leonards On Sea
East Sussex
TN38 0DX
www.cutitout.co.uk
email: oneill@dircon.co.uk
Tel: 01424 441972
Fax: 01424 441972

DAEDALIAN GLASS LTD
The Old Smithy, Cold Row, Carr Lane
Stalmine
Poulton - Le - Fylde, Fy6 9dw
FY6 9DW
www.daedalian-glass.co.uk
email: chris@daedalian-glass.co.uk
Tel: 01253 702531
Fax: 01253 702532

DROSTLE MURALS & MOSAICS
40 Strand House
Merbury Close
London
SE28 0LU
www.drostle.com
email: arts@drostle.com
Tel: 07719 529520

EDINBURGH ARTS
26-28 West Bowling Green St
Edinburgh, EH6 5PB
email: enquiries@edinburgharts.com
Tel: 0131 555 1235
Fax: 0131 555 4378

GLASSCASTS LTD
299 Haggerston Rd, London E8 4en
E8 4EN
www.glasscasts.co.uk
email: jeff@glasscasts.co.uk
Tel: 0207 2758 481
Fax: 0207 275 8481

HANNAH LOBLEY PAPERWORK
Studio 2.5, Banks Mill Studios
71, Bridge Street
Derby
DE1 3LB
www.hl-web.net
email: info@hl-web.net
Tel: 07799 832 993

KING'S COURT GALLERIES
949-953 Fulham Road,
London, SW6 5HY
Tel: +44 (0)20 7610 6939
54 West Street, Dorking,
Surrey, RH4 1BS
Tel: +44 (0)1306 881757
kcgsales@kingscourtgalleries.co.uk
www.kingscourtgalleries.co.uk

We have over 25 years experience in
supplying artwork, mirrors and
framing to the interiors business.
We provide ideas and source artwork
tailored to suit your schemes.
Our onsite framing means we can
respond quickly. We have two shops
with a huge stock of antique pictures,
maps and modern photography.
See web site for some ideas.

KESSLERS INTERNATIONAL LTD
International Business Park
Rick Roberts Way
Stratford, London
E15 2NF
www.kesslers.com
email: kesslers@kesslers.com
Tel: 02085 223000
Fax: 02085 223129

MIRRORMANIA
27 Clover Way
Bradwell
Norfolk
NR31 8RH
www.mirrormania.co.uk
email: sales@mirrormania.co.uk
Tel: 0149 304 331

MORRIS SINGER ART FOUNDERS
9 Swinborne Drive
Springwood Industrial Estate
Braintree
CM7 2YP
www.msaf.co.uk
email: chris@msaf.co.uk
Tel: 01376 343222
Fax: 01376 341793

MOSAIC WORKSHOP LTD
Unit 2 Harry Day Mews
1 Chestnut Rd
London
SE27 9EZ
www.mosaicworkshop.com
email: sales@mosaicworkshop.com
Tel: 0208 6704466
Fax: 0208 6704466

MOSQUITO / AMY CUSHING
62 Lower Ham Road, Kingston, Surrey
KT2 5AW
www.mosquito-design.com
email: amycushing@mosquito-design.com
Tel: 07957 258 620

PLATEAUX GALLERY
At Thomas Goode & Co
19 South Audley Street
Mayfair, London
W1K 2BN
www.plateaux.co.uk
email: gallery@plateaux.co.uk
Tel: +44 (0) 207 499 2823
Fax: +44 (0) 207 629 4230

PORTER DESIGN LTD
Court Farm House
Wellow
Bath
BA28PU
porter-design.com
email: service@porter-design.com
Tel: 01225 849153
Fax: 01225 849156

PRISMS GLASS DESIGN
Unit 31 Kingsgate Workshops
114 Kingsgate Road
NW6 2JG
www.prismsglass.com
email: prisms.glass@virgin.net
Tel: 02076 243240
Fax: 02076 243240

PROPORTION LONDON
9 Dallington St
London
EC1V 0LN
www.proportionlondon.com
email: info@proportionlondon.com
Tel: 020 7251 6943
Fax: 020 7250 1798

REDCOW IMAGING
Studio 17
Eaton Mews
Chester
CH4 7EJ
www.redcow.eu
email: info@redcow.eu
Tel: 01745 730514
Fax: 01745 730514

RETPEN GLAS
Urmagertoften 130
Hojbjerg
Denmark
8270
www.retpen-glas.dk
email: marie@retpen-glas.dk
Tel: 0458 629 7125

RUPERT SCOTT LTD
The Glass Studio
Broadlands Enterprise Park
St Davids
SA62 6BR
www.rupertscott.com
email: glass@rupertscott.com
Tel: 0845 450 7684
Fax: 0845 017 7685

STEPHEN EINHORN
210 Upper Street
London
N1 1RL
www.stepheneinhorn.co.uk
email: info@stepheneinhorn.co.uk
Tel: 020 7359 4977
Fax: 020 7354 0953

STONE ICONS LTD
The Swan Centre
25 Rosemary Road
London
SW17 0AR
www.stoneicons.com
email: info@stoneicons.com
Tel: 07785 394 587
Fax: 020 8541 5750

STUART AKROYD CONTEMPORARY GLASS
Unit 3 Thoroton Place
Thoroton St
Nottingham
NG7 4EW
www.stuartakroydglass.com
email: info@stuartakroydglass.com
Tel: 0115 9106016
Fax: 0115 9106016

THE MOSAIC STUDIO
54 Darlinghurst Grove
Leigh On Sea
Essex
SS9 3LG
www.themosaicstudio.com
email: fiona@themosaicstudio.demon.co.uk
Tel: 01702 712111
Fax: 01702 712111

UREDALE GLASS
42 Market Place
Masham
North Yorkshire
HG4 4EF
www.uredale.co.uk
email: info@uredale.co.uk
Tel: 01765 689780
Fax: 01765 689780

VESSEL
114 Kesington Park Road
Notting Hill
London
W112PW
www.vesselgallery.com
email: info@vesselgallery.com
Tel: 02077 278001
Fax: 02077 278661

YOUR WHITE SPACE
66 Brackendale Rd
Bournemouth
Dorset
BH8 9HZ
www.yourwhitespace.com
email: david@yourwhitespace.com
Tel: 01202 251126

ZENITH ART
C/O Dpi
Balmorall Drive
Southport
PR9 8PX
www.zenithart.me.uk
email: clarezenithart@aol.com
Tel: 07786 272 835

CHINA & GLASSWARE

BAHNE EN GROS
Tel: 01628 820082
Fax: 01628 820082

BOB CROOKS: FIRST GLASS
Thelbridge Cross Farm
Thelbridge
Crediton, Devon
EX17 5SH
www.bobcrooks.com
email: sales@bobcrooks.com
Tel: 01884 860037

CATHERINE HOUGH GLASS
Unit 11
43 Carol Street
London
NW1 0HT
www.catherinehough.com
email: houghglass@aol.com
Tel: 02072 840702

DAVID MELLOR DESIGN
4 Sloane Square
London
SW1W 8EE
www.davidmellordesign.com
email: davidmellor@davidmellordesign.co.uk
Tel: 020 7730 4259
Fax: 020 7730 7240

HERALDIC PORCELAIN
Po Box 54829
London
SW1V 3YD
www.heraldicporcelain.com
email: crests@heraldicporcelain.co.uk
Tel: 0207 8281055
Fax: 0207 8281055

ISLE OF WIGHT STUDIO GLASS LTD
Old Park
St. Lawrence
Isle Of Wight
PO38 1XR
www.isleofwightstudioglass.co.uk
email: sales@isleofwightstudioglass.co.uk
Tel: 01983 853526
Fax: 01983 854054

JARAPA LTD
12 Cole Rd
Bruton
Somerset
BA10 0DA
www.jarapa.co.uk
email: stewart@jarapa.co.uk
Tel: 01749 813067
Fax: 01749 813067

KATY HOLFORD
Tichborne Studios
18 Tichborne Street
Brighton
BN1 1UR
www.katyholford.co.uk
email: katy@katyholford.co.uk
Tel: 01273 327792

LALIQUE LTD
47 Conduit Street
London
W1S 2YP
www.cristallalique.fr
email: shop.london.cs@lalique.fr
Tel: 0207 292 0444
Fax: 02074 937249

LUXURY LIVING LONDON LIMITED
103 Wandsworth Bridge Road
London
SW6 2TE
www.luxuryliving.uk.com
email: showroom@luxuryliving.uk.com
Tel: 0207 384 9722
Fax: 020 7384 9721

MAXWELL AND WILLIAMS
No 4 Watling Gate
297-303 Edgware Road
London
NW9 6NB
www.maxwellandwilliams.co.uk
email: sales@valerie-graham.co.uk
Tel: 0208 2005100
Fax: 0208 2005150

RETPEN GLAS
Urmagertoften 130
Hojbjerg
Denmark
8270
www.retpen-glas.dk
email: marie@retpen-glas.dk
Tel: 0458 629 7125

ROBERT WELCH DESIGNS
Lower High Street
Chipping Campden
Glos
GL55 6DY
www.robertwelch.com
email: sales@welch.co.uk
Tel: 01386 840522
Fax: 01386 848804

SARAH BROADHEAD-RIALL
6 Complins,
Holybourne
Alton
GU34 4EJ
sarah-broadhead-riall-glass.com
email: sarah_broadhead@tiscali.co.uk
Tel: 01420 85083

STUART AKROYD CONTEMPORARY GLASS
Unit 3 Thoroton Place
Thoroton St
Nottingham
NG7 4EW
www.stuartakroydglass.com
email: info@stuartakroydglass.com
Tel: 0115 9106016
Fax: 0115 9106016

SUSIE WATSON DESIGN
25 Northcote Rd
Battersea
London
W11 6PS
www.susiewatsondesigns.co.uk
Tel: 0207 228 0787

SVAJA LIMITED
The Circlefifteen
Emily Davison Drive
Epsom
KT18 5QH
www.svaja.com
email: nigelb@svaja.com
Tel: 0870 444 6860
Fax: 0870 444 6861

TENTERDEN (PEWTER) COLLECTION, THE
108-110 High Street
Tenterden
Kent
TN30 6HT
email: tenterdenhouseinteriors@hotmail.com
Tel: 01580 764481
Fax: 01580 765531

VITAMIN
The Old Truman Brewery
91 Brick Lane
London
E1 6QL
email: info@vitaminliving.com
Tel: 0207 092 9191

CLOCKS

COMITTI OF LONDON
The Clock And Barometer Strore
Four Wantz Corner
Ongar, Essex
CM5 0AH
www.comitti.com
Tel: 01277 367670
Fax: 01277 369805

COMITTI OF LONDON
The Clock And Barometer Strore
Four Wantz Corner
Ongar, Essex
CM5 0AH
www.comitti.com
Tel: 01277 367670
Fax: 01277 369805

GRANDFATHER CLOCKS
Billib
Norwich Road
Bournemouth
BH2 5QZ
www.billib.co.uk†
Tel: 01202 290917

MARIANNE FORREST
3&8 Coach House Cloisters
Hitchin Street
Baldock, Herts
AL8 6QZ
www.marianneforrest.com
Tel: 01462 491992

CONTEMPORARY ART

2D:3D
263 Abbeydale Road
Wembley
London
HA0 1TW
www.2d3d.co.uk
email: rob@2d3d.co.uk
Tel: 0208 998 3199
Fax: 0208 998 7767

ART SEARCH LTD
33 Kingswood Avenue
London, NW6 6LR
www.artsearchlimited.co.uk
email: info@artsearchlimited.co.uk
Tel: 02089 699844

ARTISTIC-LICENCE
157 Harrow Road
Wollaton Park
Nottingham, NG8 1FL
www.artistic-licence.com
email: studio@artistic-licence.com
Tel: 01159 724 777

ARTIZAN EDITIONS
Ground Floor East Wing
Industrial House
Conway St
Hove
BN3 3LW
Tel: 01273 773959
Email: info@artizaneditions.co.uk
Web: www.artizaneditions.co.uk

Artizan Editions workshop is proud to bring you a collection of Original Serigraphs created by national and international artists. A diverse range of signed works on paper is shown by the broad spectrum of images which will add a visual richness to any wall space.

ARTIZAN EDITIONS
Ground Floor East, Industrial House
Conway Street
Hove
BN3 3LW
www.arizaneditions.co.uk
email: info@artizaneditions.co.uk
Tel: 01273 773959

BEAVER LODGE PRINTS LTD
Lynderswood Farm
Lynderswood Lane
Braintree, Essex
CM77 8JT
www.beaverlodgeprints.co.uk
email: sales@beaverlodgeprints.co.uk
Tel: 01245 361066
Fax: 01245 362223

BELL FINE ART
67b Parchment Street
Winchester
SO23 8AT
www.bellfineart.co.uk
email: bellfineart@btclick.com
Tel: 01962 860439
Fax: 01962 860439

BOB CROOKS: FIRST GLASS
Thelbridge Cross Farm
Thelbridge
Crediton, Devon
EX17 5SH
www.bobcrooks.com
email: sales@bobcrooks.com
Tel: 01884 860037

BRADLEY BASSO
3 Orchard Studios
Brook Green, Hammersmith
London
W6 7BU
www.bradleybasso.com
email: info@bradleybasso.com
Tel: 0207 602 1840

BURLINGTON PAINTINGS LTD
10 & 12 Burlington Gardens
W1S 3EY
www.burlington.co.uk
email: pictures@burlington.co.uk
Tel: 02077 349984
Fax: 02074 943770

CAROL MACKENZIE GALE
in progress
email: cmgale@onetel.net
Tel: 01805 804575

CATHERINE HOUGH GLASS
Unit 11
43 Carol Street
London
NW1 0HT
www.catherinehough.com
email: houghglass@aol.com
Tel: 02072 840702

COLIN RICHES SCULPTOR
Wydcombe Manor, Whitwell, Isle Of Wight
PO38 2NY
www.richesart.co.uk
email: richesart@hotmail.com
Tel: 01983 730961

ARTIZAN EDITIONS
Original Printmakers

01273 773959
www.artizaneditions.co.uk

CUT IT OUT LTD
9 Marine Court
St Leonards On Sea
East Sussex
TN38 0DX
www.cutitout.co.uk
email: oneill@dircon.co.uk
Tel: 01424 441972
Fax: 01424 441972

D'ARCY GALLERY
7 Well Walk,
Cheltenham
GL503JX
www..artbydarcy.co.uk
email: hope@artbydarcy.co.uk
Tel: 01242 511682
Fax: 01242 254767

DIANA SPRINGALL
Oast Cottage
2 Park Lane
Kemsing
TN15 6NU
email: dianaspringall@btinternet.com
Tel: 01732 761501
Fax: 01732 761501

DROSTLE MURALS & MOSAICS
40 Strand House
Merbury Close
London
SE28 0LU
www.drostle.com
email: arts@drostle.com
Tel: 07719 529520

EDINBURGH ARTS
26-28 West Bowling Green St
Edinburgh
EH6 5PB
email: enquiries@edinburgharts.com
Tel: 0131 555 1235
Fax: 0131 555 4378

FRAMANC LTD
Ashbourne Industrial Estate
Ashbourne
Co . Meath
www.framanc.com
email: tara@framanc.com
Tel: 00353 1835 0543
Fax: 00353 1835 2896

GB EYE LTD
1 Russell Street
Kelham Island
Sheffield
S3 8RW
www.gbeye.com
email: enquiries@gbeye.com
Tel: 0114 2767 454
Fax: 0114 2729599

HANNAH LOBLEY PAPERWORK
Studio 2.5, Banks Mill Studios
71, Bridge Street
Derby
DE1 3LB
www.hl-web.net
email: info@hl-web.net
Tel: 07799 832 993

 Jill George Gallery

JILL GEORGE GALLERY
38 Lexington Street, Soho,
London, W1F 0LL
Tel 0207 439 7319
Fax 0207 287 0478
info@jillgeorgegallery.co.uk
www.jillgeorgegallery.co.uk

Jill George Gallery, established in 1974,
represents paintings, drawings,
monoprints and edition prints by British
contemporary artists from the established
artist to the recent graduate with 3D
work by Mark Firth, Alessandro Gallo and
David Mach. The Gallery undertakes
commissions and provides all ancillary
services from selection to installation.
Large selection of work always available.

ISLE OF WIGHT STUDIO GLASS LTD
Old Park
St. Lawrence
Isle Of Wight
PO38 1XR
www.isleofwightstudioglass.co.uk
email: sales@isleofwightstudioglass.co.uk
Tel: 01983 853526
Fax: 01983 854054

OPEN GALLERY
375 City Road
London
EC1V 1NB
www.opengallery.co.uk
email: will@opengallery.co.uk
Tel: 020 7837 3000
Fax: 020 7833 2185

PLATEAUX GALLERY
At Thomas Goode & Co
19 South Audley Street
Mayfair, London
W1K 2BN
www.plateaux.co.uk
email: gallery@plateaux.co.uk
Tel: +44 (0) 207 499 2823
Fax: +44 (0) 207 629 4230

PW LTD
1 Church Street
Pewsey
Wilts
SN9 5DL
www.pwlimited.co.uk
email: johnny@pwlimited.co.uk
Tel: 01672 562878
Fax: 01672 563043

RILEY CONTEMPORARY ART
Far Peak
Northleach
Cheltenham
GL54 3JB
www.rileycontemporaryart.co.uk
email: rileyalbatross@btinternet.com
Tel: 07966 525187

TAMBO DESIGN LTD
Unit 1-3 Foundry Road
Bonnybridge
Falkirk
FK4 2AP
www.tambodesign.co.uk
email: sales@tambodesign.co.uk
Tel: 01324 810000
Fax: 01324 810000

THE PORTFOLIO COLLECTION (RUTLAND)
12 Midland Court
Station Approach
Oakham
LE15 6RA
www.theportfoliocollection.com
email: info@theportfoliocollection.com
Tel: 01572 770719
Fax: 01572 770729

TROWBRIDGE GALLERY
555 Kings Road
London
SW6 2EB
www.trowbridgegallery.com
email: gallery@trowbridge.co.uk
Tel: 02073 718733
Fax: 02073 718138

WILL'S ART WAREHOUSE
180 Lower Richmond Road
Putney Common
London
SW15 1LY
www.wills-art.com
email: info@wills-art.com
Tel: 020 8246 4840
Fax: 020 8246 4841

ZENITH ART
C/O Dpi
Balmorall Drive
Southport
PR9 8PX
www.zenithart.me.uk
email: clarezenithart@aol.com
Tel: 07786 272 835

ECO PRODUCTS

4 LIVING FURNITURE
24-26 Berwick Court Farm
Berwick
Polegate
BN26 5QS
www.4living.co.uk
email: office@4living.co.uk
Tel: 0800 75 65 199
Fax: 0800 75 65 199

ANNASACH
Jonah's Place
Willis Wynd, Duns
Berwickshire
TD11 3PZ
www.annasach.com
email: info@annasach.com
Tel: +44(0)1361-884 189

BE MODERN
Western Approach
South Shields
Tyne & Wear
NE33 5QZ
www.bemodern.com
email: enquiries@bemodern.com
Tel: 0191 455 3571
Fax: 0191 456 5556

BLUE MARMALADE LTD
32-36 Dalmeny Street
Edinburgh
EH6 8RG
www.bluemarmalade.co.uk
email: info@bluemarmalade.co.uk
Tel: 0131 5537766
Fax: 0131 5536659

BOTTLE ALLEY GLASS
1 Tills Courtyard
High St
Battle
TN33 0AE
www.bottlealleyglass.co.uk
email: info@bottlealleyglass.co.uk
Tel: 0845 643 2733
Fax: 0709 237 3521

CAMINOS STOVES, LANDY VENT LTD
Foster House
2 Redditch Rd
Studley, Warwickshire
B80 7AX
www.caminosstoves.co.uk
email: sales@caminosstoves.co.uk
Tel: 01527 857814
Fax: 01527 854101

DANLERS LTD
Danlers Business Centre
Vincients Road
Chippenham
SN14 6NQ
www.danlers.co.uk
email: sales@danlers.co.uk
Tel: 01249 443377
Fax: 01249 443388

DAVID COLWELL DESIGN
Trannon Studio, Llawr Y Glyn, Caersws, Powys.
SY17 5RH
www.davidcolwell.com
email: info@davidcolwell.com
Tel: 01686 430434

GLASSECO LTD
Unit 5 ,Highams Farm
Sheepbarn Lane, Warlingham
Surrey
CR6 9PQ
www.glasseco.co.uk
email: info@glasseco.co.uk
Tel: 01959 576897
Fax: 01959 575902

HANNAH LOBLEY PAPERWORK
Studio 2.5, Banks Mill Studios
71, Bridge Street
Derby
DE1 3LB
www.hl-web.net
email: info@hl-web.net
Tel: 07799 832 993

JARAPA LTD
12 Cole Rd
Bruton
Somerset
BA10 0DA
www.jarapa.co.uk
email: stewart@jarapa.co.uk
Tel: 01749 813067
Fax: 01749 813067

JETMASTER FIRES
Unit 2 Peacock Trading Estate
Goodwood Road
Eastleigh, Hants
SO50 4NT
www.jetmaster.co.uk
email: jetmastersales@aol.com
Tel: 0870 727 0105
Fax: 0870 727 0106

NATURAL HOME PRODUCTS LTD
5 Station Court
Station Lane
Hethersett
NORFOLK
www.naturalhome-products.com
email: sales@naturalhome-products.com
Tel: 01508 491 117

NATUREWARM LTD
27 Water Lane
South Witham
Grantham
NG33 5PH
www.naturewarm.co.uk
email: sales@naturewarm.co.uk
Tel: 01572 768362
Fax: 01572 767146

INTERIOR DESIGN TODAY

THE TRADE ONLY MAGAZINE FOR INTERIOR DESIGN PROFESSIONALS   NOV/DEC 2009 £5.95

PRODUCT DESIGNS

LIGHTING

BATHROOMS

DECOREX
CHELSEA WAS
CHARMED BY THE
STUNNING CREATIVITY
ON DISPLAY

100% DESIGN
THE COMPANIES AT THE TOP OF
OUR LIST ARE REVEALED IN LIGHT
OF THE RECENT SHOW

A HISTORY OF
GOOD DESIGN
BRINTON'S STEPS BACK IN TIME TO
REVEAL OUR MOST POWERFUL
DESIGN INFLUENCES

IDTMAGAZINE.CO.UK

it's a personal experience   VADO

POSH GRAFFITI LTD
The Gallery, Elmtree House,
54 Main Road, Long Bennington,
Nr Newark, Nottinghamshire
Tel: +44 1400 281563
Fax: +44 1400 281541
www.poshgraffiti.com
www.emilyreadettbayley.com

• British Design • Traditional Skills • Eco Ethics

Hand made wooden alphabets for
interior and exterior decoration and
Emily Readett-Bayley's unusual range of
interior accessories, gifts and reclaimed
teak dining tables. Use our interactive
graffiti wall on our website to plan your
wall decoration to scale.

OSMO UK
Unit 24 Anglo Business Park
Smeaton Close
Aylesbury, HP19 8UP
www.osmouk.com
email: steve@osmouk.com
Tel: 01296 481220
Fax: 01296 424090

SELTEX INTERIORS LTD
1 Horizon Trade Park
Ring Way
London, N11 2NW
www.seltex.co.uk
email: sales@seltex.co.uk
Tel: 020 8211 3107
Fax: 020 8368 0838

SPIRIT FIRES LIMITED
4 Beaumont Square
Aycliffe Industrial Park
Newton Aycliffe, Co Durham, DL5 6SW
www.spiritfires.co.uk
Tel: 01325 327221
Fax: 01325 327929

TARNSJO GARVERI AB
Garverivagen 6
740 45 TARNSJO
www.tarnsjogarveri.se
email: info@tarnsjogarveri.se
Tel: 0046 29270 750
Fax: 0046 29270 769

THE LITTLE GREENE PAINT COMPANY
Wood Street
Openshaw
Manchester, M11 2FB
www.thelittlegreene.com
email: mail@thelittlegreene.com
Tel: 0161 230 0880
Fax: 0161 223 3208

TP24 LTD
Seymour House, 12 Station Road,
Chatteris , Cambridgeshire, PE16 6AG
www.tp24.com
email: sales@tp24.com
Tel: 01354 694 591
Fax: 01354 695 879

WAVENEY RUSH INDUSTRY
The Old Maltings
Caldecott Road, Oulton Broad
Lowestoft, NR32 3PH
www.waveneyrush.co.uk
email: crafts@waveneyrush.co.uk
Tel: 01502 538777
Fax: 01502 538477

FALSE BOOKS

THE ORIGINAL BOOK WORKS LTD
1 Wilkinson Rd, Cirencester, Glos GL7 1YT
Tel: +44 1285 641664
Fax: +44 1285 641705
Philip@originalbooks.net
www.originalbooks.net
www.fauxbooks.co.uk

The Original Book Works make faux
books in traditional antique colours as
well as vellum. The products are all hand
made and hand painted in Cirencester to
replicate the genuine "look". Ideal for
use on doors, cupboards,doors to hide
TV. Now Paperbacks as faux books to
add a contemporary look.

FOUNTAIN &
WATER DISPLAYS

PRET-A-POT
6a Cow Lane Sidlesham
West Sussex, Po20 7ln
www.pret-a-pot.co.uk
email: info@pret-a-pot.co.uk
Tel: 01243 641928
Fax: 01243 641945

FRAMES & FRAMERS

55MAX
6 Lonsdale Road
Queens Park
London
NW6 6RD
www.55max.com
email: info@55max.com
Tel: 020 7625 3774
Fax: 020 7625 3776

ACRYLIC DESIGN
3a 3b Shakespeare Industrial Estate
Shakespeare Street, Watford
Hertfordshire
WD24 5RS
www.acrylicdesign.co.uk
email: sales@acrylicdesign.co.uk
Tel: 01923 241122
Fax: 01923 241144

BEAVER LODGE PRINTS LTD
Lynderswood Farm
Lynderswood Lane
Braintree, Essex
CM77 8JT
www.beaverlodgeprints.co.uk
email: sales@beaverlodgeprints.co.uk
Tel: 01245 361066
Fax: 01245 362223

BELL FINE ART
67b Parchment Street
Winchester
SO23 8AT
www.bellfineart.co.uk
email: bellfineart@btclick.com
Tel: 01962 860439
Fax: 01962 860439

D'ARCY GALLERY
7 Well Walk,
Cheltenham
GL503JX
www..artbydarcy.co.uk
email: hope@artbydarcy.co.uk
Tel: 01242 511682
Fax: 01242 254767

EDINBURGH ARTS
26-28 West Bowling Green St
Edinburgh
EH6 5PB
email: enquiries@edinburgharts.com
Tel: 0131 555 1235
Fax: 0131 555 4378

GILES COOK DESIGN
The Dove House
Astwood, Newport Pagnell
Bucks
MK16 9JX
www.gilescookdesign.co.uk
email: info@gilescookdesign.co.uk
Tel: 01234 391156
Fax: 01234 391156

PAUL FERGUSON WORKSHOP
Tel: 01525 851594

SALLY MITCHELL FINE ARTS
Askham
Newark
Nottinghamshire
NG22 0RN
www.dogart.com
email: info@dogart.com
Tel: 01777 838234
Fax: 01777 838198

SIGNWAVES LTD
Lefevre Way
Gapton Hall Industrial Estate
Great Yarmouth
NR31 0NW
www.signwavesgroup.com
email: enquiries@signwavesgroup.com
Tel: 01493 419300
Fax: 01493 419301

TAMBO DESIGN LTD
Unit 1-3 Foundry Road
Bonnybridge, Falkirk, FK4 2AP
www.tambodesign.co.uk
email: sales@tambodesign.co.uk
Tel: 01324 810000
Fax: 01324 810000

TROWBRIDGE GALLERY
555 Kings Road London, SW6 2EB
www.trowbridgegallery.com
email: gallery@trowbridge.co.uk
Tel: 02073 718733
Fax: 02073 718138

GAMES

GEOFFREY PARKER GAMES   LTD
Piglets Corner, Upper Green,
Wimbish Village, Saffron Walden,
Essex, CB10 2XJ
Tel: + 44 (0) 1799 599 100
Fax: + 44 (0) 1799 599 733
bespoke@geoffreyparker.com
www.geoffreyparker.com

Bespoke luxury games have been
made in our workshops for the past 51
years and feature all you would expect
in board gaming, from Championship
Backgammon and Chess, to gaming
compendia and tables, family
favourites Monopoly® and Scrabble®
etc. Made in sumptuous leathers,
beautiful woods or set with precious
stones and metals.

SKEELS
www.skeels.co.uk
email: rebecca@skeels.co.uk
Tel: 07715093690

INTERIOR LANDSCAPING

GILES COOK DESIGN
The Dove House
Astwood, Newport Pagnell, Bucks, MK16 9JX
www.gilescookdesign.co.uk
email: info@gilescookdesign.co.uk
Tel: 01234 391156
Fax: 01234 391156

IOTA GARDEN & HOME LTD
Wick Road, Wick St Lawerence,
North Somerset, BS22 7YQ
www.commercial.iotagarden.com
email: mail@iotagarden.com
Tel: 01934 522617
Fax: 01934 522107

DAVUKA GRP LTD
Tel: 020 8660 2854
Fax: 020 8645 2556
Email: info@davuka.co.uk
Web: www.davuka.co.uk

Suppliers of fine quality decorative
mouldings, nationwide.
Comprehensive range of interior
cornice, skirting, corbels, columns,
dado, architrave, ceiling roses etc, all
as fitted in top international hotels
and developments. See our website
for inspirational ideas and designs or
phone for catalogue and/or samples.

PELLFOLD PARTHOS LTD
1 The Quadrant
Howarth Road
Maidenhead, SL6 1AP
www.designs4space.com
email: sales@pellfoldparthos.co.uk
Tel: 01628 773353
Fax: 01628 773363

TENSARC
95 Stirling Enterprise Park
Stirling, FK7 7RP
www.tensarc.co.uk
email: info@tensarc.co.uk
Tel: 01786 450083

THE SILK FOREST
Main Street, Bagworth,
Leicestershire, LE67 1DN
www.thesilkforest.com
email: info@thesilkforest.com
Tel: 01530 231241
Fax: 01530 231240

MIRRORS
ACCENT APS
www.accent.dk
Tel: 0045 2087 9049

BAHNE EN GROS
Tel: 01628 820082
Fax: 01628 820082

BEAVER LODGE PRINTS LTD
Lynderswood Farm
Lynderswood Lane
Braintree, Essex, CM77 8JT
www.beaverlodgeprints.co.uk
email: sales@beaverlodgeprints.co.uk
Tel: 01245 361066
Fax: 01245 362223

BRIGHTON ROC
Unit 4
Fowlswick Farm
Allington Chippenham
Wiltshire
Chippenham
SN14 6QE
www.brightonroc.co.uk
email: brighton.roc@btconnect.com
Tel: 01249 782270
Fax: 01249 782270

CARVERS & GILDERS LTD
Unit 44 Spaces Business Centre
Ingate Place London SW8 3NS
www.carversandgilders.com
email: info@carversandgilders.com
Tel: 0207 498 5070
Fax: 0207 498 1221

FRAMANC LTD
Ashbourne Industrial Estate
Ashbourne, Co . Meath
www.framanc.com
email: tara@framanc.com
Tel: 00353 1835 0543
Fax: 00353 1835 2896

JP GLASS & DECOR LTD
Units 1-6 Eastcote Ind Estate
Eastcote, Middlesex, HA4 9XG
www.jpglass.com
email: sales@jpglass.com
Tel: 02084 292999
Fax: 02088 684314

MIRRORMANIA
27 Clover Way, Bradwell,
Norfolk, NR31 8RH
www.mirrormania.co.uk
email: sales@mirrormania.co.uk
Tel: 0149 304 331

JULIETTE'S INTERIORS LIMITED
Tel: 00 44 (0) 1789 721911
E-mail: sales@juliettesinteriors.co.uk
Web: www.juliettesinteriors.co.uk

Juliette's Interiors Ltd is an excellent
sourcing tool for interior designers
worldwide. Turn heads with their
astonishing, unique collection of mirrors
and furniture that can be commissioned
at a fraction of the normal price. Their
range is huge and we offer a personal
customer focused service.

NOHO MIRRORS

NOHO MIRRORS
9 Coolhurst Road, London, N8 8EP
Contact: Norma Holland
Mob: 07976829601
Email: nohonorma@aol.com
Web: www.nohomirrors.com

We are one of the few companies who still produce handmade mirrors in the traditional way. We can custom make any mirror in our range to any size specification you require. please contact us for a price quote for bespoke mirrors. Delivery is 6/10 weeks. Plus we carry a small selection of stock. please contact us for further information

PAVILLION RATTAN
The Ulvers Building
Budby Road
Notts, NG20 - 9JP
www.pavilionrattan.co.uk
email: sales@pavilionrattan.co.uk
Tel: 01623 847030
Fax: 0870 706 2159

PORTER DESIGN LTD
Court Farm House
Wellow
Bath, BA28PU
porter-design.com
email: service@porter-design.com
Tel: 01225 849153
Fax: 01225 849156

PRISMS GLASS DESIGN
Unit 31 Kingsgate Workshops
114 Kingsgate Road, NW6 2JG
www.prismsglass.com
email: prisms.glass@virgin.net
Tel: 02076 243240
Fax: 02076 243240

REINDEER ANTIQUES
81 Kensington Church Street
London, W8 4BG
www.reindeerantiques.co.uk
email: london@reindeerantiques.co.uk
Tel: 02079 373754
Fax: 02079 377199

SAPER GLASS INDUSTRIES LTD
Thames House
Longreach Road
Barking, Essex, IG11 0JR
www.saperglass.co.uk
email: tech.sales@saperglass.co.uk
Tel: 020 8594 4949
Fax: 020 8594 5252

TONY SANDLES GLASS LTD
Unit 6, Park Farm, Park Road, Great Chesterford, Essex
CB10 1RN
www.sandles-glass.co.uk
email: tony@sandles-glass.co.uk
Tel: 01799 531516
Fax: 01799 531516

TONY WILLIAMS ANTIQUE MIRRORS LTD
The Old Cottage
13 The Green, Welbourn
Lincoln
LN5 0NJ
www.williamsantiquemirrors.co.uk
email: info@williamsantiquemirrors.co.uk
Tel: 01400 273688
Fax: 07711 207551

PLANTS & ARTIFICIAL FOLIAGE

PRET-A-POT
6a Cow Lane Sidlesham
West Sussex
Po20 7ln
www.pret-a-pot.co.uk
email: info@pret-a-pot.co.uk
Tel: 01243 641928
Fax: 01243 641945

THE SILK FOREST
Main Street
Bagworth
Leicestershire
LE67 1DN
www.thesilkforest.com
email: info@thesilkforest.com
Tel: 01530 231241
Fax: 01530 231240

TABLEWARE

CANDLES DIRECT
55 Marine Drive
Paignton
TQ3 2NS
www.candlesdirect.uk.com
email: james@candlesdirect.uk.com
Tel: 01803 525365
Fax: 01803 528865

COFFEE AND CREAM
Tel: 08456 447681

CONSORZIO AX ARTIGIANEXPORT
email: consorzioax@libero.it
Tel: 0039 0759 72240
Fax: 0039 0759711757

DAVID MELLOR DESIGN
4 Sloane Square
London
SW1W 8EE
www.davidmellordesign.com
email: davidmellor@davidmellordesign.co.uk
Tel: 020 7730 4259
Fax: 020 7730 7240

DO SHOP LIMITED
G/F And Basement
47 Beak Street
London
W1F 9SE
www.do-shop.com
email: info@do-shop.com
Tel: 020 7494 9090
Fax: 020 7494 9090

GLAZEBROOK & CO
London
SW6 3XD
www.glazebrook.com
email: sales@glazebrook.com
Tel: 020 7731 7135
Fax: 020 7371 5434

ISAGI LIMITED
The Laurels
34 Sheepfold Lane
Amersham, Bucks
HP7 9EJ
www.isagi.co.uk
email: sales@isagi.co.uk
Tel: 01494 729345
Fax: 01494 729345

JB SILVERWARE
139a New Bond Street
London
W1S 2TN
www.jbsilverware.co.uk
email: elliot@jbsilverware.co.uk
Tel: 0207 6291251
Fax: 0207 4953001

MAXWELL AND WILLIAMS
No 4 Watling Gate
297-303 Edgware Road
London
NW9 6NB
www.maxwellandwilliams.co.uk
email: sales@valerie-graham.co.uk
Tel: 0208 2005100
Fax: 0208 2005150

NORMANN COPENHAGEN
Osterbrogade 70
Copenhagen
Denmark
2100
www.normann-copenhagen.com
email: normann@normann-copenhagen.com
Tel: 0045 35 554 459
Fax: 0045 35 554 439

PREMIER HOUSEWARES LLP
Premier Business Park
55 Jordanvale Avenue
Glasgow
G14 0QP
www.premierhousewares.co.uk
email: info@premierhousewares.co.uk
Tel: 0141 579 2000
Fax: 0141 579 2005

ROBERT WELCH DESIGNS
Lower High Street
Chipping Campden
Glos
GL55 6DY
www.robertwelch.com
email: sales@welch.co.uk
Tel: 01386 840522
Fax: 01386 848804

SARAH BROADHEAD-RIALL
36 Complins,
Holybourne
Alton
GU34 4EJ
sarah-broadhead-riall-glass.com
email: sarah_broadhead@tiscali.co.uk
Tel: 01420 85083

SKEELS
www.skeels.co.uk
email: rebecca@skeels.co.uk
Tel: 07715093690

TENTERDEN (PEWTER) COLLECTION, THE
108-110 High Street
Tenterden
Kent
TN30 6HT
email: tenterdenhouseinteriors@hotmail.com
Tel: 01580 764481
Fax: 01580 765531

TONE VON KROGH CERAMICS
4 Lynwood Grove
Heaton Chapel
Stockport
SK4 5DP
email: tonevonkrogh@yahoo.com
Tel: 01614 313238

VASES, SCULPTURES & ORNAMENTS

ANCIENNE AMBIANCE LUXURY CANDLES
www.ancienneambiance.com
email: info@ancienneambiance.com
Tel: 0870 199 8958
Fax: 020 7373 8583

BAHNE EN GROS
Tel: 01628 820082
Fax: 01628 820082

CATHERINE HOUGH GLASS
Unit 11
43 Carol Street
London
NW1 0HT
www.catherinehough.com
email: houghglass@aol.com
Tel: 02072 840702

GUINEVERE WAREHOUSE
Unit 5
92-104 Carnwath Road
London
SW6 3HW
www.guinevere.co.uk
email: sales@guineverewarehouse.co.uk
Tel: 020 7731 5401
Fax: 020 77368267

ISLE OF WIGHT STUDIO GLASS LTD
Old Park
St. Lawrence
Isle Of Wight
PO38 1XR
www.isleofwightstudioglass.co.uk
email: sales@isleofwightstudioglass.co.uk
Tel: 01983 853526
Fax: 01983 854054

KAREN LAWRENCE GLASS
Unit F 272, Riverside Business Centre
Brendon Valley
Wandsworth, London
SW18 4UQ
www.karenlawrenceglass.com
email: karen@karenlawrenceglass.com
Tel: 020 8874 7955

KATY HOLFORD
Tichborne Studios
18 Tichborne Street
Brighton
BN1 1UR
www.katyholford.co.uk
email: katy@katyholford.co.uk
Tel: 01273 327792

LALIQUE LTD
47 Conduit Street
London
W1S 2YP
www.cristallalique.fr
email: shop.london.cs@lalique.fr
Tel: 0207 292 0444
Fax: 02074 937249

LUXURY LIVING LONDON LIMITED
103 Wandsworth Bridge Road
London
SW6 2TE
www.luxuryliving.uk.com
email: showroom@luxuryliving.uk.com
Tel: 0207 384 9722
Fax: 020 7384 9721

MARVELLÍS LTD
The Warehouse
Station Road
Hadnall, Shrewsbury
SY4 3DD
www.marvells.com
email: louise@marvells.com
Tel: 01938 210800
Fax: 01939 210999

PLATEAUX GALLERY
At Thomas Goode & Co
19 South Audley Street
Mayfair, London
W1K 2BN
www.plateaux.co.uk
email: gallery@plateaux.co.uk
Tel: +44 (0) 207 499 2823
Fax: +44 (0) 207 629 4230

RETPEN GLAS
Urmagertoften 130
Hojbjerg
Denmark
8270
www.retpen-glas.dk
email: marie@retpen-glas.dk
Tel: 0458 629 7125

SARAH BROADHEAD-RIALL
36 Complins,
Holybourne
Alton
GU34 4EJ
sarah-broadhead-riall-glass.com
email: sarah_broadhead@tiscali.co.uk
Tel: 01420 85083

STUART AKROYD CONTEMPORARY GLASS
Unit 3 Thoroton Place
Thoroton St
Nottingham
NG7 4EW
www.stuartakroydglass.com
email: info@stuartakroydglass.com
Tel: 0115 9106016
Fax: 0115 9106016

SVAJA LIMITED
The Circlefifteen
Emily Davison Drive
Epsom
KT18 5QH
www.svaja.com
email: nigelb@svaja.com
Tel: 0870 444 6860
Fax: 0870 444 6861

THE SILK FOREST
Main Street
Bagworth
Leicestershire
LE67 1DN
www.thesilkforest.com
email: info@thesilkforest.com
Tel: 01530 231241
Fax: 01530 231240

TONE VON KROGH CERAMICS
4 Lynwood Grove
Heaton Chapel
Stockport
SK4 5DP
email: tonevonkrogh@yahoo.com
Tel: 01614 313238

UREDALE GLASS
42 Market Place
Masham
North Yorkshire
HG4 4EF
www.uredale.co.uk
email: info@uredale.co.uk
Tel: 01765 689780
Fax: 01765 689780

VESSEL
114 Kesington Park Road
Notting Hill
London
W112PW
www.vesselgallery.com
email: info@vesselgallery.com
Tel: 02077 278001
Fax: 02077 278661

VITAMIN
The Old Truman Brewery
91 Brick Lane
London
E1 6QL
email: info@vitaminliving.com
Tel: 0207 092 9191

WALL HANGINGS, PAINTINGS & PRINTS

ANDREA MAFLIN
44 Albert Road
Stroud Green
London
N4 3RP
www.andreamaflin.co.uk
email: design@andreamaflin.co.uk
Tel: 0207 272 7972

ART & IMAGE LTD
Gerrards Cross
SL9 8QF
www.artandimage.co.uk
email: valerie@artandimage.co.uk
Tel: 01753 884535
Fax: 08704 601546

ART SEARCH LTD
33 Kingswood Avenue
London
NW6 6LR
www.artsearchlimited.co.uk
email: info@artsearchlimited.co.uk
Tel: 02089 699844

ARTISTIC-LICENCE
157 Harrow Road
Wollaton Park
Nottingham
NG8 1FL
www.artistic-licence.com
email: studio@artistic-licence.com
Tel: 01159 724 777

ARTIZAN EDITIONS
Ground Floor East, Industrial House
Conway Street
Hove
BN3 3LW
www.arizaneditions.co.uk
email: info@artizaneditions.co.uk
Tel: 01273 773959

ATELIERS PINTON
9 Rue Preville
Felletin
France
23500
www.ateliers-pinton.com
email: l.dixon@ateliers-pinton.com
Tel: 00 33 630 640 534
Fax: 00 33 555 664 322

BURLINGTON PAINTINGS LTD
10 & 12 Burlington Gardens
W1S 3EY
www.burlington.co.uk
email: pictures@burlington.co.uk
Tel: 02077 349984
Fax: 02074 943770

CARINA HASLAM ART
2 Reyners Green
Little Kingshill, Great Missenden
Bucks
HP16 0EQ
www.carinahaslamart.com
email: art@carinahaslamart.com
Tel: 01494866914 or 0797 3322397

CAROL MACKENZIE GALE
in progress
email: cmgale@onetel.net
Tel: 01805 804575

CUT IT OUT LTD
9 Marine Court
St Leonards On Sea
East Sussex
TN38 0DX
www.cutitout.co.uk
email: oneill@dircon.co.uk
Tel: 01424 441972
Fax: 01424 441972

D'ARCY GALLERY
7 Well Walk,
Cheltenham
GL503JX
www..artbydarcy.co.uk
email: hope@artbydarcy.co.uk
Tel: 01242 511682
Fax: 01242 254767

DIANA SPRINGALL
Oast Cottage
2 Park Lane
Kemsing
TN15 6NU
email: dianaspringall@btinternet.com
Tel: 01732 761501
Fax: 01732 761501

DOVECOT STUDIOS LTD
Dovecot
10 Infirmary Street
Edinburgh
EH1 1LT
www.dovecotstudios.com
email: info@dovecotstudios.com
Tel: 0131 550 3660
Fax: 0131 550 3669

FAMILY COPIES
1 Chapel Cottages
Ashmansworth
Newbury
RG20 9SL
www.familycopies.com
email: derekbird@familycopies.com
Tel: 01635 254592

FRAMANC LTD
Ashbourne Industrial Estate
Ashbourne
Co . Meath
www.framanc.com
email: tara@framanc.com
Tel: 00353 1835 0543
Fax: 00353 1835 2896

FRENCH FABRIC DESIGN
37
Duke Street St James's
St Jamesis , London
SW1Y 6DF
email: info@julianhartnoll.com
Tel: 020 7839 3842

J.MORTON LEE (FINE WATERCOLOURS)
Cedar House
Bacon Lane
Hayling Island
PO11 0DN
www.edenbridgegalleries.com
email: j.mortonlee@btinternet.com
Tel: 023 92464444

MARVELLÍS LTD
The Warehouse
Station Road
Hadnall, Shrewsbury
SY4 3DD
www.marvells.com
email: louise@marvells.com
Tel: 01938 210800
Fax: 01939 210999

MIRRORMANIA
27 Clover Way
Bradwell
Norfolk
NR31 8RH
www.mirrormania.co.uk
email: sales@mirrormania.co.uk
Tel: 0149 304 331

MOLLIE REGAN TEXTILES
The Studio
99 Dorchester Road, Oakdale
Poole, Dorset
BH15 3QZ
www.mollieregantextiles.co.uk
email: rosalyn@mollieregantextiles.co.uk
Tel: 01202 675944
Fax: 01202 675944

MOSQUITO / AMY CUSHING
62 Lower Ham Road, Kingston, Surrey
KT2 5AW
www.mosquito-design.com
email: amycushing@mosquito-design.com
Tel: 07957 258 620

PAISNEL GALLERY
9, Bury Street,
St.james's
London
SW1Y 6AB
www.paisnelgallery.co.uk
email: info@paisnelgallery.co.uk
Tel: 020 7930 9293
Fax: 020 7930 7282

PORTER DESIGN LTD
Court Farm House
Wellow
Bath
BA28PU
porter-design.com
email: service@porter-design.com
Tel: 01225 849153
Fax: 01225 849156

RILEY CONTEMPORARY ART
Far Peak
Northleach
Cheltenham
GL54 3JB
www.rileycontemporaryart.co.uk
email: rileyalbatross@btinternet.com
Tel: 07966 525187

SALLY MITCHELL FINE ARTS
Askham
Newark
Nottinghamshire
NG22 0RN
www.dogart.com
email: info@dogart.com
Tel: 01777 838234
Fax: 01777 838198

STICKYUPS
1-6 Clay Street
London
W1U 6DA
www.stickyups.com
email: sales@stickyups.com
Tel: 0845 257 0642

TAMBO DESIGN LTD
Unit 1-3 Foundry Road
Bonnybridge
Falkirk
FK4 2AP
www.tambodesign.co.uk
email: sales@tambodesign.co.uk
Tel: 01324 810000
Fax: 01324 810000

THE ART SURGERY
33-35 Tib Street
Northern Quarter
Manchester
M4 1LX
www.theartsurgery.co.uk
email: info@theartsurgery.co.uk
Tel: 0161 8192888

THE PORTFOLIO COLLECTION (RUTLAND)
12 Midland Court
Station Approach
Oakham
LE15 6RA
www.theportfoliocollection.com
email: info@theportfoliocollection.com
Tel: 01572 770719
Fax: 01572 770729

TROWBRIDGE GALLERY
555 Kings Road
London
SW6 2EB
www.trowbridgegallery.com
email: gallery@trowbridge.co.uk
Tel: 02073 718733
Fax: 02073 718138

WILL'S ART WAREHOUSE
180 Lower Richmond Road
 Putney Common
London
SW15 1LY
www.wills-art.com
email: info@wills-art.com
Tel: 020 8246 4840
Fax: 020 8246 4841

YOUR WHITE SPACE
66 Brackendale Rd
Bournemouth
Dorset
BH8 9HZ
www.yourwhitespace.com
email: david@yourwhitespace.com
Tel: 01202 251126

ZARDI & ZARDI
Podgwell Barn
Edge
Gloucestershire
GL6 6NJ
www.zardiandzardi.co.uk
email: enquiries@zardiandzardi.co.uk
Tel: 01452 814777
Fax: 01452 814 433

ZENITH ART
C/O Dpi
Balmorall Drive
Southport
PR9 8PX
www.zenithart.me.uk
email: clarezenithart@aol.com
Tel: 07786 272 835

Entertainment Technology & Electronics

POWELL BLINDS
Sunblind House, Holmbush Potteries,
Faygate, Horsham,
West Sussex, RH12 4SE
Tel: +44 (0) 1293 851010
Fax: +44 (0) 1293 851999
www.powellblinds.com
sales@powellblinds.com

Whether your installing a full home automation system or just looking for stand alone motorised blinds, Powell Blinds are the specialists in the field. We offer a full range of automated shading products with a comprehensive consultation, survey and installation service and are the UK's leading Luton shade specialist.

D2C LTD
7 Hazel Rd
St Albans
Hertfordshire
AL22AH
www.d2c.co.uk
email: daviddavies@d2c.co.uk
Tel: 07973 751272
Fax: 01727 873338

SMARTCOMM LTD
45 Cressex Enterprise Centre
Lincoln Road
High Wycombe, Bucks
HP12 3RL
www.smartcomm.co.uk
email: info@smartcomm.co.uk
Tel: 01494 471912
Fax: 01494 472464

ACOUSTIC & NOISE CONTROL

BICESTER PRODUCTS LTD
Unit 7
Crawley Mill
Witney
OX29 9TJ
www.bicpro.co.uk
email: bicpro@btconnect.com
Tel: 01993 704810
Fax: 01933 779569

KNAUF AMF CEILINGS LTD
Thames House
6 Church Street
Twickenham
TW1 3NJ
www.amfceilings.co.uk
email: sales@amfceilings.co.uk
Tel: 020 8892 3216
Fax: 020 8892 6866

LA DRAPE INTERNATIONAL LTD
Internet House
Aston Lane North
Preston Brook
WA7 3PE
www.thequiltedwall.co.uk
email: info@ladrape.com
Tel: 01928 713 330
Fax: 01928 713 094

SAS INTERNATIONAL
31 Suttons Business Park
London Road
Reading
RG6 1AZ
www.sasint.co.uk
email: enquiries@sasint.co.uk
Tel: 0118 929 0900
Fax: 0118 929 0901

STRETCHED FABRIC SYSTEMS
68a Compton Street, London
EC1V 0BN
www.stretchedfabricsystems.com
email: sales@stretchedfabricsystems.com
Tel: 02072 534608
Fax: 02072 535746

AUDIO SOLUTIONS

ALBION DESIGN & FABRICATION LTD
4-16 Gosforth Close
Middlefield Industrail Estate
Sandy
SG191RB
www.albion-manufacturing.com
email: info@albion-manufacturing.com
Tel: 01767 692313
Fax: 01767 683157

ARMOUR HOME
Stortford Hall Industrial Park
Dunmow Road
Bishops Stortford, Hertfordshire
CM23 5GZ
www.armourhome.co.uk
email: info@armourhome.co.uk
Tel: 01279 501111
Fax: 01279 501080

BRETFORD MANUFACTURING LTD
2 Etongate, 110 Windsor Rd
Slough
Berkshire
SL1 2JA
www.bretforduk.com
email: sales@bretforduk.com
Tel: 01753 539955
Fax: 01753 539478

KAURUS LTD
135 Lord Street
Hoddesdon
Herts
EN11 8NG
www.kaurus.com
email: info@kaurus
Tel: 01992 460591

MUSIC IN EVERY ROOM LTD
16 The Sidings
Guiseley
Leeds
LS20 8BX
www.musicineveryroom.co.uk
email: sales@musicineveryroom.co.uk
Tel: 0845 094 1857
Fax: 01943 872768

PEL SERVICES LTD
Belvue Business Centre
Belvue Road
Northolt
UB5 5QQ
www.pel.co.uk
email: info@pel.co.uk
Tel: 020 8839 2100
Fax: 020 8841 1948

REVO TECHNOLOGIES LTD
The Inox Building
Caldwellside
Lanark, Scotland
ML11 7SR
www.revo.co.uk
email: enquiries@revo.co.uk
Tel: 01555 666161
Fax: 01555 663344

SMARTCOMM LTD
45 Cressex Enterprise Centre
Lincoln Road
High Wycombe, Bucks
HP12 3RL
www.smartcomm.co.uk
email: info@smartcomm.co.uk
Tel: 01494 471912
Fax: 01494 472464

THE SOUND WORKSHOP LTD
19-21 Queens Road
Halifax
West Yorkshire
HX1 3NS
www.thesoundworkshop.com
email: info@thesoundworkshop.com
Tel: 01422 345021
Fax: 01422 363440

INTEGRATED SOUND, LIGHT & VIDEO SYSTEMS

ARMOUR HOME
Stortford Hall Industrial Park
Dunmow Road
Bishops Stortford, Hertfordshire
CM23 5GZ
www.armourhome.co.uk
email: info@armourhome.co.uk
Tel: 01279 501111
Fax: 01279 501080

OPEN GALLERY
375 City Road
London
EC1V 1NB
www.opengallery.co.uk
email: will@opengallery.co.uk
Tel: 020 7837 3000
Fax: 020 7833 2185

PEL SERVICES LTD
Belvue Business Centre
Belvue Road
Northolt, UB5 5QQ
www.pel.co.uk
email: info@pel.co.uk
Tel: 020 8839 2100
Fax: 020 8841 1948

SON ET LUMIERE AV & LIGHTING CONSULTANTS
Design House
39a High Street
East Malling
ME19 6AJ
www.son-et-lumiere.co.uk
Tel: 01732 521111

SMART3 LTD
2nd Floor Titan Court
Bishop Square
Hatfield, AL10 9NA
Tel: +44 (0) 870 351 6082
Fax: +44 (0) 870 351 6083
E-mail: info@smart3.co.uk
Web: www.smart3.co.uk

Smart3 is a provider of highly flexible home automation systems comprising security, multi-room audio and video, light control and much more. Smart3 is the bridge that makes it possible for multiple consumer electronics and home systems to work seamlessly together - with a single remote. So, find out what's possible with Smart3!

THE SOUND WORKSHOP LTD
19-21 Queens Road
Halifax
West Yorkshire
HX1 3NS
www.thesoundworkshop.com
email: info@thesoundworkshop.com
Tel: 01422 345021
Fax: 01422 363440

WIZARD LIGHTING
Springfieldschurch Lane
Bisley
Woking
GU24 9EA
wizardlighting.co.uk
email: wizlightin@aol.com
Tel: 01483 489080
Fax: 01473 489030

SECURITY

ACCESS CONTROLS
72 Boston Road Leicester
LE4 1HB
www.accesscontrolsolutions.co.uk
email: info@accesscontrolsolutions.co.uk
Tel: 01162 366044
Fax: 01162 366360

CODELOCKS LTD
Castle Industrial Park
Kiln Road
Newbury
RG14 2EZ
www.codelocks.co.uk
email: sales@codelocks.co.uk
Tel: 01635 239645
Fax: 01636 239644

FRANCHI LOCKS & TOOLS LTD
278 Holloway Road
London
N7 6NE
www.franchi.co.uk
email: info@franchi.co.uk
Tel: 020 7607 2200
Fax: 020 7700 4050

I-DESK SOLUTIONS LTD
11 Ivanhoe Road
Finchampstead
Berkshire
RG40 4QQ
www.i-desk.co.uk
email: info@i-desk.co.uk
Tel: 01189 739700
Fax: 01189 8731058

PEL SERVICES LTD
Belvue Business Centre
Belvue Road
Northolt
UB5 5QQ
www.pel.co.uk
email: info@pel.co.uk
Tel: 020 8839 2100
Fax: 020 8841 1948

SECURIKEY
Po Box 18
Aldershot
GU12 4UH
www.securikey.co.uk
email: enquiries@securikey.co.uk
Tel: 01252 311 888
Fax: 01252 343939

R&D MARKETING (*demista*™) LTD

DIGITAL DOOR VIEWER ™
Land House
Anyards Road
Cobham
Surrey, KT11 2LW
Tel: +44 (0)1932 866600
Fax: +44 (0)1932 866688
E-mail: rd@demista.co.uk
Web: www.demista.co.uk

The wireless Digital Door Viewer (DDV) is an innovative product designed to replace the conventional peepholes in doors. It is simple to fit and has a system delivering clear images at the touch of a button with full extended views so giving security and peace of mind.

TELGUARD
Units 2/3, The Old Stables, Ockley Court Farm, Coles Lane, Ockley, Surrey, RH5 5LS
Tel: 01306 710120
Fax: 01306 713769
Web: www.doorentry.co.uk

TelGuard offer a wide range of telephone/GSM based intercom entry systems. The main benefits of telephone/GSM based entry systems are: no hard wiring, no dedicated handsets, flexibility, quick and easy to install. Our products are designed for operation with doors, gates, barriers, bollards, turnstiles and other forms of automated access.

SON ET LUMIERE AV & LIGHTING CONSULTANTS
Design House
39a High Street
East Malling, ME19 6AJ
www.son-et-lumiere.co.uk
Tel: 01732 521111

SMART HOME TECHNOLOGY

AV INSPIRATIONS LTD
Units 8 - 10 Shorade Ind Est
Watling Street, Bridgtown
Cannock, WS11 0DH
email: tracey@avinspirations.co.uk
Tel: 01543 506766

D2C LTD
7 Hazel Rd, St Albans,
Hertfordshire, AL22AH
www.d2c.co.uk
email: daviddavies@d2c.co.uk
Tel: 07973 751272
Fax: 01727 873338

GOELST UK LTD
Crimple Court
Hornbeam Park
Harrogate, HG2 8PB
www.goelstuk.com
email: info@goelstuk.com
Tel: 01423 873 002
Fax: 01423 874 006

IO-HOMECONTROL
47 Rue Maurice Flandin, 69003 LYON
www.io-homecontrol.com
email: contact@io-homecontrol.com
Tel: +33 4 72 13 24 01
Fax: +33 4 72 13 23 12

LEGRAND ELECTRIC LTD
Great King Street North
Birmingham
B19 2LF
Tel: 0870 608 9000

MIRRORMEDIA LTD
15 Southmill Trading Centre
Southmill Road
Bishop's Stortford
CM23 3DY
www.mirrormedia.com
email: sales@mirrormedia.com
Tel: 0870 386 6333
Fax: 0870 386 6111

SMARTCOMM LTD
45 Cressex Enterprise Centre
Lincoln Road
High Wycombe, Bucks
HP12 3RL
www.smartcomm.co.uk
email: info@smartcomm.co.uk
Tel: 01494 471912
Fax: 01494 472464

SUNPROJECT (U K)
6 Waterloo Park Ind. Est.
Wellington Road
Bidford On Avon
B50 4JG
email: sales@sunproject.co.uk
Tel: 01789 773377
Fax: 01789 773388

SMART3 LTD
2nd Floor Titan Court
Bishop Square
Hatfield, AL10 9NA
Tel: +44 (0) 870 351 6082
Fax: +44 (0) 870 351 6083
E-mail: info@smart3.co.uk
Web: www.smart3.co.uk

Smart3 is a provider of highly flexible home automation systems comprising security, multi-room audio and video, light control and much more. Smart3 is the bridge that makes it possible for multiple consumer electronics and home systems to work seamlessly together - with a single remote. So, find out what's possible with Smart3!

VASSALLO MELLOR PARRIS
8 Plato Place
72-74 St Dionis Road
London
SW6 4TU
www.vmpdesign.co.uk
email: mail@vmpdesign.co.uk
Tel: 02077 317903

SOUND & VISION

ANTHONY GALLO ACOUSTICS
The Inox Building
Caldwellside
Lanark, Scotland
ML11 7SR
www.anthonygallo.co.uk
email: david@anthonygallo.co.uk
Tel: 01555 666444
Fax: 01555 663344

AQUAVISION WATERPROOF TELEVISIONS
Ibroc House
Essex Road
Hoddesdon
EN11 0QS
www.aquavision.co.uk
email: info@aquavision.co.uk
Tel: 01992 708333
Fax: 01992 708308

ARMOUR HOME
Stortford Hall Industrial Park
Dunmow Road
Bishops Stortford, Hertfordshire
CM23 5GZ
www.armourhome.co.uk
email: info@armourhome.co.uk
Tel: 01279 501111
Fax: 01279 501080

AV INSPIRATIONS LTD
Units 8 - 10
Shorade Ind Est
Watling Street
Bridgtown
Cannock
WS11 0DH
email: tracey@avinspirations.co.uk
Tel: 01543 506766

D2C LTD
7 Hazel Rd
St Albans
Hertfordshire
AL22AH
www.d2c.co.uk
email: daviddavies@d2c.co.uk
Tel: 07973 751272
Fax: 01727 873338

KAURUS LTD
135 Lord Street
Hoddesdon
Herts
EN11 8NG
www.kaurus.com
email: info@kaurus
Tel: 01992 460591

LASERPOD
Highmoor Park
Highmoor
Henley On Thames
RG9 5DH
www.laserpod.com
email: andy@laserpod.com
Tel: 01491 641 000

MIRRORMEDIA LTD
15 Southmill Trading Centre
Southmill Road
Bishop's Stortford
CM23 3DY
www.mirrormedia.com
email: sales@mirrormedia.com
Tel: 0870 386 6333
Fax: 0870 386 6111

REVO TECHNOLOGIES LTD
The Inox Building
Caldwellside
Lanark
Scotland
ML11 7SR
www.revo.co.uk
email: enquiries@revo.co.uk
Tel: 01555 666161
Fax: 01555 663344

SHARP
4 Furzeground Way
Stockley Park
Uxbridge
UB11 1EZ
www.sharp.co.uk
email: martin.arnold@sharp-uk.co.uk
Tel: 0208 734 2000   0800 262 958

THE SOUND WORKSHOP LTD
19-21 Queens Road
Halifax
West Yorkshire
HX1 3NS
www.thesoundworkshop.com
email: info@thesoundworkshop.com
Tel: 01422 345021
Fax: 01422 363440

THE HIDDEN TV COMPANY
Coleham Head, Shrewsbury,
Shropshire, SY3 7BJ
Tel: 01743 351120
Mobile: 0797 401 5755
mansers@theantiquedealers.com
www.thehiddentvcompany.com

Designers and creators of traditional
television cabinets. We offer a unique
product of beautifully handcrafted
cabinets in quality woods. We are also
a part of Mansers Antiques, est. since
1944.

VIDEO & AUDIO SOLUTIONS

BANG & OLUFSEN

Bang & Olufsen
Peter Bangs Vej 15, DK-7600 Struer
Tel: +45 96841122
www.bang-olufsen.com

Bang & Olufsen is a world-renowned
manufacturer of television, audio and
loudspeaker systems. Our story goes
back to 1925 and includes the
creation of some of the world's most
epoch-making products and solutions
in our field. At Bang & Olufsen we
strive to create products that combine
unrivalled performance with ingenuity
and emotional appeal. We believe
people should not be forced to adapt
to complicated technology; instead,
technology should adapt to people.
**All our products and solutions
have one goal: creating ultimate
pleasure and experiences.**

Exterior & Landscaping

CH WHITEHOUSE LTD
Buckhurst Works,
Bells Yew Green,
Tunbridge Wells
TN3 9BN
greenhouse.uk.net
Tel: 01892 750247
Fax: 01892 750247

CH WHITEHOUSE LTD
Buckhurst Works,
Bells Yew Green,
Tunbridge Wells
TN3 9BN
greenhouse.uk.net
Tel: 01892 750247
Fax: 01892 750247

FUSION GLASS DESIGNS LIMITED
365 Clapham Road
London
SW9 9BT
www.fusionglass.co.uk
email: info@fusionglass.co.uk
Tel: 020 7738 5888
Fax: 020 7738 4888

PARMAR AND PARMAR
9 Beechcroft Road
Bushey
Herts
WD23 2JU
www.parmarandparmar.com
email: info@parmarandparmar.com
Tel: 0845 450 3714

SMP PLAYGROUNDS LTD
Ten Acre Lane
Thorpe, Egham
TW20 8RJ
www.smp.co.uk
email: sales@smp.co.uk
Tel: 01784 489100
Fax: 01784 431079

WHICHFORD POTTERY
Whichford
Nr. Shipston-On-Stour
Warwickshire
CV36 5PG
www.whichfordpottery.com
Tel: 01608 684416
Fax: 01608 684833

FENCING & GATES

ATLAS GROUP
868 Plymouth Road
Slough
Berkshire
SL1 4LP
www.atlasgroup.co.uk
email: info@atlasgroup.co.uk
Tel: 01753 696166
Fax: 01753 696916

BALCONY SYSTEMS LTD
Unit 5 Forest Row Business Pk
Station Road
Forest Row
RH18 5DW
www.balconette.co.uk
email: enquiries@balconette.co.uk
Tel: 01342 410 411
Fax: 01342 410412

HADDONCRAFT FORGE
The Forge House
East Haddon
Northampton
NN6 8DB
www.haddoncraft.co.uk
email: info@haddoncraft.co.uk
Tel: 01604 772 027
Fax: 01604 770 027

LINCARE LTD
15 Chiltern Business Village
Arundel Road
UB8 2SN
www.linkcare.net
email: info@linkcare.net
Tel: 01895 232626

TOWNSCAPE PRODUCTS LIMITED
Fulwood Road South
Sutton In Ashfield
Nottinghamshire
NG17 2JZ
www.townscape24.com
email: sales@townscape-products.co.uk
Tel: 01623 513355
Fax: 01623 440267

FOUNTAINS & WATER DISPLAYS

BULBECK FOUNDRY
Reach Road
Burwell
Cambridgeshire
CB25 0GH
www.bulbeckfoundry.co.uk
email: info@bulbeckfoundry.co.uk
Tel: 01638 743153
Fax: 01638 743374

CAPITAL GARDEN PRODUCTS LTD
Gibbs Reed Barn
Pashley Road
Ticehurst
TN5 7HE
www.capital-garden.com
email: sales@capital-garden.com
Tel: 01580 201092
Fax: 01580 201093

FENG SHUI WITH RÈNUKA
Tel: 07958 204916

HADDONSTONE LTD
The Forge House
East Haddon
Northampton
NN6 8DB
www.haddonstone.com
email: info@haddonstone.co.uk
Tel: 01604 770711
Fax: 01604 770027

REDFIELDS
Unit1 Cluster Ind Est
Rodney Rd
Portsmouth
PO4 8ST
www.redfields.co.uk
email: sales@redfields.co.uk
Tel: 02392 870000

TOWNSCAPE PRODUCTS LIMITED
Fulwood Road South
Sutton In Ashfield
Nottinghamshire
NG17 2JZ
www.townscape24.com
email: sales@townscape-products.co.uk
Tel: 01623 513355
Fax: 01623 440267

GARDEN ORNAMENT

ANDREW CRACE
Bourne Lane, Much Hadham, Hertfordshire
SG10 6ER
www.andrewcrace.com
email: sales@andrewcrace.com
Tel: 01279 842685
Fax: 01279 843646

BULBECK FOUNDRY
Reach Road
Burwell
Cambridgeshire
CB25 0GH
www.bulbeckfoundry.co.uk
email: info@bulbeckfoundry.co.uk
Tel: 01638 743153
Fax: 01638 743374

CADIX UK LTD
Unit 5
2 Counties Estate, Falconer Road
Haverhill , Suffolk
CB9 7XZ
www.cadix.co.uk
email: sales@cadix.co.uk
Tel: 01440 713 704
Fax: 01440 713 708

DROSTLE MURALS & MOSAICS
40 Strand House
Merbury Close
London
SE28 0LU
www.drostle.com
email: arts@drostle.com
Tel: 07719 529520

HADDONSTONE LTD
The Forge House
East Haddon
Northampton, NN6 8DB
www.haddonstone.com
email: info@haddonstone.co.uk
Tel: 01604 770711
Fax: 01604 770027

IOTA GARDEN & HOME LTD
Wick Road
Wick St Lawerence
North Somerset BS22 7YQ
www./commercial.iotagarden.com/
email: mail@iotagarden.com
Tel: 01934 522617
Fax: 01934 522107

MINSTERSTONE LTD
Pondhayes Farm
Dinnington
Hinton St George, TA17 8SU
www.minsterstone.com
email. sales@minsterstone.ltd.uk
Tel: 01460 52277
Fax: 01460 57865

PARMAR AND PARMAR
9 Beechcroft Road
Bushey
Herts, WD23 2JU
www.parmarandparmar.com
email: info@parmarandparmar.com
Tel: 0845 450 3714

PRET-A-POT
6a Cow Lane Sidlesham
West Sussex, Po20 7ln
www.pret-a-pot.co.uk
email: info@pret-a-pot.co.uk
Tel: 01243 641928
Fax: 01243 641945

THE THIRD NATURE
Tel 07909 695204
sales@thethirdnature.co.uk

www.thethirdnature.co.uk for
contemporary concrete planters,
plinths and furniture, in a range of
colours. Based in Cornwall, we offer a
reasonably priced range of mid-
bespoke products that can be made
and delivered to you within 3-6 weeks.
We also make and distribute concrete
wall and floor tiles for Jethro Macey.

REDFIELDS
Unit1 Cluster Ind Est
Rodney Rd
Portsmouth
PO4 8ST
www.redfields.co.uk
email: sales@redfields.co.uk
Tel: 02392 870000

WHICHFORD POTTERY
Whichford
Nr. Shipston-On-Stour
Warwickshire
CV36 5PG
www.whichfordpottery.com
Tel: 01608 684416
Fax: 01608 684833

LANDSCAPING
BALMORAL TANKS
Balmoral Park
Loirston
Aberdeen
AB12 3GY
www.balmoraltanks.com
email: tanks@balmoral.co.uk
Tel: 01224 859000
Fax: 01224 859123

BURLINGTON SLATE LTD
Cavendish House
Kirkby In Furness
Cumbria
LA17 7UN
burlingtonstone.co.uk
email: sales@burlingtonstone.co.uk
Tel: 01229 889661
Fax: 01229 889466

FLOWCRETE UK LTD
The Flooring Technology Centre
Booth Lane
Sandbach, Cheshire
CW11 3QF
www.flowcrete.com
email: uk@flowcrete.com
Tel: 01270 753 000
Fax: 01270 753 333

FOUR SEASONS SUN ROOMS
Lakeside House
Quarry Lane
Chichester, West Sussex
PO19 8NY
email: info@roomoutside.com
Tel: 01243 538999
Fax: 01243 776313

HADDONSTONE LTD
The Forge House
East Haddon
Northampton
NN6 8DB
www.haddonstone.com
email: info@haddonstone.co.uk
Tel: 01604 770711
Fax: 01604 770027

PLANTAZIA LANDSCAPES LTD
49 Derry Downs
Orpington
Kent
BR5 4DU
www.plantazia.co.uk
email: info@plantazia.co.uk
Tel: 01689 819974
Fax: 01689 819974

SPARTAN TILES
Slough Lane
Ardleigh
Colchester
CO11 2PY
www.spartantiles.com
email: sales@spartantiles.com
Tel: 01206 230553
Fax: 01206 230516

SSQ GROUP
301 Elveden Road
Park Royal
London
NW10 7SS
www.ssqgroup.com
email: info@ssq.co.uk
Tel: 020 8961 7725
Fax: 020 8965 7013

WHICHFORD POTTERY
Whichford
Nr. Shipston-On-Stour
Warwickshire
CV36 5PG
www.whichfordpottery.com
Tel: 01608 684416
Fax: 01608 684833

OUTDOOR FURNITURE
ANDREW CRACE
Bourne Lane, Much Hadham, Hertfordshire
SG10 6ER
www.andrewcrace.com
email: sales@andrewcrace.com
Tel: 01279 842685
Fax: 01279 843646

BARLOW TYRIE LTD
Springwood Industrial Estate
Braintree
Essex
CM7 2RN
www.teak.com
email: devans@teak.com
Tel: 01376 557 600
Fax: 0870 460 1100

CADIX UK LTD
Unit 5
2 Counties Estate, Falconer Road
Haverhill , Suffolk
CB9 7XZ
www.cadix.co.uk
email: sales@cadix.co.uk
Tel: 01440 713 704
Fax: 01440 713 708

CAPITAL GARDEN PRODUCTS LTD
Gibbs Reed Barn
Pashley Road
Ticehurst
TN5 7HE
www.capital-garden.com
email: sales@capital-garden.com
Tel: 01580 201092
Fax: 01580 201093

CLASSIC FURNITURE GROUP LTD
Audley Avenue
Newport
Shropshire
TF10 7BX
www.classicfurniture.co.uk
email: sales@classicfurniture.co.uk
Tel: 01952 825000
Fax: 01952 811948

THE HEVENINGHAM COLLECTION LIMITED

THE HEVENINGHAM COLLECTION is the ultimate in stylish, elegant iron furniture custom-made in Great Britain. Only the highest quality materials are used throughout the manufacturing process and all furniture is hot zinc coated, followed by powder coating, thus ensuring that the furniture is both luxurious and highly durable. Perfect for the home, terrace, conservatory or poolside. Designs include, elegant dining sets, single and double chaise longue, armchairs and tables in a variety of sizes, bar stools, benches, Versailles tubs and swing seats which have proved extremely popular with clients in a wide range of locations and climates such as The Cote d' Azure, Tuscany, Geneva, Palm Beach, Palm Springs, Barbados, New York, Chicago, Toronto and Aspen.

www.heveningham.co.uk
Tel: + 44 (0) 1489 893481
email: sales@heveningham.co.uk

DW WINDSOR LIGHTING
Pindar Road, Hodderson, Herts
EN11 0DX
www.dwwindsor.co.uk
email: info@dwwindsor.co.uk
Tel: 01992 474 600
Fax: 01992 474 601

EDEN CONTRACT FURNITURE
Unit 12 Weights Farm Business Park
Weights Lane
Redditch
B97 6RG
www.edencontractfurniture.co.uk
email: sales@edencontractfurniture.co.uk
Tel: 01527 592455
Fax: 08450 536001

FEEK BVBA
Fao Sofie Couwenberg
Klapdorp 52, B-2000
Antwerp, Belgium
B-2000
www.feek.be
email: info@feek.be
Tel: 0032 3475 1765

GAZE BURVILL
Garden Showroom, Redloh House
The Gas Works, 2 Michael Road
London
SW6 2AD
www.gazeburvill.com
email: info@gazeburvill.com
Tel: 020 7471 8500
Fax: 0207 736 6020

HADDONCRAFT FORGE
The Forge House
East Haddon
Northampton
NN6 8DB
www.haddoncraft.co.uk
email: info@haddoncraft.co.uk
Tel: 01604 772 027
Fax: 01604 770 027

INFORM FURNITURE LIMITED
99 St John's Hill
London
SW11 1SY
www.informfurniture.co.uk
email: info@informfurniture.co.uk
Tel: 020 7228 3335
Fax: 020 7924 5955

IOTA GARDEN & HOME LTD
Wick Road
Wick St Lawerence
North Somerset
BS22 7YQ
www.commercial.iotagarden.com/
email: mail@iotagarden.com
Tel: 01934 522617
Fax: 01934 522107

KATIE WALKER FURNITURE
Cox Farm Studios
Warnham
West Sussex
RH12 3RZ
www.katiewalkerfurniture.com
email: katie@kwf.biz
Tel: 01403 211323
Fax: 01403 211323

LIVING IT UP
Tel: 0116 2695 960

MAKASIHOME
138 Oatlands Drive
Weybridge
Surrey
KT13 9HJ
www.makasihome.co.uk
email: info@makasihome.co.uk
Tel: 01932 860841
Fax: 01932 860841

MARVELLÍS LTD
The Warehouse
Station Road
Hadnall, Shrewsbury
SY4 3DD
www.marvells.com
email: louise@marvells.com
Tel: 01938 210800
Fax: 01939 210999

MHF CONTRACT FURNITURE LTD
The Hollins
Merrington
Shrewsbury
SY4 3QF
www.mhf-furniture.co.uk
email: info@mhf-furniture.co.uk
Tel: 01939 290280
Fax: 01939 291173

NATIONWIDE HOME INNOVATIONS LTD
www.nationwideltd.co.uk
Tel: 01929 554901
Fax: 01929 551023

NEW DAWN FURNITURE
Rose Cottage, Westbourne, Emsworth,
Hampshire, Po10 8td
PO10 8TD
www.newdawnfurniture.co.uk
email: info@newdawnfurniture.co.uk
Tel: 01243 375535

PAVILION RATTAN LTD
The Ulvers Building
Budby Road
Cuckney, Nr. Mansfield
NG20 9JP
www.pavilionrattan.co.uk
email: sales@pavilionrattan.co.uk
Tel: 01623 847030
Fax: 0870 706 2159

SMART FIRE LTD
Lyon House
160-166 Borough High St
SE1 1JR
www.ecosmartfire.com
email: uk(at)ecosmartfire.com
Tel: 020 7173 5000
Fax: 020 7173 5001

SMARTSTREETS
94 Sutton Court
Chiswick
London
W4 3JF
www.smartstreets.co.uk
email: sales@smartstreets.co.uk
Tel: 020 8742 3210
Fax: 0208 742 3226

THE DESIGN NET LTD
8 Rudolf Place
Miles Street
London
SW8 1RP
www.thedesignnet.co.uk
email: info@thedesignnet.co.uk
Tel: 02078 207771
Fax: 02078 201820

THOMAS BRAMWELL COLLECTION
Tides Reach 127 East Beach Rd Selsey West
Sussex
PO20 0HA
www.thomasbramwell.co.uk
email: info@thomasbramwell.co.uk
Tel: 01243 381207

TOWNSCAPE PRODUCTS LIMITED
Fulwood Road South
Sutton In Ashfield
Nottinghamshire
NG17 2JZ
www.townscape24.com
email: sales@townscape-products.co.uk
Tel: 01623 513355
Fax: 01623 440267

VINCENT SHEPPARD
Industriepark 5
Spiere - Belgium
8587
www.vincentsheppard.com
email: sales@vincentsheppard.com
Tel: 0032 5646 1111
Fax: 0032 56461112

WESTMINSTER
Westminster House
Bellbrook Business Park
Uckfield, East Sussex
TN221QZ
www.westminsterfurniture.eu
email: sales@westminsterfurniture.eu
Tel: +44 (0)1825 764222
Fax: +44 (0)1825 749444

WRIGHTS FINE FURNITURE LTD
Stretton Heath
Yockleton
Shrewsbury
SY5 9QQ
www.wrightsfinefurniture.com
email: margo@wrightsfinefurniture.com
Tel: 01743 821800
Fax: 01743 821333

POOLS

THE MOSAIC STUDIO
54 Darlinghurst Grove
Leigh On Sea
Essex
SS9 3LG
www.themosaicstudio.com
email: fiona@themosaicstudio.demon.co.uk
Tel: 01702 712111
Fax: 01702 712111

REPRO ORNAMENTS

BRIGHTON ROC
Unit 4, Fowlswick Farm, Allington Chippenham
Wiltshire Sn14 6qe United Kingdom
Chippenham
Wiltshire
SN14 6QE
www.brightonroc.co.uk/
email: brighton.roc@btconnect.com
Tel: 01249 782270
Fax: 01249 782270

SCULPTURES

BULBECK FOUNDRY
Reach Road
Burwell
Cambridgeshire
CB25 0GH
www.bulbeckfoundry.co.uk
email: info@bulbeckfoundry.co.uk
Tel: 01638 743153
Fax: 01638 743374

CARINA HASLAM ART
2 Reyners Green
Little Kingshill, Great Missenden
Bucks
HP16 0EQ
www.carinahaslamart.com
email: art@carinahaslamart.com
Tel: 01494866914 or 0797 3322397

CATRIN JONES ARCHITECTURAL GLASS
www.catrinjones.co.uk
email: catrin@catrinjones.co.uk
Tel: 01792 469256
Fax: 08701 302830

COLIN RICHES SCULPTOR
Wydcombe Manor, Whitwell, Isle Of Wight
PO38 2NY
www.richesart.co.uk
email: richesart@hotmail.com
Tel: 01983 730961

DOVERHAY FORGE STUDIOS LTD
Porlock
Minehead
Somerset
TA24 8QB
www.doverhay.co.uk
email: jh@doverhay.co.uk
Tel: 01643 862444

FAIRHAVEN AND WOODS LTD
Northfield Farm Stoneyard
Lode Road, Bottisham
Cambridge, CB25 9DN
www.fairhavengroup.co.uk
email: office@fairhavengroup.co.uk
Tel: 01223 812555
Fax: 01223 812554

HERITAGE STONEWORKS LTD
Unit 2 Southview Ind Est
Off Richard Lane
Tideswell, SK17 8PR
www.heritagestoneworks.co.uk
email: info@heritagestoneworks.co.uk
Tel: 01298 873173
Fax: 01298 873178

KATY HOLFORD
Tichborne Studios
18 Tichborne Street
Brighton, BN1 1UR
www.katyholford.co.uk
email: katy@katyholford.co.uk
Tel: 01273 327792

MARIANNE FORREST
3&8 Coach House Cloisters
Hitchin Street
Baldock, Herts
AL8 6QZ
www.marianneforrest.com
Tel: 01462 491992

LANDSCAPE ORNAMENT COMPANY
Tel: 01380 840533
info@landscapeornament.com
www.landscapeornament.com

Fantastically large fruit, wonderful wall
plaques, beautiful benches, snuffling
piglets and much more are to be found
amongst LOC's unique range of
handcrafted ornaments, designed for the
discriminating garden lover who cares
about quality and style and is looking for
something distinctively different. In a
market place where so much appears the
same, LOC sets out to change the
mould, designing simple ideas that are
eye-catching, meticulously made and
affordable. Full details and images online.

MORRIS SINGER ART FOUNDERS
9 Swinborne Drive
Springwood Industrial Estate
Braintree
CM7 2YP
www.msaf.co.uk
email: chris@msaf.co.uk
Tel: 01376 343222
Fax: 01376 341793

PW LTD
1 Church Street
Pewsey
Wilts
SN9 5DL
www.pwlimited.co.uk
email: johnny@pwlimited.co.uk
Tel: 01672 562878
Fax: 01672 563043

REDFIELDS
Unit1 Cluster Ind Est
Rodney Rd
Portsmouth
PO4 8ST
www.redfields.co.uk
email: sales@redfields.co.uk
Tel: 02392 870000

RILEY CONTEMPORARY ART
Far Peak
Northleach
Cheltenham
GL54 3JB
www.rileycontemporaryart.co.uk
email: rileyalbatross@btinternet.com
Tel: 07966 525187

Fabrics & Soft Furnishings

ASHBURN UPHOLSTERY
Unit 3 Western Units
Pottery Road
Bovey Tracey, Devon
TQ13 9DS
www.ashburn-upholstery.co.uk
email: mail@ashupohl.plus.com
Tel: 01626 832532
Fax: 01626 832532

BENNISON FABRICS LTD
16 Holbein Place, London
SW1W 8NL
email: bennisonfabrics@btinternet.com
Tel: 02077 308076
Fax: 02078 234997

CAROL MACKENZIE GALE
in progress
email: cmgale@onetel.net
Tel: 01805 804575

CHESHIRE CURTAINS & INTERIORS LIMITED
Stanley Studio
Stanley Street
Macclesfield
SK11 6AU
www.cheshirecurtains.co.uk
email: mail@cheshirecurtains.co.uk
Tel: 01625 434121
Fax: 01625 618857

DECOWARE
1030 Kamato Road Unit 22 Mississauga On
L4w 4b6 Canada
email: decowarecanada@rogers.com
Tel: +1 9052901302
Fax: +1 9052901902

G & H INTERIORS
The Chantry
Combe Raleigh
Honiton
EX14 4TQ
www.gandhinteriors.co.uk
email: info@gandhinteriors.co.uk
Tel: 01404 42063
Fax: 01404 45112

GREEN COMMERCIAL
88
Gillespie Road
Highbury
N5 1LN
www.interior4u.co.uk
email: james@interior4u.co.uk
Tel: 0207 359 7924
Fax: 0207 354 0077

HARLEQUIN HARRIS
Tel: 0844 5430100
Fax: 0844 5430101

HELEN GREEN DESIGN
29 Milner Street
London
SW3 3QD
www.helengreendesign.com
email: mail@helengreendesign.com
Tel: 020 7352 3344
Fax: 020 7352 5544

JUDY HOLME LIMITED
The Watermark
9-15 Ribbleton Lane
Preston
PR1 5EZ
www.judyholme.com
email: sales@judyholme.com
Tel: 0845 389 3131
Fax: 0845 389 3121

KOBE UK LTD
Suite D, Loddon Vale House, Hurricane Way,
Woodley
Reading
Berkshire, United Kingdom
RG5 4UX
www.kobefab.com
Tel: 0118 969 1020
Fax: 0118 969 2400

MARVIC TEXTILES
G26
Design Centre Chelsea Harbour
London
SW10 0XE
www.marvictextiles.co.uk
email: showroom@marvictextiles.co.uk
Tel: 0207 352 3119
Fax: 0207 352 3135

MARYLYN LARKIN
6 Queens Court
230 West End Lane
London
NW61UT
email: marylyn.larkin@blueyonder.co.uk
Tel: 02074 353001
Fax: 02074 353001

NOBILIS FONTAN
Bellevue House
Althorp Road
London
SW17 7EP
www.nobilis.fr
email: nobilis@nobilis-fontan.co.uk
Tel: 020 8767 0774
Fax: 020 8682 4904

NOCHINTZ LTD
Carvers Warehouse
77 Dale Street
Manchester
M1 2HG
www.nochintz.co.uk
email: info@nochintzltd.co.uk
Tel: 0161 236 1412
Fax: 0161 880 2407

NORDIC STYLE
109 Lots Road
London
SW10 0RN
www.nordicstyle.com
email: sales@nordicstyle.com
Tel: 0207 351 1755
Fax: 0207 351 4966

O ECOTEXTILES LTD
Gardiner House
3-9 Broomhill Road
London
SW18 4JQ
www.oecotextiles.com
email: carole@oecotextiles.com
Tel: 0208 8755777
Fax: 0208 8759088

ORCHARD FABRICS LTD
Unit 2 Avondale Ind. Est
Avondale Road
Edgeley, Stockport, Cheshire
SK8 7DX
www.orchardfabrics.com
email: orchardfabrics@btconnect.com
Tel: 01614 774225
Fax: 01614 290993

PRESTIGIOUS TEXTILES
4 Cross Lane
Westgate Hill Street
Bradford
BD4 0SG
www,prestigious.co.uk
email: mail@prestigious.co.uk
Tel: 01274 688 448
Fax: 01274 689 560

PRETTY FRILLS BLIND COMPANY
Unit 45 The Royal Arsenal
The Io Centre
Woolwich
SE18 6RS
www.prettyfrills.co.uk
Tel: 0208 331 4383
Fax: 0208 331 4378

RALPH LAUREN HOME
1 New Bond Street
London
W1S 3RL
www.ralphlaurenhome.com
Tel: 020 7535 4557

ROMO LTD
Lowmoor Road
Kirkby-In-Ashfield
Nottinghamshire
NG17 7DE
www.romo.com
email: sales@romo.com
Tel: 01623 750005
Fax: 01623 750031

SMD TEXTILES
Unit F2, Pittman Way
Fulwood
Preston
PR2 9ZD
www.swatchbox.co.uk
email: sarah_johnston@smd-textiles.co.uk
Tel: 01772 651199
Fax: 01772 654034

THE CAMPBELL GROUP
Units 1-3, Block 1
Alva Industrial Estate
Alva
FK12 5JA
www.thecampbellgroup.co.uk
email: info@thecampbellgroup.co.uk
Tel: 01259 760572
Fax: 01259 769434

UNIVERSAL TEXTILE MILLS
44 Gudahatti Main Road
Neralur Post
Attibele Hobli 562 107, Bangalore, Karnataka
INDIA
www.univeraltextile.com
email: utm@utm.co.in
Tel: 0091 8022897400
Fax: 0091 022897500

ACCESSORIES

DN DESIGNS COLLECTION LTD
13 Whitecome Mews, Kew,
Richmond, TW9 4BT
Tel/Fax: 0044 2088 763903
www.dndesignscollection.com
By Appointment Only

Jewel like curtain accessories, using precious
materials and finishes, all handcrafted and
produced in a limited number.

Whether Inlaid with mother of pearl, a 300
year old tradition that we passionately
preserve, gilded with silver or gold leaf, or
made of acrylic, with brass or aluminium in-
serts, they will dress up the simplest
curtain for the ultimate glamorous look,
in a very contemporary way.

AWNINGS & CANOPIES

DORSET INTERIORS
415a Lymington Road, Highcliffe-On-Sea,
Christchurch, BH23 5EN
www.dorsetinteriors.co.uk
email: joy@dorsetinteriors.co.uk
Tel: 01425 280011
Fax: 01425 280011

FABRIC ARCHITECTURE
Unit B4 Nexus
Hurricane Rd
Brockworth, Glos
GL3 4AG
www.fabricarchitecture.co.uk
email: info@fabarc.co.uk
Tel: 01452 612 800
Fax: 01452 621 200

LELLIOTTS SUNBLINDS LTD
80 Sompting Road
Worthing
West Sussex
BN14 9ES
www.lelliotts.co.uk
email: info@lelliotts.co.uk
Tel: 01903 204676
Fax: 01903 538052

SAXON BLINDS LTD
7 Magee Street
Northampton
NN1 4JT
www.saxonblinds.co.uk
email: sales@saxonblinds.co.uk
Tel: 01604 603111
Fax: 01604 631212

SUN FASHION LTD
Unit 8 Northbrook Industrial Estate
Vincent Avenue
Southampton
SO16 6PB
www.sun-fashion.co.uk
email: sales@sun-fashion.co.uk
Tel: 02380 773533
Fax: 02380 878942

SUN FASHION LTD
Unit 8 Northbrook Industrial Estate
Vincent Avenue
Southampton
SO16 6PB
www.sun-fashion.co.uk
email: sales@sun-fashion.co.uk
Tel: 02380 773533
Fax: 02380 878942

SUNPROJECT (U K)
6 Waterloo Park Ind. Est.
Wellington Road
Bidford On Avon
B50 4JG
email: sales@sunproject.co.uk
Tel: 01789 773377
Fax: 01789 773388

SWIFT BLINDS & CURTAINS LTD
Aldon Works
Lockwood Rd
Huddersfield
HD1 3TG
swifttradeblinds.com
email: info@switblinds-curtains.co.uk
Tel: 01484 512741
Fax: 01484 542954

WORTH & COMPANY BLINDS
R/O 30 Christchurch Road
Southend On Sea
Essex
SS2 4JS
www.worthblinds.com
email: info@worthblinds.com
Tel: 01702 467581
Fax: 01702 467560

BESPOKE FABRICS

ATELIERS PINTON
9 Rue Preville
Felletin
France
23500
www.ateliers-pinton.com
email: l.dixon@ateliers-pinton.com
Tel: 00 33 630 640 534
Fax: 00 33 555 664 322

BERNARD THORP & CO LIMITED
53 Chelsea Manor Street
Chelsea
London
SW3 5RZ
www.bernardthorp.co.uk
email: bernardthorp@btconnect.com
Tel: 020 7352 1022/ 5745
Fax: 020 7376 3640

DE GOURNAY
112 Old Church Street
London, United Kingdom
SW3 6EP
www.degournay.com
email: info@degournay.com
Tel: 0207 352 9988
Fax: 0207 795 0447

ELANBACH
Llangoed Hall
Llyswen
Brecon
LD3 0YP
www.elanbach.com
email: sales@elanbach.com
Tel: 01874 754 631
Fax: 01874 754 588

HENRY BERTRAND SILK FABRICS
Chelsea Harbour Design Centre
Lots Road
London
SW10
www.henrybertrand.co.uk
email: interiors@henrybertrand.co.uk
Tel: 020 7349 1477
Fax: 020 7349 1479

**MARK FINZEL DESIGN &
PHOTOGRAPHY**
www.markfinzel.co.uk
email: mark@markfinzel.co.uk
Tel: 0771 259 0706

ROYAL SCHOOL OF NEEDLEWORK
Apartment 12a
Hampton Court Palace
Surrey
KT8 9AU
www.royal-needlework.org.uk
email: studio.enquiries@royal-
needlework.org.uk
Tel: +44 (0) 020 3166 6944
Fax: +44 (0) 20 8943 4916

VANDERHURD
276, 56 Gloucester Road
London
SW7 4UB
email: info@vanderhurd.co.uk
Tel: 0207 313 5400
Fax: 0207 229 7776

COMMERCIAL TEXTILES

CASAMANCE LTD
Greytown House
221-227 High Street
Orpington, Kent
BR6 0NZ
www.casamance.co.uk
email: d.wilson@texdecor.com
Tel: 0844 369 0104
Fax: 0844 369 0103

ELANBACH
Llangoed Hall
Llyswen
Brecon
LD3 0YP
www.elanbach.com
email: sales@elanbach.com
Tel: 01874 754 631
Fax: 01874 754 588

ERICA WAKERLY
Studio 5
96 De Beauvoir Road
London
N1 4EN
www.printpattern.com
email: info@printpattern.com
Tel: 07940 577 620

POLLACK
150 Varick Street
New York Ny
Usa
10013-1218
www.pollackassociates.com
Tel: 001 212 627 7766
Fax: 001 212 924 8396

ROMO LTD
Lowmoor Road
Kirkby-In-Ashfield
Nottinghamshire
NG17 7DE
www.romo.com
email: sales@romo.com
Tel: 01623 750005
Fax: 01623 750031

CURTAIN POLES & HARDWARE

ACRYLIC DESIGN
3a 3b Shakespeare Industrial Estate
Shakespeare Street, Watford
Hertfordshire
WD24 5RS
www.acrylicdesign.co.uk
email: sales@acrylicdesign.co.uk
Tel: 01923 241122
Fax: 01923 241144

DECOWARE
1030 Kamato Road Unit 22 Mississauga On
L4w 4b6 Canada
email: decowarecanada@rogers.com
Tel: +1 9052901302
Fax: +1 9052901902

GOELST UK LTD
Crimple Court
Hornbeam Park
Harrogate
HG2 8PB
www.goelstuk.com
email: info@goelstuk.com
Tel: 01423 873 002
Fax: 01423 874 006

HALLIS HUDSON GROUP LTD
Unit B1
Red Scar Business Park
Preston
PR2 5NJ
www.hallishudson.com
email: sales@hallishudson.com
Tel: 01772 202 202
Fax: 01772 515 515

JAGO DESIGNS LTD
337 Athlon Road
Wembley
Middx
jagodesigns.co.uk
email: info@jagodesigns.co.uk
Tel: 020 8810 5432
Fax: 020 8810 8765

JIM LAWRENCE
The Ironworks
Lady Lane Industrial Estate
Hadleigh
IP7 6BQ
www.jim-lawrence.co.uk
email: sales@jim-lawrence.co.uk
Tel: 01473 828176
Fax: 01473 824074

LELLIOTTS SUNBLINDS LTD
80 Sompting Road
Worthing
West Sussex
BN14 9ES
www.lelliotts.co.uk
email: info@lelliotts.co.uk
Tel: 01903 204676
Fax: 01903 538052

MCCORMICK-WEEKS
Unit 2 Springfield Farm
Perrotts Brook
Cirencester, Glos
GL7 7DT
www.mcormickweeks.com
email: enquiries@mccormickweeks.com
Tel: 01285 831771
Fax: 01285 831881

MERRICK & DAY
Redbourne Road
Redbourne
Gainsborough, Lincs
DN21 4TG
www.merrick-day.com
email: sales@merrick-day.com
Tel: 01652 648814
Fax: 01652 648104

PENBRICE INTERIORS
4 Kingsway
West Wickham
Kent
BR4 9JF
www.penbriceinteriors.co.uk
email: info@penbriceinteriors.co.uk
Tel: 0208 462 8787

PRETTY FRILLS BLIND COMPANY
Unit 45 The Royal Arsenal
The Io Centre
Woolwich
SE18 6RS
www.prettyfrills.co.uk
Tel: 0208 331 4383
Fax: 0208 331 4378

PRICE & COMPANY (REGENCY) LIMITED
North Street
Portslade
East Sussex
BN41 1ES
www.price-regency.co.uk
email: enquiries@price-regency.co.uk
Tel: 01273 439 527
Fax: 01273 421888

PROPRESS
Unit 3, Pavillions
2 East Road
South Wimbledon
SW19 1UW
www.propress.co.uk
email: info@propress.co.uk
Tel: 020 8417 0660
Fax: 020 8544 9468

ROGER DAVIS INTERIORS LTD
43, Tentercroft Street
Lincoln
Lincolnshire
LN5 7DB
www.roger-davis-interiors.co.uk
email: info@roger-davis-interiors.co.uk
Tel: 01522 531371
Fax: 01522 528349

THE BLACKSMITH COLLECTION
West Park
Kings Nympton
Umberleigh
EX37 9TN
www.blacksmithcollection.com
Tel: 01769 580004
Fax: 01769 581125

THE BRADLEY COLLECTION
Lion Barn
Maitland Road
Needham Market, Suffolk
IP6 8NS
www.bradleycollection.com
email: info@bradleycollection.com
Tel: 0845 118 7224
Fax: 0845 118 7228

WEMYSS HOULES
7a Nobel Road
Wester Gourdie Ind. Est.
Dundee, Scotland
DD2 4UH
www.houles.com
email: sales@wemysshoules.co.uk
Tel: 01946 517506/02073764430
Fax: 01946 517507

CURTAINS & BLINDS

ALBERT E. CHAPMAN LTD
17 Crouch Hill
London
N4 4AP
albertechapman.com
Tel: 020 7272 2536
Fax: 020 7263 1033

BERY DESIGNS
8 Rosehill Rd
London
SW18 2NX
www.berydesigns.com
email: colleen@berydesigns.co.uk
Tel: 0208 874 5454
Fax: 0560 311 2481

BLENDWORTH INTERNATIONAL
Crookley Park
Horndean
Hampshire
PO8 0AD
www.blendworth.co.uk
email: sales@blendworth.co.uk
Tel: +44 23 9259 4911
Fax: +44 23 9259 7040

CHESHIRE CURTAINS & INTERIORS LIMITED
Stanley Studio
Stanley Street
Macclesfield
SK11 6AU
www.cheshirecurtains.co.uk
email: mail@cheshirecurtains.co.uk
Tel: 01625 434121
Fax: 01625 618857

DORSET INTERIORS
415a Lymington Road
Highcliffe-On-Sea
Christchurch
BH23 5EN
www.dorsetinteriors.co.uk
email: joy@dorsetinteriors.co.uk
Tel: 01425 280011
Fax: 01425 280011

ENGLISH HOME.COM LTD
2b Seagrave Road
London
SW6 1RR
www.englishhome.com
email: sales@englishhome.com
Tel: 020 7381 3020
Fax: 020 738 3238

FELICITY THORPE INTERIOR DESIGN LTD.
Allfrey's House
Bolney Road
Cowfold
RH13 8AZ
www.felicitythorpeinteriors.co.uk
email: enquiries@felicitythorpeinteriors.co.uk
Tel: 01403 864 784
Fax: 01403 865 035

FIONA CAMPBELL LTD
259 New Kings Road
Parsons Green
London
SW6 4RB
www.fionacampbelldesign.co.uk
email: info@fionacampbelldesign.co.uk
Tel: 0207 731 3681
Fax: 0207 736 7436

GOELST UK LTD
Crimple Court
Hornbeam Park
Harrogate
HG2 8PB
www.goelstuk.com
email: info@goelstuk.com
Tel: 01423 873 002
Fax: 01423 874 006

HILLARY'S BLINDS LTD
Private Road No 2
Colwick Business Park, Colwick
Nottingham
NG4 2JR
www.hillarys.co.uk
email: enquiries@hillarys.co.uk
Tel: 0800 916 7720
Fax: 0115 9614176

HUNG, DRAWN & CORDED
1 Tudor Close, Dean Court Road
Rottingdean, Brighton
BN2 7DF
hungdrawnandcorded.com
email: ally_pollock@hotmail.com
Tel: 01273 390070
Fax: 01273 390070

INTERIORS OF CHISWICK
454 Chiswick High Road
London
W4 5TT
www.interiorsofchiswick.co.uk
Tel: 02089 940073
Fax: 02089 944144

JEFFREYS INTERIORS
8 North West Circus Place
Edinburgh
EH3 6ST
www.jeffreys-interiors.co.uk
email: mail@jeffreys-interiors.co.uk
Tel: 0131 247 8010
Fax: 0845 882 2656

LELLIOTTS SUNBLINDS LTD
80 Sompting Road
Worthing
West Sussex
BN14 9ES
www.lelliotts.co.uk
email: info@lelliotts.co.uk
Tel: 01903 204676
Fax: 01903 538052

LEON NORELL LTD
Correspondence: 25a Woodstock Road,
London Nw11 8es
Warehouse: 403-405 Edgware Road, London
Nw2 6ln
www.leonnorell.com
email: sales@leonnorell.com
Tel: 020 837 7708
Fax: 020 8458 7147

MARGARET SHERIDAN
36 Market Place
Hingham
Norwich
NR9 4AF
www.margaretsheridan.co.uk
email: enquiries@margaretsheridan.co.uk
Tel: 01953 850691
Fax: 01953 851447

MERRICK & DAY
Redbourne Road
Redbourne
Gainsborough, Lincs
DN21 4TG
www.merrick-day.com
email: sales@merrick-day.com
Tel: 01652 648814
Fax: 01652 648104

PENBRICE INTERIORS
4 Kingsway
West Wickham
Kent
BR4 9JF
www.penbriceinteriors.co.uk
email: info@penbriceinteriors.co.uk
Tel: 0208 462 8787

PRET A VIVRE LTD
160 Wandsworth Bridge Road,
London
SW6 2UH
www.pretavivre.com
email: sales@pretavivre.com
Tel: 0845 130 5161
Fax: 0845 130 5262

powell blinds

POWELL BLINDS
Sunblind House, Holmbush Potteries,
Faygate, Horsham,
West Sussex, RH12 4SE
Tel : +44 (0) 1293 851010
Fax: +44 (0) 1293 851999
www.powellblinds.com
sales@powellblinds.com

Not only offering all types of blinds & awnings, Powell Blinds are the leaders in bespoke shading solutions for difficult areas such as atria, skylights, shaped & high level windows. We specialise in automated shading and are the leading Lutron shade dealer for London & the South East.

PRETTY FRILLS BLIND COMPANY
Unit 45 The Royal Arsenal
The Io Centre
Woolwich, SE18 6RS
www.prettyfrills.co.uk
Tel: 0208 331 4383
Fax: 0208 331 4378

PROPRESS
Unit 3, Pavillions
2 East Road
South Wimbledon, SW19 1UW
www.propress.co.uk
email: info@propress.co.uk
Tel: 020 8417 0660
Fax: 020 8544 9468

ROGER DAVIS INTERIORS LTD
43, Tentercroft Street
Lincoln
Lincolnshire, LN5 7DB
www.roger-davis-interiors.co.uk
email: info@roger-davis-interiors.co.uk
Tel: 01522 531371
Fax: 01522 528349

SAXON BLINDS LTD
7 Magee Street
Northampton, NN1 4JT
www.saxonblinds.co.uk
email: sales@saxonblinds.co.uk
Tel: 01604 603111
Fax: 01604 631212

SUNPROJECT (U K)
6 Waterloo Park Ind. Est.
Wellington Road
Bidford On Avon
B50 4JG
email: sales@sunproject.co.uk
Tel: 01789 773377
Fax: 01789 773388

SWIFT BLINDS & CURTAINS LTD
Aldon Works
Lockwood Rd
Huddersfield
HD1 3TG
swifttradeblinds.com
email: info@switblinds-curtains.co.uk
Tel: 01484 512741
Fax: 01484 542954

THE CAMPBELL GROUP
Units 1-3, Block 1
Alva Industrial Estate
Alva
FK12 5JA
www.thecampbellgroup.co.uk
email: info@thecampbellgroup.co.uk
Tel: 01259 760572
Fax: 01259 769434

VOLGA LINEN
Unit 1 Eastlands Industrial Estate
Leiston
Suffolk
IP16 4LL
www.volgalinen.co.uk
email: info@volgalinen.co.uk
Tel: 01728 635 020
Fax: 01728 635 021

WORTH & COMPANY BLINDS
R/O 30 Christchurch Road
Southend On Sea
Essex
SS2 4JS
www.worthblinds.com
email: info@worthblinds.com
Tel: 01702 467581
Fax: 01702 467560

CUSHIONS & THROWS

009 TEXTILES
Studio 009
Westbourne Studios
242 Acklam Road, London
W10 5JJ
www.009textiles.co.uk
email: 009textiles@gmail.com
Tel: 020 7575 3209
Fax: 020 7575 3209

ACCENT APS
www.accent.dk
Tel: 0045 2087 9049

BBD INTERIORS
Unit 18c Euro Business Park
Little Island
Cork
IRELAND
www.bbd.ie
email: info@bbd.ie
Tel: 0353 21435 1999
Fax: 00353 21435 1998

BERY DESIGNS
8 Rosehill Rd
London
SW18 2NX
www.berydesigns.com
email: colleen@berydesigns.co.uk
Tel: 0208 874 5454
Fax: 0560 311 2481

BRUNO TRIPLET LTD
23 Elystan Street
SW3 3NT
www.brunotriplet.com
email: info@brunotriplet.com
Tel: 02078 239990
Fax: 02078 239989

BURKE BY DESIGN WHOLESALE LTD
18c Euro Business Park
Little Island
Cork
IRELAND
www.bbd.ie
email: info@bbd.ie
Tel: 00353 21 435 1999
Fax: 00353 21 435 1998

DESIGN HOUSE EUROPE
Design House
Balme Road
Cleckheaton
BD19 4EW
www.prontex.co.uk
email: louisemarren@designhouseeurope.com
Tel: 01274 863747
Fax: 01274 863748

ENGLISH HOME.COM LTD
2b Seagrave Road
London
SW6 1RR
www.englishhome.com
email: sales@englishhome.com
Tel: 020 7381 3020
Fax: 020 738 3238

FELJOY ANTIQUES
Chelsea Galleries. 69-73 Portobello Road,
London
W11 2QB
www.feljoy-antiques.co.uk
email: joy@feljoy-antiques.co.uk
Tel: 02084 458706
Fax: 0208 446 0933

JEREMY LOXTON & COMPANY
P O Box 5588
Thatcham
RG19 8XY
Tel: 0870 385 1086
Fax: 0870 385 1086

JYSK
Melford Road
Hazel Grove
Stockport
SK3 0JD
www.jysk.co.uk
email: dgoo@jysk.com
Tel: 0845 389 3089

KIT MOOI
email: info@kitmooi.com
Tel: 07944691119

KOBE UK LTD
Suite D, Loddon Vale House, Hurricane Way,
Woodley
Reading
Berkshire, United Kingdom
RG5 4UX
www.kobefab.com
Tel: 0118 969 1020
Fax: 0118 969 2400

LA DRAPE INTERNATIONAL LTD
Internet House
Aston Lane North
 Preston Brook
WA7 3PE
www.thequiltedwall.co.uk
email: info@ladrape.com
Tel: 01928 713 330
Fax: 01928 713 094

MYAKKA LTD
Tythings Commercial Centre
Wincanton
Somerset
BA9 9EQ
www.myakka.co.uk
email: sales@myakka.co.uk
Tel: 0845 460 3122

UNIVERSAL TEXTILE MILLS
44 Gudahatti Main Road
Neralur Post
Attibele Hobli 562 107, Bangalore, Karnataka
INDIA
www.univeraltextile.com
email: utm@utm.co.in
Tel: 0091 8022897400
Fax: 0091 022897500

ECO FABRICS

ISAGI LIMITED
The Laurels
34 Sheepfold Lane
Amersham, Bucks
HP7 9EJ
www.isagi.co.uk
email: sales@isagi.co.uk
Tel: 01494 729345
Fax: 01494 729345

NATUREWARM LTD
27 Water Lane
South Witham
Grantham
NG33 5PH
www.naturewarm.co.uk
email: sales@naturewarm.co.uk
Tel: 01572 768362
Fax: 01572 767146

PRET A VIVRE LTD
160 Wandsworth Bridge Road,
London
SW6 2UH
www.pretavivre.com
email: sales@pretavivre.com
Tel: 0845 130 5161
Fax: 0845 130 5262

EMBROIDERY

CONSORZIO AX ARTIGIANEXPORT
email: consorzioax@libero.it
Tel: 0039 0759 72240
Fax: 0039 0759711757

MOLLIE REGAN TEXTILES
The Studio
99 Dorchester Road, Oakdale
Poole, Dorset
BH15 3QZ
www.mollieregantextiles.co.uk
email: rosalyn@mollieregantextiles.co.uk
Tel: 01202 675944
Fax: 01202 675944

ROYAL SCHOOL OF NEEDLEWORK
Apartment 12a
Hampton Court Palace
Surrey
KT8 9AU
www.royal-needlework.org.uk
email: studio.enquiries@royal-needlework.org.uk
Tel: +44 (0) 020 3166 6944
Fax: +44 (0) 20 8943 4916

WHALEYS BRADFORD LTD
Tel: 01274 576718
Fax: 01274 521309

FABRICS & TEXTILES

009 TEXTILES
Studio 009
Westbourne Studios
242 Acklam Road, London
W10 5JJ
www.009textiles.co.uk
email: 009textiles@gmail.com
Tel: 020 7575 3209
Fax: 020 7575 3209

ABBEY QUILTING LTD
Selinas Lane
Dagenham
RM8 1ES
www.abbey-quilting.co.uk
email: enquiries@abbey-quilting.co.uk
Tel: 02085 922233
Fax: 02085 933787

ALHAMBRA UK
126 Whitby Street South
Hartlepool
Cleveland
TS24 7LP
email: joanne@norfolhouse-uk.com
Tel: 01429 260860
Fax: 01429 224418

ANNA FRENCH
36 Hinton Road
London
SE24 0HJ
www.annafrench.co.uk
email: enquiries@annafrench.co.uk
Tel: 02077 376555

ARC COLLECTIONS LIMITED
1 Andrew Place
London
SW8 4RA
www.arccollections.com
email: sales@arccollections.com
Tel: 020 7720 1628
Fax: 020 7622 6214

BLENDWORTH INTERNATIONAL
Crookley Park
Horndean
Hampshire
PO8 0AD
www.blendworth.co.uk
email: sales@blendworth.co.uk
Tel: +44 23 9259 4911
Fax: +44 23 9259 7040

BRIAN YATES (INTERIORS) LTD
Lansil Way
Caton Road
Lancaster
LA1 3QY
www.brian-yates.co.uk
email: sales@brian-yates.co.uk
Tel: 01524 35035
Fax: 01524 32232

BENNISON

Tel: 0207 730 8076
Fax: 0207 823 4997
bennisonfabrics@btinternet.com
www.bennisonfabrics.com

BENNISON is an English company specializing in hand-printed archive fabrics. These document designs are faithfully reproduced on beige or oyster linen and silk for traditional interiors or deconstructed and re-coloured for contemporary spaces. A custom colouring service is available and most of the designs can be printed on our special wallpaper.

Berber Interiors

BERBER INTERIORS
Bayfield Brecks, Holt,
Norfolk, NR25 7DZ
Tel: 01263 715555
enquiries@berberinteriors.com
www.berberinteriors.com

Berber Interiors is a new business featuring Moroccan design. The showroom is set in a magnificent barn in North Norfolk, stocked with stunning mirrors, traditional rugs, lamps and candles, colourful fabrics, leather furniture and garden chairs and tables. The showroom is open Wednesday to Saturday from 11 am to 4 pm. Should you wish to visit at any other time please contact us for an appointment.

BRUNO TRIPLET LTD
23 Elystan Street
SW3 3NT
www.brunotriplet.com
email: info@brunotriplet.com
Tel: 02078 239990
Fax: 02078 239989

CATHERINE HAMMERTON
Cockpit Arts, Cockpit Yard
Northington Street
London
WC1N 2NP
www.catherinehammerton.com
email: info@catherinehammerton.com
Tel: ex directory.

COLEFAX AND FOWLER
19/23 Grosvenor Hill
LONDON W1K 3QD
Tel: 020 7493 2231
Fax: 020 7318 6043

COLONY FABRICS LTD
2/14 Chelsea Harbour Design Centre
Chelsea Harbour
London
SW10 0XE
www.colonyfabrics.com
email: colonyfabrics@aol.com
Tel: 0207 3513232
Fax: 020 73512242

DOVECOT STUDIOS LTD
Dovecot
10 Infirmary Street
Edinburgh
EH1 1LT
www.dovecotstudios.com
email: info@dovecotstudios.com
Tel: 0131 550 3660
Fax: 0131 550 3669

CELC MASTERS OF LINEN
sue.spencer@mastersoflinen.com
www.mastersoflinen.com

European linen is the eco-friendly and sustainable fibre - the world's oldest known textile is synonymous with luxury fabrics for home interiors - from table and bed-linens to furnishings and curtains. Linen compliments every mood, mixing texture with tones from the intensely rich to the softest of natural hues.

CHRISTOPHER MOORE STUDIO
48 Cromwell Avenue,
Hammersmith, London W6 9LA
(By Appointment Only)
Tel: 020 8741 3699
info@thetoileman.com
www.thetoileman.com

Well known for over twenty years as
The Toile Man, Christopher Moore now
also hand-prints fine re-editions of 18th
and early 19th century Indiennes and
Chintzes reproduced from his own
archive. Hand-printed wallpapers and a
bespoke making-up service, from
cushions and curtains to a fully-dressed
bed, are other specialities on offer.

DZ DESIGNS
The Old Mill House
Stanwell Moor
Staines, TW19 6BQ
email: dz_designs@btconnect.com
Tel: 01753 682266
Fax: 01753 682203

ECHELON
Po Box 1295
Bradford, BD4 0WU
www.echelon.uk.com
Tel: 0845 1800 880
Fax: 0845 1800 881

ELANBACH
Llangoed Hall
Llyswen
Brecon, LD3 0YP
www.elanbach.com
email: sales@elanbach.com
Tel: 01874 754 631
Fax: 01874 754 588

FIONA CAMPBELL LTD
259 New Kings Road
Parsons Green
London, SW6 4RB
www.fionacampbelldesign.co.uk
email: info@fionacampbelldesign.co.uk
Tel: 0207 731 3681
Fax: 0207 736 7436

FROMENTAL
The Saga Centre
326 Kensal Road
London
W10 5BZ
www.fromental.co.uk
email: info@fromental.co.uk
Tel: 020 8960 8899
Fax: 020 7681 2343

GUINEVERE WAREHOUSE
Unit 5
92-104 Carnwath Road
London
SW6 3HW
www.guinevere.co.uk
email: sales@guineverewarehouse.co.uk
Tel: 020 7731 5401
Fax: 020 77368267

HAINSWORTH INTERIOR FABRICS
Spring Valley Mills
Stanningley
Pudsey, West Yorkshire
LS28 6DW
www.hainsworth.co.uk
email: interiors@hainsworth.co.uk
Tel: 0113 395 5695
Fax: 0113 3955686

HALLIS HUDSON GROUP LTD
Unit B1
Red Scar Business Park
Preston
PR2 5NJ
www.hallishudson.com
email: sales@hallishudson.com
Tel: 01772 202 202
Fax: 01772 515 515

J. ROBERT SCOTT
500 North Oak Street
Inglewood
California
90302
www.jrobertscott.com
email: london@jrobertscott.com
Tel: 001 310 680 4380
Fax: 001 310 680 4323

HAINSWORTH INTERIOR FABRICS
Spring Valley Mills, Stanningley,
Pudsey, West Yorkshire LS28 6DW
Tel: 0113 395 5695
Fax: 0113 395 5686
Email: interiors@hainsworth.co.uk
www.hainsworth.co.uk

Hainsworth is a specialist textile
company that has been an unrivalled
market leader for over 225 years.
Our Interior Fabrics range offers a
wealth of fabrics from the finest
upholstery, the plushest curtains
and drapes to elegant wall and table
coverings. We also offer luxurious
cabinet linings, divine bed covers,
hand-finished blankets and throws
and the fastest snooker and pool cloth.

JAMES BRINDLEY
FABRICS & WALLCOVERINGS
Hookstone Park
Harrogate
HG2 7DB
Tel: 01423 880400
www.jamesbrindley.com

James Brindley Fabrics & Wallcoverings
offer an extensive range of exquisite
fabrics including plains, prints, jacquards
and embroideries, with a worldwide
reputation for pure silk and silk blends.
Traditional and contemporary, the
collections span a myriad of colours and
designs. Available from leading
independent interior design showrooms
across the UK.

JIM DICKENS
48 Britannia Way
Britannia Enterprise Park
Lichfield
Staffordshire, WS14 9UY
Tel: 01543 415588
Fax: 01543 410548
Email: jimdickens@btconnect.com
Web: www.jimdickens.co.uk

Are you looking for inspiration, for
fabrics with a distinctive quality and
feel, look no further than Jim Dickens.
Our Collection is suitable for
upholstery, curtains and soft
furnishings. For details of stockists
please contact us or see website.

JUST FAB

Inscape Design Services Ltd,
Dockacre Road, Launceston,
Cornwall, PL15 8YY
Tel: 01566 773863
Contact: Richard JH Taylor
www.justfab.co.uk

The most extensive designer fabrics and
wallpaper showroom in the
Westcountry. All major names supplied.
Visit us for expert advice and ideas for
your home or interior, from fabrics on
the roll, made to measure curtains and
blinds, bespoke upholstered furniture,
fabric-related interior design service, all
to the highest quality.

LELIEVRE

108-110 Design Centre
Chelsea Harbour
London, SW10 0XE
www.lelievre.eu
email: enquiries@lelievre.eu
Tel: 020 7352 4798
Fax: 020 7352 9569

MARGARET SHERIDAN

36 Market Place
Hingham
Norwich, NR9 4AF
www.margaretsheridan.co.uk
email: enquiries@margaretsheridan.co.uk
Tel: 01953 850691
Fax: 01953 851447

MARVIC TEXTILES

G26
Design Centre Chelsea Harbour
London, SW10 0XE
www.marvictextiles.co.uk
email: showroom@marvictextiles.co.uk
Tel: 0207 352 3119
Fax: 0207 352 3135

NATASHA MARSHALL FABRICS AND WALLCOVERINGS

The Printworks, 10 Otago Street
Glasgow, G12 8JH
www.natashamarshall.com
email: info@natashamarshall.com
Tel: 01413 390120

NICHOLAS HASLAM LTD

12-14 Holbein Place
London
SW1W 8NL
www.nicholashaslam.com
Tel: 020 7730 8623
Fax: 020 7730 6679

NYA NORDISKA TEXTILES GMBH

An den Ratswiesen 4,
29451 Dannenberg I Germany
Tel: +49 5861 809500
www.nya.com
nya@nya.com

Clarity of form and the highest
standards are the principles of Nya
Nordiska. For more than 40 years,
the internationally recognized textile
editeur, based in Germany has been
designing and producing high class
decoration and upholstery fabrics.
In 2008, Nya Nordiska took over the
renowed brand Artline; Nya Artline,
that means first class curtain poles,
rope tensioners and tie back objects.
The collections are mainly
manufactured by workmanship and in
small series.

PETA SMYTH ANTIQUE TEXTILES

42 Moreton Street
London, SW1V 2PB
email: petasmyth@ukonline.co.uk
Tel: 020 7630 9898
Fax: 020 7630 5398

POLLACK

150 Varick Street
New York Ny
Usa, 10013-1218
www.pollackassociates.com
Tel: 001 212 627 7766
Fax: 001 212 924 8396

PRESTIGIOUS TEXTILES

4 Cross Lane
Westgate Hill Street
Bradford, BD4 0SG
www,prestigious.co.uk
email: mail@prestigious.co.uk
Tel: 01274 688 448
Fax: 01274 689 560

PRET A VIVRE LTD

160 Wandsworth Bridge Road,
London
SW6 2UH
www.pretavivre.com
email: sales@pretavivre.com
Tel: 0845 130 5161
Fax: 0845 130 5262

ROBERT ALLEN

Chiltern House, The Valley Centre
Gordon Road
High Wycombe
HP13 6EQ
www.robertallendesign.com
email: sales@robertallendesign.co.uk
Tel: 01494 474741
Fax: 01494 603400

ROYAL SCHOOL OF NEEDLEWORK

Apartment 12a
Hampton Court Palace
Surrey
KT8 9AU
www.royal-needlework.org.uk
email: studio.enquiries@royal-
needlework.org.uk
Tel: +44 (0) 020 3166 6944
Fax: +44 (0) 20 8943 4916

SCOTMAT CARPETS

10 Westerton Road
East Mains Ind. Estate
Broxburn
EH52 5AU
www.scotmat.co.uk
email: sales@scotmat.co.uk
Tel: 01506 859995
Fax: 01506 859996

SELVEDGE LTD

162 Archway Road
London
N6 5BB
www.selvedge.com
email: editor@selvedge.org
Tel: +44 (0)208 341 9721

SUSIE WATSON DESIGN

125 Northcote Rd
Battersea
London
SW11 6PS
www.susiewatsondesigns.co.uk
Tel: 0207 228 0787

THE LINEN PRESS LTD

Hartley Fold
Hartley
Kirkby Stephen
CA17 4JH
www.thelinenpress.co.uk
email: sales@thelinenpress.co.uk
Tel: 01768 372777
Fax: 01768 372794

TODAY INTERIORS

Hollis Road
Grantham
Lincolnshire
NG31 7QH
www.todayinteriors.com
email: info@today-interiors.co.uk
Tel: 01476 574 401
Fax: 01476 590208

TROYNORTH

High Ardley,
Hexham
NE46 2LG
email: mail@troynorth.com
Tel: 01434 607 366
Fax: 01434 608 415

VOLGA LINEN

Unit 1 Eastlands Industrial Estate
Leiston
Suffolk
IP16 4LL
www.volgalinen.co.uk
email: info@volgalinen.co.uk
Tel: 01728 635 020
Fax: 01728 635 021

WARWICK FABRICS UK LTD
Hackling House
Bourton Industrial Park
Bourton-On-The-Water
GL54 2HQ
www.warwick.co.uk
email: sales@warwick.co.uk
Tel: +44 (0)1451 822383
Fax: +44 (0)1451 822369

WEMYSS HOULES
7a Nobel Road
Wester Gourdie Ind. Est.
Dundee, Scotland
DD2 4UH
www.houles.com
email: sales@wemysshoules.co.uk
Tel: 01946 517506/02073764430
Fax: 01946 517507

WENDY EDMONDS TEXTILE DESLGN
Tel: 0208 9401512
Fax: 0208 9401512

WHALEYS BRADFORD LTD
Tel: 01274 576718
Fax: 01274 521309

ZARDI & ZARDI
Podgwell Barn
Edge
Gloucestershire
GL6 6NJ
www.zardiandzardi.co.uk
email: enquiries@zardiandzardi.co.uk
Tel: 01452 814777
Fax: 01452 814 433

FURNISHING FABRIC

009 TEXTILES
Studio 009
Westbourne Studios
242 Acklam Road, London
W10 5JJ
www.009textiles.co.uk
email: 009textiles@gmail.com
Tel: 020 7575 3209
Fax: 020 7575 3209

ANNA FRENCH
36 Hinton Road
London
SE24 0HJ
www.annafrench.co.uk
email: enquiries@annafrench.co.uk
Tel: 02077 376555

ANNE & ROBERT SWAFFER LTD
Bakewell Road
Orton Southgate
Peterborough
PE2 6WQ
www.swaffer.co.uk
email: sales@swaffer.co.uk
Tel: 01733 371727
Fax: 01733 371247

ARC COLLECTIONS LIMITED
1 Andrew Place
London
SW8 4RA
www.arccollections.com
email: sales@arccollections.com
Tel: 020 7720 1628
Fax: 020 7622 6214

BEAUDESERT
The Square
Tisbury
Wiltshire
SP3 6JP
www.beaudesert.co.uk
email: showroom@beaudesert.co.uk
Tel: 0845 838 8720
Fax: 01747 871016

BLENDWORTH INTERNATIONAL
Crookley Park
Horndean
Hampshire
PO8 0AD
www.blendworth.co.uk
email: sales@blendworth.co.uk
Tel: +44 23 9259 4911
Fax: +44 23 9259 7040

BRIAN YATES (INTERIORS) LTD
Lansil Way
Caton Road
Lancaster
LA1 3QY
www.brian-yates.co.uk
email: sales@brian-yates.co.uk
Tel: 01524 35035
Fax: 01524 32232

CASAMANCE LTD
Greytown House
221-227 High Street
Orpington, Kent
BR6 0NZ
www.casamance.co.uk
email: d.wilson@texdecor.com
Tel: 0844 369 0104
Fax: 0844 369 0103

COLONY FABRICS LTD
2/14 Chelsea Harbour Design Centre
Chelsea Harbour
London
SW10 0XE
www.colonyfabrics.com
email: colonyfabrics@aol.com
Tel: 0207 3513232
Fax: 020 73512242

ECHELON
Po Box 1295
Bradford
BD4 0WU
www.echelon.uk.com
Tel: 0845 1800 880
Fax: 0845 1800 881

ERICA WAKERLY
Studio 5
96 De Beauvoir Road
London
N1 4EN
www.printpattern.com
email: info@printpattern.com
Tel: 07940 577 620

GAINSBOROUGH LOUNGE SUITES
1 Northmoor Ind Est
Moor Street
Brierley Hill
DY5 3 SU
www.gainsboroughloungesuites.co.uk
email: sales@gainsboroughloungesuites.co.uk
Tel: 01384 261009
Fax: 01384 480226

HAINSWORTH INTERIOR FABRICS
Spring Valley Mills
Stanningley
Pudsey, West Yorkshire, LS28 6DW
www.hainsworth.co.uk
email: interiors@hainsworth.co.uk
Tel: 0113 395 5695
Fax: 0113 3955686

HENRY BERTRAND SILK FABRICS
Chelsea Harbour Design Centre
Lots Road
London, SW10
www.henrybertrand.co.uk
email: interiors@henrybertrand.co.uk
Tel: 020 7349 1477
Fax: 020 7349 1479

INTERIORS OF CHISWICK
454 Chiswick High Road
London, W4 5TT
www.interiorsofchiswick.co.uk
Tel: 02089 940073
Fax: 02089 944144

JAMES BRINDLEY
FABRICS & WALLCOVERINGS
Hookstone Park
Harrogate, HG2 7DB
Tel: 01423 880400
www.jamesbrindley.com

KNOWLES & CHRSITOU
116 Lots Road
Chelsea
London
SW10 0RN
www.knowles-christou.com
email: info@knowles-christou.com
Tel: 02073 527000
Fax: 02073 528877

KAI
Emmanuel House, Travellers Close,
Welham Green, Hertfordshire, AL9 7LD
Tel: + 44 (0) 1707 635 258
Fax: + 44 (0) 1707 635 233
Email: simonb@ashleywildegroup.com
Website: www.kaidistribution.co.uk

KAI offers an exciting and inspirational
portfolio of fabrics and wall coverings
which will add infinite style to your
home. Every collection creates a totally
different 'lifestyle' look, with fabrics
selected for their comfort and quality,
together with complementary wallpapers
that will enhance any interior.

KOBE UK LTD
Suite D, Loddon Vale House, Hurricane Way,
Woodley
Reading
Berkshire, United Kingdom
RG5 4UX
www.kobefab.com
Tel: 0118 969 1020
Fax: 0118 969 2400

LELIEVRE
108-110 Design Centre
Chelsea Harbour
London
SW10 0XE
www.lelievre.eu
email: enquiries@lelievre.eu
Tel: 020 7352 4798
Fax: 020 7352 9569

LEON NORELL LTD
Correspondence: 25a Woodstock Road,
London Nw11 8es
Warehouse: 403-405 Edgware Road, London
Nw2 6ln
www.leonnorell.com
email: sales@leonnorell.com
Tel: 020 837 7708
Fax: 020 8458 7147

MARVIC TEXTILES
G26
Design Centre Chelsea Harbour
London
SW10 0XE
www.marvictextiles.co.uk
email: showroom@marvictextiles.co.uk
Tel: 0207 352 3119
Fax: 0207 352 3135

MERRICK & DAY
Redbourne Road
Redbourne
Gainsborough, Lincs
DN21 4TG
www.merrick-day.com
email: sales@merrick-day.com
Tel: 01652 648814
Fax: 01652 648104

POLLACK
150 Varick Street
New York Ny
Usa
10013-1218
www.pollackassociates.com
Tel: 001 212 627 7766
Fax: 001 212 924 8396

THE CECIL BEATON FABRIC COLLECTION
The Square
Tisbury
Wiltshire
SP3 6JP
www.cecilbeatonfabrics.com
email: beaton@beaudesert.co.uk
Tel: 0845 838 8720
Fax: 01747 871016

THE NATURAL FABRIC COMPANY
Dovedale Farmhouse
Blockley
Gloucestershire
GL56 9TS
www.naturalfabriccompany.com
email: info@naturalfabriccompany.com
Tel: 01386 700900
Fax: 01386 700504

THE NATURAL FABRIC COMPANY
Dovedale Farmhouse
Blockley
Gloucestershire
GL56 9TS
www.naturalfabriccompany.com
email: info@naturalfabriccompany.com
Tel: 01386 700900
Fax: 01386 700504

THE NATURAL FABRIC COMPANY
Dovedale Farmhouse
Blockley
Gloucestershire
GL56 9TS
www.naturalfabriccompany.com
email: info@naturalfabriccompany.com
Tel: 01386 700900
Fax: 01386 700504

TODAY INTERIORS
Hollis Road
Grantham
Lincolnshire
NG31 7QH
www.todayinteriors.com
email: info@today-interiors.co.uk
Tel: 01476 574 401
Fax: 01476 590208

WARWICK FABRICS UK LTD
Hackling House
Bourton Industrial Park
Bourton-On-The-Water
GL54 2HQ
www.warwick.co.uk
email: sales@warwick.co.uk
Tel: +44 (0)1451 822383
Fax: +44 (0)1451 822369

WHALEYS BRADFORD LTD
Tel: 01274 576718
Fax: 01274 521309

LEATHER
CASADOR
Tel: 0049 30 78991854
Fax: 0049 30 78991855

GAINSBOROUGH LOUNGE SUITES
1 Northmoor Ind Est
Moor Street
Brierley Hill
DY5 3 SU
www.gainsboroughloungesuites.co.uk
email: sales@gainsboroughloungesuites.co.uk
Tel: 01384 261009
Fax: 01384 480226

**GUARDSMAN FURNITURE SOLUTIONS
GROUP**
Valspar Industries (Uk) Ltd
152 Milton Park
Abingdon, Oxfordshire
OX14 4SD
www.guardsman.co.uk
email: marketing@valspareurope.com
Tel: 01235 444700
Fax: 01235 862730

RYAN LEATHERS LTD
33 Wadeson Street
London
E29DR
email: info@ryanleathers.com
Tel: 02089 831182
Fax: 02089 831483

YARWOOD LEATHER LTD
Treefield Industrial Estate
Gelderd Road
Leeds, LS27 7JU
Tel: +44 113 252 1014
sales@yarwood.co.uk
www.yarwood.co.uk

Yarwood Leather Ltd manufactures and
supplies upholstery leathers with the
highest levels of aesthetic and
performance quality at competitive
prices. A wide variety of ranges and
colours are stocked and available for
next day delivery. We also offer bespoke
leather grains and colours to optimise
your project's design element.

TARNSJO GARVERI AB
Garverivagen 6
740 45 TARNSJO
www.tarnsjogarveri.se
email: info@tarnsjogarveri.se
Tel: 0046 29270 750
Fax: 0046 29270 769

SILK
DE GOURNAY
112 Old Church Street
London, United Kingdom
SW3 6EP
www.degournay.com
email: info@degournay.com
Tel: 0207 352 9988
Fax: 0207 795 0447

ENGLISH HOME.COM LTD
2b Seagrave Road
London, SW6 1RR
www.englishhome.com
email: sales@englishhome.com
Tel: 020 7381 3020
Fax: 020 738 3238

HENRY BERTRAND SILK FABRICS
Chelsea Harbour Design Centre
Lots Road, London, SW10
www.henrybertrand.co.uk
email: interiors@henrybertrand.co.uk
Tel: 020 7349 1477
Fax: 020 7349 1479

**JAMES BRINDLEY
FABRICS & WALLCOVERINGS**
Hookstone Park
Harrogate
HG2 7DB
Tel: 01423 880400
www.jamesbrindley.com

TRADE EIGHTY
63-65 Riding House Street
London
W1W 7EH
Tel: +44 (0)20 7637 5188
Fax: +44 (0)20 7637 5187
E-mail: trade80@btconnect.com
Web: www.trade80silks.co.uk

Trade Eighty have been inspiring the
interiors industry with their unique
collection of Silks for over 20 years.
Be it plains, shot, metallic silks,
Jacquards, emroideries or Prints, we can
help. Special commissions have always
been offered with nominal or reasonable
minimums and quick delivery schedules
making it all very welcome.

PETA SMYTH ANTIQUE TEXTILES
42 Moreton Street
London
SW1V 2PB
email: petasmyth@ukonline.co.uk
Tel: 020 7630 9898
Fax: 020 7630 5398

TASSELS & TRIMMINGS

COLEFAX AND FOWLER
19/23 Grosvenor Hill
LONDON
W1K 3QD
Tel: 020 7493 2231
Fax: 020 7318 6043

HALLIS HUDSON GROUP LTD
Unit B1
Red Scar Business Park
Preston
PR2 5NJ
www.hallishudson.com
email: sales@hallishudson.com
Tel: 01772 202 202
Fax: 01772 515 515

JAMES BRINDLEY
FABRICS & WALLCOVERINGS
Hookstone Park
Harrogate
HG2 7DB
Tel: 01423 880400
www.jamesbrindley.com

L & E BARNETT
Taylor Lane
Denton
Manchester, M34 3NR
email: janet@l-ebarnett.co.uk
Tel: 0161 336 2401
Fax: 0161 335 9134

NADA DESIGNS LTD
2/9 Chelsea Harbour Design Centre,
London SW10 0XE
Tel: 0207 351 6496
Fax: +44 (0)1638 552 189
Mob: +44 (0)7803729019
Email: sherine@nadadesignsltd.com
Web: www.nadadesignsltd.com

Nada Designs manufacture exclusive
historic and contemporary bespoke
trimmings and tiebacks. They pride
themselves in using the finest Egyptian
silk and cotton and are dedicated to
preserving the tradition of handmade
trimmings even down to the small detail
of the hand turned wood used in the
trimmings and tiebacks.

PRICE & COMPANY (REGENCY) LIMITED
North Street
Portslade
East Sussex, BN41 1ES
www.price-regency.co.uk
email: enquiries@price-regency.co.uk
Tel: 01273 439 527
Fax: 01273 421888

SPINA DESIGN
12 Kingsgate Place
London, NW6 4TA
www.spinadesign.co.uk
email: info@spinadesign.co.uk
Tel: 0207 328 5274
Fax: 0207 624 2078

TROYNORTH
High Ardley,
Hexham, NE46 2LG
email: mail@troynorth.com
Tel: 01434 607 366
Fax: 01434 608 415

WARWICK FABRICS UK LTD
Hackling House
Bourton Industrial Park
Bourton-On-The-Water, GL54 2HQ
www.warwick.co.uk
email: sales@warwick.co.uk
Tel: +44 (0)1451 822383
Fax: +44 (0)1451 822369

WEMYSS HOULES
7a Nobel Road
Wester Gourdie Ind. Est.
Dundee, Scotland
DD2 4UH
www.houles.com
email: sales@wemysshoules.co.uk
Tel: 01946 517506/02073764430
Fax: 01946 517507

Flooring

DALSOUPLE
Showground Road
Bridgwater
Somerset, TA6 6AJ
www.dalsouple.com
email: info@dalsouple.com
Tel: 01278 727777
Fax: 01278 727788

FLOWCRETE UK LTD
The Flooring Technology Centre
Booth Lane
Sandbach, Cheshire
CW11 3QF
www.flowcrete.com
email: uk@flowcrete.com
Tel: 01270 753 000
Fax: 01270 753 333

JOSEPH HAMILTON & SEATON
Tel: 01827 831400
Fax: 01827 831401

PERGO
Po Box 1313
Kingbury Link
Picadilly ,Amworth
B77 9DJ
www.pergo.com
email: customercare.uk@pergo.com
Tel: 01827 871840
Fax: 01827 871850

**THE NATURAL WOOD FLOOR
COMPANY**
20 Smugglers Way Wandsworth London
SW181EG
www.naturalwoodfloor.co.uk
email: sales@naturalwoodfloor.co.uk
Tel: 020 8871 9771
Fax: 020 8877 0273

THE TILE ASSOCIATION
Forum Court
83 Copers Cope Road
Beckenham
BR3 1NR
www.tiles.org.uk
email: info@tiles.org.uk
Tel: 020 8663 0946
Fax: 020 8663 0949

VORWERK CARPETS
Po Box 10206
South Woodham Ferrers
Essex.
CM3 9AA
www.vorwerk-carpet.com
email: sales@vorwerkcarpets.co.uk
Tel: 08700 10 44 84
Fax: 01245 425 371

ACCESS FLOORING

CMD LTD, POWERPLAN
Brockholes Way
Claughton-On-Brock
Preston
PR3 0PZ
www.powerplan.co.uk
email: enquiries@powerplan.co.uk
Tel: 01995 640844
Fax: 01995 640798

GO INTERIORS LTD
Units C & D Lea Industrial Estate
Lower Luton Road
Harpenden, AL5 5EQ
www.gointeriors.co.uk
email: customercare@gointeriors.co.uk
Tel: 08700 111167
Fax: 08700 111168

LEGRAND ELECTRIC LTD
Great King Street, North Birmingham, B19 2LF
Tel: 0870 608 9000

BESPOKE
CARPETS & RUGS

ART RUGS
Contact: Annalisa Pascoe
Tel: 01273 770877
Email: info@artrugs.co.uk
Web: www.artrugs.co.uk

ART RUGS create exclusive hand tufted
rugs of the very highest quality. Working
with you to any commission, large or
small, traditional or contemporary, from
designing a rug from scratch to a simple
re-colouring of an existing design, Art
Rugs will create your own unique rug to
suit your interior.

Prices start at £250.

CARPETS & RUGS

AHWAZIAN LTD
Occ, 105 Eade Road, London, N4 1TJ
www.ahwazian.com
Tel: 02088 029990
Fax: 02088 029991

ATELIERS PINTON
9 Rue Preville, Felletin,
France, 23500
www.ateliers-pinton.com
email: l.dixon@ateliers-pinton.com
Tel: 00 33 630 640 534
Fax: 00 33 555 664 322

BAZAAR VELVET
2 New Kings Road
London
SW6 4SA
www.bazaarvelvet.com
email: info@bazaarvelvet.com
Tel: 020 7736 9693

BAZAAR VELVET
2 New Kings Road
London
SW6 4SA
www.bazaarvelvet.com
email: info@bazaarvelvet.com
Tel: 020 7736 9693

BAZAAR VELVET
2 New Kings Road
London
SW6 4SA
www.bazaarvelvet.com
email: info@bazaarvelvet.com
Tel: 020 7736 9693

BBD INTERIORS
Unit 18c Euro Business Park
Little Island
Cork
IRELAND
www.bbd.ie
email: info@bbd.ie
Tel: 00353 21435 1999
Fax: 00353 21435 1998

BRITISH WOOL MARKETING BOARD
Wool House, Roydsdale Way,
Euroway Trading Estate,
Bradford, BD4 6SE
Tel: 01274 688666
Fax: 01274 652233
Email: info@britishwool.org.uk
web: www.aboutwool.com

The BWMB sells and promotes British
Wool to the international carpet and
textile industry on behalf of wool
producers in the UK. The Shepherd's
Crook mark highlights British Wool
content in finished product and is only
available to licensed partners. British
Wool is a natural, biodegradable and
sustainable fibre and the brand enjoys
a quality reputation across the world.

BERY DESIGNS
8 Rosehill Rd
London
SW18 2NX
www.berydesigns.com
email: colleen@berydesigns.co.uk
Tel: 0208 874 5454
Fax: 0560 311 2481

BLENHEIM CARPETS
41 Pimlico Road
London
SW1W 8NE
www.blenheim-carpets.com
email: info@blenheim-carpets.com
Tel: 020 7823 6333
Fax: 020 7823 5210

BRINTONS LTD
Unit 107
Design Centre Chelsea Harbour
London
SW10 0XE
www.brintons.net
email: jules@brintons.co.uk
Tel: 0207 349 0020
Fax: 0207 351 0746

BUGHETTI
www.bughetti.com
email: www.bughetti@bughetti.com
Tel: 01474 871143

BURKE BY DESIGN WHOLESALE LTD
18c Euro Business Park
Little Island
Cork
IRELAND
www.bbd.ie
email: info@bbd.ie
Tel: 00353 21 435 1999
Fax: 00353 21 435 1998

CALDERDALE CARPETS
Dewsbury Mills,
Thornhill Road
Dewsbury, West Yorkshire
WF12 9QE
www.calderdalecarpets.com
email: sales@calderdalecarpets.com
Tel: 01924 487800
Fax: 01924 487801

CASADOR
Tel: 0049 30 78991854
Fax: 0049 30 78991855

CHARLOTTE GASKELL ORIENTAL CARPETS
183 Trinity Road
Wandsworth Common
London
SW17 7HL
www.charlottegaskell.com
email: info@charlottegaskell.com
Tel: 0208 672 3224

CREATIVE CARPETS LTD
Unit 8
Mill Hill Ind Est
Quarry Lane
LE19 4AU
www.creativecarpetsltd.co.uk
email: info@creativecarpetsltd.co.uk
Tel: 0116 2841455
Fax: 0116 275 2550

DEBORAH ROLT RUGS
www.deborahroltrugs.co.uk
email: anne@deborahroltrugs.co.uk
Tel: 020 8780 5288

DEIRDRE DYSON
554 Kings Road
London
SW6 2DZ
www.deirdredyson.com
Tel: 020 7384 4464
Fax: 020 7384 2232

DENTRO HOME
Calle Cobalto 152, 1-A
L'h De Llobregat
Barcelona
8907
www.dentrohome.com
email: info@dentrohome.com
Tel: 0034 93 337 8300

DORSET INTERIORS
415a Lymington Road
Highcliffe-On-Sea
Christchurch
BH23 5EN
www.dorsetinteriors.co.uk
email: joy@dorsetinteriors.co.uk
Tel: 01425 280011
Fax: 01425 280011

DOVECOT STUDIOS LTD
Dovecot
10 Infirmary Street
Edinburgh
EH1 1LT
www.dovecotstudios.com
email: info@dovecotstudios.com
Tel: 0131 550 3660
Fax: 0131 550 3669

GUARDSMAN FURNITURE SOLUTIONS GROUP
Valspar Industries (Uk) Ltd
152 Milton Park
Abingdon, Oxfordshire
OX14 4SD
www.guardsman.co.uk
email: marketing@valspareurope.com
Tel: 01235 444700
Fax: 01235 862730

HELEN YARDLEY
A-Z Studios
3-5 Hardwidge Street
London
SE1 3SY
www.helenyardley.com
email: info@helenyardley.com
Tel: 020 7403 7114
Fax: 020 7403 8906

JARAPA LTD
12 Cole Rd
Bruton
Somerset
BA10 0DA
www.jarapa.co.uk
email: stewart@jarapa.co.uk
Tel: 01749 813067
Fax: 01749 813067

JOCELYN WARNER LTD
23 Links Yard
Spelman Street
London, United Kingdom
E1 5LX
www.jocelynwarner.com
Tel: 0207 3753754

KAPPA LAMBDA RUGS
Unit 8 Regis Road
London
NW5 3EW
www.kappa-lambda.co.uk
email: post@kappa-lambda.co.uk
Tel: 020 74858822
Fax: 020 74858866

LECAFLOR LTD
Alanbrooke Industrial Park
Station Road
Topcliffe
YO7 3SE
www.lecaflor.com
email: sales@lecaflor.com
Tel: 01845 577522
Fax: 01485 577193

LEON NORELL LTD
Correspondence: 25a Woodstock Road,
London Nw11 8es
Warehouse: 403-405 Edgware Road, London
Nw2 6ln
www.leonnorell.com
email: sales@leonnorell.com
Tel: 020 837 7708
Fax: 020 8458 7147

LOOPHOUSE
88 Southwark Bridge Road
London
SE1 0EX
www.loophouse.com
email: info@loophouse.com
Tel: 020 7207 7619
Fax: 020 7207 7834

M. A. SAMAD
Tel: 02088 022929
Fax: 02088 022777

LUKE IRWIN

LUKE IRWIN
The Old Foundry
Tollard Royal
Salisbury
Wiltshire
SP5 5PS
Tel +44(0)1725 553 000
Email luke@lukeirwin.com
Web: www.lukeirwin.com

Luke Irwin has been designing hand knotted custom made rugs since 2003. The driving principle behind the company since it's inception has been to give the customer complete choice and control over their own rug. With choices to be made for the size, colour, weave, textile and design each individual can receive a truly bespoke and personal service.

MASTERCRAFT RUGS
19 Kenyon Road
Lomeshaye Industrial Estate
Nelson Lancashire
BB8 7EG
www.mastercraftrugs.co.uk
email: enquires@mastercraftrugs.co.uk
Tel: 01282 694565
Fax: 01282 447650

NANIMARQUINA
C/ Esglèsia 10 3JD
Barcelona
Spain
8024
www.nanimarquina.com
email: info@nanimarquina.com
Tel: 0034 932 376 465
Fax: 0034 932 175 774

PARSUA - LA HAUTE COUTURE DU TAPIS
Fairbank Studios 2
65-69 Lots Road
London
SW10 0RN
www.cbparsua.com
email: info@parsua.co.uk
Tel: 020 7351 6111
Fax: 020 7351 6222

RAMA CARPETS LTD
41 Humber Road
London
NW2 6EN
www.ramacarpets.com
email: info@ramacarpets.com
Tel: 0845 521 1010
Fax: 0845 521 1009

RIVIERE
Riviere, Unit 112 Avro House,
Havelock Terrace, London, SW8 4AS
Tel: 020 7627 0031
Email: info@jamtse.co.uk
Web: www.riviererugs.com

Riviere - Contemporary Handknotted
Rugs create timeless and elegant
handmade carpets of exceptional
quality. Using only the finest Tibetan
wool and Chinese silk, our collection is
woven exclusively by childfree workshops in Nepal. In addition to our
designs, we work closely with both
retail and trade clients to offer a
completely bespoke service.

Ryalux is the UK's leading manufacturer
of innovative, high quality wool carpets.
The Ryalux product range comprises of
well designed collections of twists,
velvets, saxonies, loops and shag piles.
The Ryalux Ultimate collection offers the
opportunity for a bespoke carpet in any
colour and size up to 7 metres wide.

For stockists details visit
www.ryalux.com

ROBERT CLEMENTS LTD
11 The Sidings
Hainault Road
London, E11 1HD
www.robertclements.co.uk
email: info@robertclements.co.uk
Tel: 020 8556 6595
Fax: 020 8556 6596

RUDE RUGS
Haggs Farm
Haggs Road
Follifoot, HG3 1EQ
www.ruderugs.com
email: info@ruderugs.com
Tel: 0142 387 1155
Fax: 0142 384 4803

RUGS WITH FLAIR
Unit 3 Grey Street
Denton, Manchester, M34 3RU
www.rugswithflair.com
email: enquiries@rugswithflair.com
Tel: 0161 320 7146
Fax: 0161 335 9095

SAMAD BROTHERS (UK)
105 Eade Road
Occ Building D
London, N4 1TJ
www.samad.com
email: jack@samad.com
Tel: 020 880 4406
Fax: 020 88024149

SANDRINGHAM CARPETS
The Studio, 83 Middle Mead
Hook, RG27 9TE
www.sandringhamcarpets.com
email: sales@sandringhamcarpets.com
Tel: 01256 762900
Fax: 01256 762727

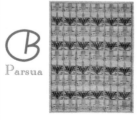

PARSUA – LA HAUTE COUTURE DU TAPIS
Fairbanks Studios 2,
65-69 Lots Road,
London, SW10 0RN
Tel: +44 (0)20 7351 6111
Fax: + 44 (0)20 7351 6222
info@parsua.co.uk
www.cbparsua.com

Parsua specialises in updating traditional
styles to create the "Haute Couture"
concept: a unique, hand-made carpet,
tailored to the interior using design, scale
and colours.
Each creation is knotted using traditional
methods with hand-spun wool, dyes
extracted from natural sources and sun
patina.
Wide range in stock also available.

RUDE RUGS
Hilary Mennell & Jan Mackaness,
The Wool Store, Haggs Farm, Haggs Rd,
Follifoot, Harrogate, HG3 1EQ
Tel: 01423 871155
Email: info@ruderugs.com
Web: www.ruderugs.com

Rude Rugs is a unique collection of
beautiful rug designs featuring shapely
bodies and sensuous silhouettes. The
latest collection 'Body Art' celebrates
man's timeless fascination with body
paint and ink! Made to order in British
Wool in England the rugs are available
in any size or colourway.
For more information and to view the
Rude Rugs Collection please visit the
website at **www.ruderugs.com**.

SCOTMAT CARPETS
10 Westerton Road
East Mains Ind. Estate
Broxburn
EH52 5AU
www.scotmat.co.uk
email: sales@scotmat.co.uk
Tel: 01506 859995
Fax: 01506 859996

SOLID FLOOR
53 Pembridge Road
Notting Hill
London
W11 3HG
www.solidfloor.co.uk
email: nottinghill@solidfloor.co.uk
Tel: 0207 221 9166
Fax: 0207 221 8193

STAIRRODS (UK) LTD
Unit 6, Park Rd North Industrial Estate
Blackhill
Consett, Co Durham
DH8 5UN
www.stairrods.co.uk
email: sales@stairrods.co.uk
Tel: 01207 591 176
Fax: 01207 591 911

STARK CARPET
Chelsea Harbour Design Centre
3rd Floor
South Dome, London
SW10 0XE
Tel: 020 7352 6001
Fax: 020 7376 4908

STEPEVI
274 King's Road
London
SW3 5AW
email: info@stepevi.com
Tel: 020 7376 7574
Fax: 020 7376 7577

THE ALTERNATIVE FLOORING COMPANY
3b Stephenson Close, East Portway
Andover
Hampshire, United Kingdom
SP10 3RU
www.alternativeflooring.com/
email: sales@alternativeflooring.com
Tel: 01264 335 111
Fax: 01264 336 445

THE CARPET LIBRARY
148 Wandsworth Bridge Road
Fulham
London
SW6 2UH
www.thecarpetlibrary.co.uk
email: sales@thecarpetlibrary.co.uk
Tel: 02077 363664
Fax: 02077 367554

THE RUG COMPANY
124 Holland Park Avenue
London
W11 4UE
www.therugcompany.info
Tel: 020 7229 5148
Fax: 020 7792 3384

THE NATURAL RUG STORE
Tel: 0845 076 0086
Web: www.naturalrugstore.co.uk
Email: info@naturalrugstore.co.uk

Our website accepts orders 24 hours a day, 7 days a week. Our customer service department is open between 9am-4:30pm, Monday to Friday.

The Natural Rug Store supply custom made natural rugs and runners in Coir, Jute, Seagrass, Sisal, Sisool and Wool via their online store. Design your own custom natural rug or runner via their online Rug Builder application which offers a surprisingly affordable method of shopping as you only pay for the sizes you need. They also offer a free sample service for accurate colour matching, telephone ordering and free delivery within the UK.

THOMAS WITTER
Parkside House
167 Chorley New Road
Bolton, BL1 4RA
www.thomaswitter.com
email: sales@thomaswitter.com
Tel: 0870 1128318
Fax: 0870 1128219

TIM PAGE CARPETS
Design Centre, Chelsea Harbour
Lots Road
London, SW10 0XE
www.timpagecarpets.com
email: sales@timpagecarpets.com
Tel: 0207 259 7282
Fax: 0207 376 8277

ULSTER CARPETS LTD
Castleisland Factory
Craigavon, Northern Ireland, BT62 1EE
www.ulstercarpets.com
email: marketing@ulstercarpets.com
Tel: 028 3839 5105
Fax: 028 3833 3142

VANDERHURD
276, 56 Gloucester Road
London, SW7 4UB
email: info@vanderhurd.co.uk
Tel: 0207 313 5400
Fax: 0207 229 7776

VORWERK CARPETS
Po Box 10206
South Woodham Ferrers
Essex.
CM3 9AA
www.vorwerk-carpet.com
email: sales@vorwerkcarpets.co.uk
Tel: 08700 10 44 84
Fax: 01245 425 371

WAVENEY RUSH INDUSTRY
The Old Maltings
Caldecott Road, Oulton Broad
Lowestoft
NR32 3PH
www.waveneyrush.co.uk
email: crafts@waveneyrush.co.uk
Tel: 01502 538777
Fax: 01502 538477

WESTON CARPETS LTD
16-17 Byford Court
Crockatt Road
Hadleigh
IP7 6RD
www.weston-carpets.co.uk
email: info@westonhammer.com
Tel: 0845 6449090
Fax: 0845 6449191

COMMERCIAL FLOORING

BLENHEIM CARPETS
41 Pimlico Road
London
SW1W 8NE
www.blenheim-carpets.com
email: info@blenheim-carpets.com
Tel: 020 7823 6333
Fax: 020 7823 5210

BONA LIMITED
www.bona.com
email: info.uk@bona.com
Tel: 01908 399740
Fax: 01908 232722

BRINTONS LTD
Unit 107
Design Centre Chelsea Harbour
London
SW10 0XE
www.brintons.net
email: jules@brintons.co.uk
Tel: 0207 349 0020
Fax: 0207 351 0746

CREATIVE CARPETS LTD
Unit 8
Mill Hill Ind Est
Quarry Lane
LE19 4AU
www.creativecarpetsltd.co.uk
email: info@creativecarpetsltd.co.uk
Tel: 0116 2841455
Fax: 0116 275 2550

DALSOUPLE
Showground Road
Bridgwater
Somerset
TA6 6AJ
www.dalsouple.com
email: info@dalsouple.com
Tel: 01278 727777
Fax: 01278 727788

DEBOLON DESSAUER BODENBEL‰GE GMBH & CO. KG
Ebertallee 209
Dessau
6846
www.debolon.de
Tel: +49 340 65000
Fax: +49 340 6500 202

GRADUS LIMITED
Park Green
Macclesfield
Cheshire
SK11 7LZ
www.gradusworld.com
email: sales@gradusworld.com
Tel: 01625 428 922
Fax: 01625 433 949

HARMONY CONTRACT FLOORING
Low Moor Business Park
Common Road
Bradford
BD12 0NB
www.harmonycontractflooring.co.uk
email: info@harmonycontractflooring.co.uk
Tel: 01274 693144
Fax: 01274 363908

INTERIOR PROPERTY SOLUTIONSLTD
Units 1-3 South Mundells
Welwyn Garden City
Hertfordshire
AL7 1EP
www.ips-interiors.co.uk
email: contact@ips-interiors.co.uk
Tel: 01707 331 078
Fax: 01707 328 828

KARELIA WOOD FLOORING
Highfield Drive
Churchfields Industrial Estate
St Leonards On Sea
TN38 9TG
www.kareliaparketti.com
email: enquiries@kareliawoodflooring.co.uk
Tel: 01424 856805
Fax: 01424 856855

KENT FLOORING SUPPLIES LTD
Unit 7/8 Revenge Road
Lordswood Industrial Estate
Chatham Kent
ME5 8UD
www.kentflooring.co.uk
email: sales@kentflooring.co.uk
Tel: 01634 668668
Fax: 01634 684550

KENTWOOD FLOORING GMBH
Ulrich-Lichtenstein-Gasse 21
Graz
Austria
8041
europe.kentwoodfloors.com
email: graz@kentwoodfloors.com
Tel: 0043 3162 25213
Fax: 0043 3162 2521315

LECAFLOR LTD
Alanbrooke Industrial Park
Station Road
Topcliffe
YO7 3SE
www.lecaflor.com
email: sales@lecaflor.com
Tel: 01845 577522
Fax: 01485 577193

MODULYSS/INNERSPACE
Brook House
Salford
Audlem
CW3 0AZ
www.innerspaceltd.co.uk
email: office@innerspaceltd.co.uk
Tel: 01270 812 380

PARAGON CARPETS
Farfield Park
Manvers
Rotherham
S63 5DB
www.paragon-carpets.co.uk
email: apotts@paragon-carpets.co.uk
Tel: 01709 763 800
Fax: 01709 763 818

RAMA CARPETS LTD
41 Humber Road
London
NW2 6EN
www.ramacarpets.com
email: info@ramacarpets.com
Tel: 0845 521 1010
Fax: 0845 521 1009

SCOTMAT CARPETS
10 Westerton Road
East Mains Ind. Estate
Broxburn
EH52 5AU
www.scotmat.co.uk
email: sales@scotmat.co.uk
Tel: 01506 859995
Fax: 01506 859996

STARK CARPET
Chelsea Harbour Design Centre
3rd Floor
South Dome, London
SW10 0XE
Tel: 020 7352 6001
Fax: 020 7376 4908

STEPEVI
274 King's Road
London
SW3 5AW
email: info@stepevi.com
Tel: 020 7376 7574
Fax: 020 7376 7577

STRATUM RESIN FLOORING
The Studio
4 Erringham Road
Shoreham By Sea
BN43 5NQ
www.stratum.uk.com
email: info@stratum.uk.com
Tel: 0870 770 4316
Fax: 0870 770 4317

TAYLORED FLOORING
Ennis Close, Wythenshawe, Manchester
Ennis Close, Wythenshawe, Manchester
M23 9LE
www.info@tayloredflooring.co.uk
Tel: 0161 498 0325
Fax: 0161 498 0327

VORWERK CARPETS
Po Box 10206
South Woodham Ferrers
Essex.
CM3 9AA
www.vorwerk-carpet.com
email: sales@vorwerkcarpets.co.uk
Tel: 08700 10 44 84
Fax: 01245 425 371

WESTON CARPETS LTD
16-17 Byford Court
Crockatt Road
Hadleigh
IP7 6RD
www.weston-carpets.co.uk
email: info@westonhammer.com
Tel: 0845 6449090
Fax: 0845 6449191

ENTRANCE MATTING
CONSTRUCTION SPECIALTIES (U K) LTD
1010 Westcott Venture Park
Westcott
Buckinghamshire
HP18 0XB
www.c-sgroup.co.uk
email: info@c-sgroup.co.uk
Tel: 01296 652800
Fax: 01296 652888

GRADUS LIMITED
Park Green
Macclesfield
Cheshire
SK11 7LZ
www.gradusworld.com
email: sales@gradusworld.com
Tel: 01625 428 922
Fax: 01625 433 949

KENT FLOORING SUPPLIES LTD
Unit 7/8 Revenge Road
Lordswood Industrial Estate
Chatham Kent
ME5 8UD
www.kentflooring.co.uk
email: sales@kentflooring.co.uk
Tel: 01634 668668
Fax: 01634 684550

PARAGON CARPETS
Farfield Park
Manvers
Rotherham
S63 5DB
www.paragon-carpets.co.uk
email: apotts@paragon-carpets.co.uk
Tel: 01709 763 800
Fax: 01709 763 818

FLOORING CONTRACTORS
CREATIVE CARPETS LTD
Unit 8
Mill Hill Ind Est
Quarry Lane
LE19 4AU
www.creativecarpetsltd.co.uk
email: info@creativecarpetsltd.co.uk
Tel: 0116 2841455
Fax: 0116 275 2550

HARMONY CONTRACT FLOORING
Low Moor Business Park
Common Road
Bradford
BD12 0NB
www.harmonycontractflooring.co.uk
email: info@harmonycontractflooring.co.uk
Tel: 01274 693144
Fax: 01274 363908

FLOORING

HITT OAK LTD
10 Park Parade,
Gunnersbury Av.
Acton
W3 9BD
www.hittoak.co.uk
email: info@hittoak.co.uk
Tel: 020 8896 1900

PARAGON CARPETS
Farfield Park
Manvers
Rotherham
S63 5DB
www.paragon-carpets.co.uk
email: apotts@paragon-carpets.co.uk
Tel: 01709 763 800
Fax: 01709 763 818

STRATUM RESIN FLOORING
The Studio
4 Erringham Road
Shoreham By Sea
BN43 5NQ
www.stratum.uk.com
email: info@stratum.uk.com
Tel: 0870 770 4316
Fax: 0870 770 4317

WELDON
The Grange
Hill Holt Farm
Norton Disney
LN6 9JP
www.weldon.co.uk
email: floors@weldon.co.uk
Tel: 01636 894838
Fax: 01636 894839

WELDON
The Grange
Hill Holt Farm
Norton Disney
LN6 9JP
www.weldon.co.uk
email: floors@weldon.co.uk
Tel: 01636 894838
Fax: 01636 894839

FSC FLOORING

HITT OAK LTD
10 Park Parade,
Gunnersbury Av.
Acton
W3 9BD
www.hittoak.co.uk
email: info@hittoak.co.uk
Tel: 020 8896 1900

JAMES LATHAM
www.lathams.co.uk
Tel: 0116 257 3415

KENTWOOD FLOORING GMBH
Ulrich-Lichtenstein-Gasse 21
Graz
Austria
8041
europe.kentwoodfloors.com
email: graz@kentwoodfloors.com
Tel: 0043 3162 25213
Fax: 0043 3162 2521315

THE NATURAL WOOD FLOOR COMPANY
20 Smugglers Way Wandsworth London
SW181EG
www.naturalwoodfloor.co.uk
email: sales@naturalwoodfloor.co.uk
Tel: 020 8871 9771
Fax: 020 8877 0273

WESTCO GROUP LTD
307 Penarth Road
Cardiff
CF11 8YN
westcofloors.co.uk
email: westco@westcodiy.co.uk
Tel: 029 20 376700
Fax: 029 20383573

RESIN FLOORING

SOLID FLOOR
53 Pembridge Road
Notting Hill
London
W11 3HG
www.solidfloor.co.uk
email: nottinghill@solidfloor.co.uk
Tel: 0207 221 9166
Fax: 0207 221 8193

STRATUM RESIN FLOORING
The Studio
4 Erringham Road
Shoreham By Sea
BN43 5NQ
www.stratum.uk.com
email: info@stratum.uk.com
Tel: 0870 770 4316
Fax: 0870 770 4317

RUBBER

THE RUBBER FLOORING COMPANY
Tel: 0800 849 6386
www.therubberflooringcompany.co.uk

The Rubber Flooring Company supplies flexible, durable, water resistant, easy to clean rubber flooring that is uniquely stylish and suitable for a wide range of applications in the home, office and large scale commercial or industrial sites. The current stock range alone includes over 40 colours across 4 styles.

DALSOUPLE
Showground Road
Bridgwater
Somerset
TA6 6AJ
www.dalsouple.com
email: info@dalsouple.com
Tel: 01278 727777
Fax: 01278 727788

STYLO
Attn Vicky House
Hille Business Centre
132 St Albans Road, Watford
WD24 4AJ
Tel: 01923 800777

STONE FLOORING

AMARESTONE
Hogwood Farm Industrial Estate
Sheerlands Road
Finchampstead
RG40 4QY
www.amarestone.com
email: sales@amarestone.com
Tel: 0845 260 8070
Fax: 01189 760371

BURLINGTON SLATE LTD
Cavendish House
Kirkby In Furness
Cumbria
LA17 7UN
burlingtonstone.co.uk
email: sales@burlingtonstone.co.uk
Tel: 01229 889661
Fax: 01229 889466

CAESARSTONE
Gorrels Way
Trans-Pennine Industrial Estate
WF3 3LY
www.caesarstone.uk.com
email: info@ebor.co.uk
Tel: 01706 863 600

DE FERRANTI
E1 The Engineering Offices
2 Michael Road
London
SW6 2AD
www.deferranti.com
email: ask@deferranti.com
Tel: 0870 321 0511
Fax: 0870 321 0512

FAIRHAVEN AND WOODS LTD
Northfield Farm Stoneyard
Lode Road, Bottisham
Cambridge
CB25 9DN
www.fairhavengroup.co.uk
email: office@fairhavengroup.co.uk
Tel: 01223 812555
Fax: 01223 812554

FRANCIS N LOWE LTD
The Marble Works
New Road
Middleton
DE4 4NA
www.lowesmarble.com
email: info@lowesmarble.com
Tel: 01629 822216
Fax: 01629 824348

KIRKSTONE
Skelwith Bridge
Ambleside
Cumbria
LA22 9NN
www.kirkstone.com
email: info:kirkstone.com
Tel: 01539 433296
Fax: 015394 34006

M. J. WRIGHT & SONS LTD.
Units 104 - 106, Northwick Business Centre
Blockley, Moreton-In-Marsh
Gloucestershire
GL56 9RF
www.wrightsofcampden.co.uk
email: office@mjwrights.fsnet.co.uk
Tel: (01386) 700497
Fax: (01386) 701144

MINSTERSTONE LTD
Pondhayes Farm
Dinnington
Hinton St George
TA17 8SU
www.minsterstone.com
email: sales@minsterstone.ltd.uk
Tel: 01460 52277
Fax: 01460 57865

R.I.M TILE AND MOSAIC BOUTIQUE
Unit 311 Design Centre Chelsea Harbour
London
SW10 0XE
www.rim.ru
email: info@rimdesign.co.uk
Tel: 020 7376 5820

SNOWDONIA SLATE & STONE
North Wales
www.snowdoniaslate.co.uk
email: richard@snowdoniaslate.co.uk
Tel: 01766 832525
Fax: 01766 832404

SSQ GROUP
301 Elveden Road
Park Royal
London
NW10 7SS
www.ssqgroup.com
email: info@ssq.co.uk
Tel: 020 8961 7725
Fax: 020 8965 7013

STONE THEATRE LTD
Newnham Terrace
Hercules Road
Waterloo, London
SE1 7DR
www.stonetheatre.com
email: london@stonetheatre.com
Tel: 020 7021 0020
Fax: 0207 021 0049

STONEHOUSE TILES LTD
2-10 Ossory Road
London
SE1 5AN
www.stonehousetiles.co.uk
email: sales@stonehousetiles.co.uk
Tel: 0207 237 5375
Fax: 0207 231 7597

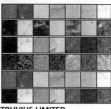

Vitruvius Limited
marble, granite, limestone
and slate specialists

VITRUVIUS LIMITED
44 Linford Street, London, SW8 4UN
Tel: 020 7627 8034
Fax: 020 7627 4578
enquiries@vitruviusltd.co.uk
www.vitruviusltd.co.uk

Vitruvius is a supplier, manufacturer
and fixer of all forms of natural stone.
The company is based in Central
London with its own modern factory
and skilled fabricators and fixers. As a
company, we strive to make our clients
the raison d'etre of our business - we
are proud that, after 20 years, we are
still working creatively with many of
the same private customers,
contractors and developers. We are
small, professional and committed.

TOUCHSTONE WORKTOPS LTD
Unit 2 Chase Rd. Trading Est.
51 Chase Rd.
London, NW10 6LG
www.touchstoneworktops.com
email: sales@touchstoneworktops.com
Tel: 020 8963 7450
Fax: 020 8963 7455

TILE FLOORING

AMARESTONE
Hogwood Farm Industrial Estate
Sheerlands Road, Finchampstead, RG40 4QY
www.amarestone.com
email: sales@amarestone.com
Tel: 0845 260 8070
Fax: 01189 760371

CERAMIQUE INTERNATIONALE LTD
Unit 1 Royds Lane
Lower Wortley Ring Road
Leeds, LS12 6DU
www.tilesandmosaics.co.uk
email: info@ceramiqueinternationale.co.uk
Tel: 01132 310218
Fax: 01132 310353

DE FERRANTI
E1 The Engineering Offices
2 Michael Road, London, SW6 2AD
www.deferranti.com
email: ask@deferranti.com
Tel: 0870 321 0511
Fax: 0870 321 0512

DOMINIC CRINSON
274 Richmond Road, E8 3QW
www.crinson.com
email: info@crinson.com
Tel: 0207 241 7467
Fax: 02076 132783

DEUTSCHE STEINZEUG **AGROB BUCHTAL**

AGROB BUCHTAL
www.agrob-buchtal.de

The German brand AGROB BUCHTAL
offers ceramic tiles for all public and
private areas of application. Its USP's
are the wide range of styles, product
quality made in Germany and the
revolutionary "Hydrotect"
surface-coating lending ceramic tiles
amazing characteristics: extremely
easy to clean, antibacterial effect and
elimination of unwelcome odours.

H & E SMITH LTD
Broom Street
Hanley
Stoke-On-Trent, ST1 2ER
www.hesmith.co.uk
email: sales@hesmith.co.uk
Tel: 01782 281617
Fax: 01782 269882

INTERSTYLE CERAMIC & GLASS
3625 Brighton Ave
Burnaby, Bc
Canada, V5A 3H5
www.interstyle.ca
email: info@interstyle.ca
Tel: 1 604 421 7229
Fax: 1 604 421 7544

JASBA MOSAIK GMBH
Im Petersborn 2
D-56244
www.jasba.de
email: info@jasba.de
Tel: +49 2602 682-0

JOHNSON TILES
Harewood Street, Tunstall,
Stoke On Trent, ST6 5JZ
www.johnson-tiles.com
email: sales@johnson-tiles.com
Tel: 01782 575575
Fax: 01782 524138

MAPEI UK LTD
Mapei House, Steel Park Rd
Halesowen
West Midlands
B62 8HD
www.mapei.co.uk
email: s.ridgway@mapei.co.uk
Tel: 0121 508 6970 - option 4
Fax: 0121 508 6960

JOHNSON TILES
Stoke on Trent
ST6 5JZ
Tel: 01782 575575
Web: www.johnson-tiles.com
MATERIAL LAB
10 Great Titchfield Street
London
W1W 8BB
Tel: 020 7436 8629

For a comprehensive choice of ceramic and porcelain floor designs the Johnson Tiles portfolio offers an extensive range of designs, size formats and styles. The choice includes the Absolute range which is featured at Material Lab in London.

MARLBOROUGH TILES
www.marlboroughtiles.com
Tel: 01672 512422
Fax: 01672 515791

MASS CONCRETE
Black Hill Rd Holton Heath Ind Estate
Poole Dorset
BH16 6LS
www.mass-concrete.com
email: sales@mass-concrete.com
Tel: 01202 628 140
Fax: 01202 628 149

RAK CERAMICS UK LTD
Paris House,
Frenchmans Road,
Petersfield, Hampshire, GU32 3AW.
Tel: 01730 237850
Email: info@rakceramics.co.uk
Web: www.rakceramics.co.uk

TAYLOR ETC
Beaufort Road
Plasmarl
Swansea
SA6 8JG
www.taylorsetc.co.uk
email: info@taylortiles.co.uk
Tel: 01792 797712
Fax: 01792 791103

TILES OF STOW LTD
Langston Priory Workshops
Station Road
Kingham
OX7 6UP
www.tilesofstow.co.uk
email: info@tilesofstow.co.uk
Tel: 01608 658993
Fax: 01608 658951

SURFACE TILES
London Stores in Battersea & Islington and West Molesey, Surrey.
Tel: 020 7819 2300 (Battersea)
Email: info@surfacetiles.com
Web: www.surfacetiles.com

Surface's innovative showrooms feature beautifully crafted room-sets with collections by international designers including Andrée Putman and Patricia Urquiola. There are thousands of tiles, mosaic and stone samples to take home and product brochures for key ranges. The friendly, expert team is always on hand to assist with any questions.

TAU CERAMICA, TAULELL, S.A.
Ctra. Alcora, Qdra. La Torta n°2
12006-CASTELLON (SPAIN)
Tel: 00 34 964 25 01 05
Fax: 00 34 964 25 27 71
tau@tauceramica.com
www.tauceramica.com

Colore is a TAU Ceramica response to the Consumers' demands when covering their needs in new projects for façades, exteriors, and large-scales surfaces, which has detected a clear lack of chromatic diversity in the available supply.

VIA ARKADIA LTD
3rd Floor, 19/20 Centre Dome,
Chelsea Harbour Design Centre,
London, SW10 0XE
Tel: 020 7351 7057
84 Heath Street, Hampstead, NW3 1DN
Tel: 020 7794 2341
Fax: 020 7351 7087
Email: mail@via-arkadia.co.uk
Web: via-arkadia.co.uk

Via Arkadia Ltd is an experienced tile supplier of top quality Italian stone, marble, porcelain, ceramic, mosaics and many other materials. Serving both the professional and domestic markets, Via Arkadia selects its comprehensive products on the following criteria: exceptional quality, inspiring design, timeless beauty and exceeding all European standards for hardness, and durability specifically for commercial use, and resistance to frost, chemicals etc, for both inside and outside areas.

WAXMAN CERAMICS LTD
Grove Mills
Elland
West Yorkshire
HX5 9DZ
www.waxmanceramics.co.uk
email: sales@waxmanceramics.co.uk
Tel: 01422 311331
Fax: 01422 310654

WILTON STUDIOS
Jackson Place
Wilton Road Ind. Est.
Grimsby, N E Lincolnshire
DN36 4AS
www.wiltonstudios.co.uk
email: postbox@wiltonstudios.co.uk
Tel: 01472 210820
Fax: 01472 812602

ZENITH MOSAIC & TILES LTD
Zenith House, Units 5-6 Monarch Industrial Estate
198 Kings Road, Tyseley
Birmingham
B11 2AP
www.zenithtiles.com
email: info@zenithtiles.com
Tel: 0121 706 6456
Fax: 0121 706 7509

VINYL
DEBOLON DESSAUER BODENBEL‰GE GMBH & CO. KG
Ebertallee 209
Dessau
6846
www.debolon.de
Tel: +49 340 65000
Fax: +49 340 6500 202

KARNDEAN INTERNATIONAL LTD
Crab Apple Way
Vale Park, Evesham
Worcestershire
WR11 1GP
www.karndean.co.uk
email: commercial@karndean.co.uk
Tel: 01386 820104
Fax: 01386 761249

MAPEI UK LTD
Mapei House, Steel Park Rd
Halesowen
West Midlands
B62 8HD
www.mapei.co.uk
email: s.ridgway@mapei.co.uk
Tel: 0121 508 6970 - option 4
Fax: 0121 508 6960

WESTCO GROUP LTD
307 Penarth Road
Cardiff
CF11 8YN
westcofloors.co.uk
email: westco@westcodiy.co.uk
Tel: 029 20 376700
Fax: 029 20383573

WOOD & LAMINATE FLOORING

ANTIQUE BUILDINGS LTD
Dunsfold
Godalming
Surrey, GU8 4NP
antiquebuildings.com
email: info@antiquebuildings.com
Tel: 01483 200477

BELVEDERE
11 Dove Street
Ipswich
IP4 1NG
www.belvederereproductions.co.uk†
Tel: 01473 214573

BHK FLOORING LTD
Davy Drive
Northwest Industrial Estate
Peterlee
SR8 2JF
www.bhkonline.com
email: philipgriffiths2000@yahoo.com
Tel: 0191 5186538
Fax: 0191 5186536

BLENHEIM CARPETS
41 Pimlico Road
London
SW1W 8NE
www.blenheim-carpets.com
email: info@blenheim-carpets.com
Tel: 020 7823 6333
Fax: 020 7823 5210

BONA LIMITED
www.bona.com
email: info.uk@bona.com
Tel: 01908 399740
Fax: 01908 232722

DRUMMOND'S
78 Royal Hospital Raod
Chelsea
London
SW3 4HN
www.drummonds-uk.com
email: info@drummonds-uk.com
Tel: 0207 376 4499
Fax: 0207 376 4488

EBECO UK LTD
Unit N
Kingsfield Business Centre
Redhill , Surrey
RH1 4DP
www.ebeco.com
email: uksales@ebeco.com
Tel: 01737 761767
Fax: 01737 507907

HARMONY CONTRACT FLOORING
Low Moor Business Park
Common Road
Bradford
BD12 0NB
www.harmonycontractflooring.co.uk
email: info@harmonycontractflooring.co.uk
Tel: 01274 693144
Fax: 01274 363908

HITT OAK LTD
10 Park Parade,
Gunnersbury Av.
Acton, W3 9BD
www.hittoak.co.uk
email: info@hittoak.co.uk
Tel: 020 8896 1900

JAMES LATHAM
www.lathams.co.uk
Tel: 0116 257 3415

KARELIA WOOD FLOORING
Highfield Drive
Churchfields Industrial Estate
St Leonards On Sea
TN38 9TG
www.kareliaparketti.com
email: enquiries@kareliawoodflooring.co.uk
Tel: 01424 856805
Fax: 01424 856855

KENT FLOORING SUPPLIES LTD
Unit 7/8 Revenge Road
Lordswood Industrial Estate
Chatham Kent
ME5 8UD
www.kentflooring.co.uk
email: sales@kentflooring.co.uk
Tel: 01634 668668
Fax: 01634 684550

KENTWOOD FLOORING GMBH
Ulrich-Lichtenstein-Gasse 21
Graz
Austria
8041
europe.kentwoodfloors.com
email: graz@kentwoodfloors.com
Tel: 0043 3162 25213
Fax: 0043 3162 2521315

KNIGHT WOOD UK LTD
Unit 3a, Becks Green Lane
St Andrew
Beccles
NR34 8NB
www.knight-wood.com
email: info@knight-wood.com
Tel: 01986 781 654
Fax: 01986 781 768

LECAFLOR LTD
Alanbrooke Industrial Park
Station Road
Topcliffe
YO7 3SE
www.lecaflor.com
email: sales@lecaflor.com
Tel: 01845 577522
Fax: 01485 577193

MAPEI UK LTD
Mapei House, Steel Park Rd
Halesowen
West Midlands
B62 8HD
www.mapei.co.uk
email: s.ridgway@mapei.co.uk
Tel: 0121 508 6970 - option 4
Fax: 0121 508 6960

MILLENNIUM HARDWOODS
Tel: 01388 777122
Fax: 01388 777408

OSMO UK
Unit 24 Anglo Business Park
Smeaton Close
Aylesbury, HP19 8UP
www.osmouk.com
email: steve@osmouk.com
Tel: 01296 481220
Fax: 01296 424090

PERGO
Po Box 1313
Kingbury Link
Picadilly ,Amworth
B77 9DJ
www.pergo.com
email: customercare.uk@pergo.com
Tel: 01827 871840
Fax: 01827 871850

SOLID FLOOR
53 Pembridge Road
Notting Hill
London
W11 3HG
www.solidfloor.co.uk
email: nottinghill@solidfloor.co.uk
Tel: 0207 221 9166
Fax: 0207 221 8193

ROVER'S FLOORING LTD.
Unit 33 Jubilee Trade Center,
Jubilee Road, Letchworth Garden City,
Hertfordshire SG6 1SP
Tel: +44 1462 486586
Fax: +44 1462 486584
E-mail: info@roversflooring.co.uk
Web: www.roversflooring.co.uk

Rover's Flooring was established in the
UK as an international wooden flooring
import and distribution company
originating from The Netherlands 12
years ago and now in its 10th year in
Letchworth. Offering solid hardwood
and engineered flooring from mainly
Western Europe, produced in Holland
and Germany, according to European
quality specifications, and supplying from
stock in its large warehouse in the UK.

WALKING ON WOOD
Design and installation of
custom-made wooden floors.
They specialise in bespoke,
hand-made, wooden floors that
are tailored to each client's style,
requirements and budget.
Visit the showroom at
490 King's Road, London, SW10.
Showrooms also in Kensington and
Notting Hill.
Call **020 7352 7311** or view
www.walkingonwood.co.uk

TAYLORED FLOORING
Ennis Close, Wythenshawe, Manchester
Ennis Close, Wythenshawe, Manchester
M23 9LE
www.info@tayloredflooring.co.uk
Tel: 0161 498 0325
Fax: 0161 498 0327

VICTORIAN WOODWORKS
Redhouse, Lower Dunton Road
Bulphan, Upminster
Essex
RM14 3TD
www.victorianwoodworks.co.uk
email: sales@victorianwoodworks.co.uk
Tel: 020 8534 1000
Fax: 020 8434 2000

WELDON
The Grange
Hill Holt Farm
Norton Disney
LN6 9JP
www.weldon.co.uk
email: floors@weldon.co.uk
Tel: 01636 894838
Fax: 01636 894839

WESTCO GROUP LTD
307 Penarth Road
Cardiff
CF11 8YN
westcofloors.co.uk
email: westco@westcodiy.co.uk
Tel: 029 20 376700
Fax: 029 20383573

Furniture

2020 TECHNOLOGIES
10b Eagley House, Deakins Business Park
The Hall Coppice
Egerton, Bolton, BL7 9RP
www.2020technologies.com
email: uksales@2020.net
Tel: 01204 304 040
Fax: 01204 304 422

ALEXANDER MILES
58 Welbeck Street
London
W1G 0AS
www.alexandermiles.co.uk
email: office@alexandermiles.co.uk
Tel: 0207 486 4545
Fax: 0207 935 2684

ANTHONY OUTRED ANTIQUES LTD
72 Pimlico Road
London
SW1W 8LS
www.outred.co.uk
email: antiques@outred.co.uk
Tel: 0207 730 7948

ART FURNITURE
20 Century Road
London
E17 6JB
www.artfurniture.co.uk
email: arts-and-crafts@artfurniture.co.uk
Tel: 020 8527 0676

ASHBURN UPHOLSTERY
Unit 3 Western Units
Pottery Road
Bovey Tracey, Devon
TQ13 9DS
www.ashburn-upholstery.co.uk
email: mail@ashupohl.plus.com
Tel: 01626 832532
Fax: 01626 832532

AUTHENTIC MODELS
24 Lintot Sq.
Fairbank Rd
Southwater, West Sussex
RH13 9LA
www.authenticmodels.com
email: info@am-uk.eu
Tel: 01403 734 999
Fax: 01403 734888

BENCHMARK
Bath Road
Kintbury
Hungerford
RG17 9SA
www.benchmarkfurniture.com
email: sales@benchmarkfurniture.com
Tel: 01488 608020
Fax: 01488 608030

BENTLEY DESIGNS (UK) LTD
Unit 1, Tera 40
Auriol Drive
Greenford
UB6 0TP
www.bentleydesigns.com†
email: emma@bentleydesigns.com
Tel: 020 8833 7500
Fax: 020 8578 2696

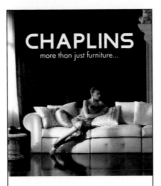

CLIVE CHRISTIAN
1st Floor, South Dome
Chelsea Harbour Design Centre
London
SW10 0XE
www.clive.com
email: london@clive.com
Tel: 020 73499200

CONNECTIONS INTERIORS LTD
286 -288 Leigh Road
Leigh-On-Sea
Essex, SS9 1BW
www.connectionsinteriors.co.uk
email: sales@connectionsinteriors.co.uk
Tel: 01702 470 939
Fax: 01702 480 238

DAVID SEYFRIED LTD
1/5 Chelsea Harbour Design Centre
London
SW10 0XE
www.davidseyfried.com
email: info@davidseyfried.com
Tel: 020 7823 3848
Fax: 020 7823 3221

DESIGN WRIGHT
Lf3.4, The Leathermarket
11/13 Weston St
London, SE1 3ER
www.designwright.co.uk
email: studio@designwright.co.uk
Tel: 020 7357 7788

DOVETAIL ENTERPRISES LTD
Dunsinane Avenue,
Dundee, DD2 3QN
Tel: 01382 810099
Fax: 01382 817272
sales@dovetailenterprises.co.uk
www.dovetailenterprises.co.uk

Dovetail is an established manufacturer
of high quality furniture, beds and doors.
We can offer supply and installation of
bespoke as well as our standard ranges.
Our long standing reputation has
resulted in undertaking many large
prestigious contracts for all our products.
We are also very happy to provide for
smaller establishments.

DIPLOMAT DESIGN
www.diplomatdesign.com
email: info@diplomatdesign.com
Tel: 02083 425285

GAINSBOROUGH LOUNGE SUITES
1 Northmoor Ind Est,
Moor Street,
Brierley Hill,
DY5 3 SU
www.gainsboroughloungesuites.co.uk
email: sales@gainsboroughloungesuites.co.uk
Tel: 01384 261009
Fax: 01384 480226

HARROW GREEN DESIGN & BUILD
16 Bastwick Street,
London,
EC1V 3PS
www.hgdb.co.uk
email: hgdb@harrowgreen.com
Tel: 020 014 3088
Fax: 020 014 3089

HELEN GREEN DESIGN
29 Milner Street,
London, SW3 3QD
www.helengreendesign.com
email: mail@helengreendesign.com
Tel: 020 7352 3344
Fax: 020 7352 5544

HERITAGE TABLES
Tel: 01580 852316

Hi Portia,

Sorry about Jonathan's End of Term Review Party - Oh dear, I don't know what came over me!

Look, I've Stumbled on Scumble! You HAVE to go to <u>www.scumblegoosie.com</u> & check these guys out. They're an Interior Designers' dream!

They hand make the MOST AMAZING FURNITURE in VIRTUALLY ANY SIZE & COLOUR (& in sustainably sourced hardwood)!!!

Beautiful Gustavian pieces & other traditional styles,......Chests of Drawers, Armoires, Chairs, Consoles, Bedside Tables - just about everything,....

Anyway must dash - Jonathan has apparently just found an item of clothing belonging to me stuck on one of the chandeliers. Don't ask......!!!

Clem X

www.scumblegoosie.com

P.S. Let's go and see Scumble Goosies' Cotswolds' Showroom - gather it's lovely! Txt me!

ERCOL FURNITURE LTD.
Summerleys Road,
Princes Risborough,
Bucks HP27 9PX
Tel: 01844 271800
Fax: 01844 271888
sales@ercol.com
www.ercol.com

Ercol Furniture based in Buckinghamshire
for 90 years, design and manufacturer
high quality, hard wood furniture.
Ranges consist of classic and
contemporary style dining tables, chairs
and cabinets, upholstered and show
wood sofas, and bedroom furniture.
Made to order and available in a choice
of wood finishes, fabrics and leathers.

LEPORELLO
4 - 5 Old Char Wharf, Station Road,
Dorking, Surrey, RH4 1EF
T 01483 284109 Sales & Enquiries
T 01306 875550 Surrey Showroom
F 01306 877107
E info@leporello.co.uk
www.leporello.co.uk

Hand made furniture made in England.
Leporello, family run business specialises
in the design & manufacture of an
exceptional range of painted dining &
bedroom furniture and accessories in
both classic and contemporary styles -
made to exacting standards. Available in
a range of paint colours & treatments,
bespoke sizes. Furniture design service.
Home delivery & installation.

KABILJO INC.
Gonzagagasse 5, Vienna, Austria
1010
www.kabiljo.com
email: wisdom@kabiljo.com
Tel: +43 1 5321094

LITTON FURNITURE
White Lane Close
Sturminster, Dorset, DT10 1EJ
www.littonfurniture.com
email: info@littonfurniture.com
Tel: 01258 472359
Fax: 01258 473542

MOOOI
Minervum 7003
4817 ZL BREDA
www.moooi.com
email: info@moooi.com
Tel: 0031 765784444
Fax: 0031 765710621

NOBILIS FONTAN
Bellevue House
Althorp Road
London, SW17 7EP
www.nobilis.fr
email: nobilis@nobilis-fontan.co.uk
Tel: 020 8767 0774
Fax: 020 8682 4904

NOCHINTZ LTD
Carvers Warehouse
77 Dale Street
Manchester, M1 2HG
www.nochintz.co.uk
email: info@nochintzltd.co.uk
Tel: 0161 236 1412
Fax: 0161 880 2407

NORDIC STYLE
109 Lots Road
London, SW10 0RN
www.nordicstyle.com
email: sales@nordicstyle.com
Tel: 0207 351 1755
Fax: 0207 351 4966

RALPH LAUREN HOME
1 New Bond Street
London
W1S 3RL
www.ralphlaurenhome.com
Tel: 020 7535 4557

REINHARD DESIGN
Kyffhaeuserstrasse 7
Koeln
D- 50674
www.claasreinhard.de
email: buero@claasreinhard.de
Tel: 0049 221 721 2366

**SASHA WADDELL FURNITURE (TEED
INTERIORS LTD)**
Tel: 0208 979 9189
Fax: 0208 979 0804

TAG FURNITURE CONSULTANCY
Tel: 0151 924 6036

WALTER MOORES & SON
Po Box 5338
Market Harborough
United Kingdom
LE16 7WG
www.waltermoores.co.uk
email: waltermoores@btinternet.com
Tel: +44(0)7071 226202 or +44(0)77 100
19045
Fax: +44(0)7071 226202

WAMBAMBOO
54 Swan Terrace
Windsor Qld
Australia
4030
www.wambamboo.com.au
email: info@wambamboo.com.au
Tel: 0061 73315 6605

WWW.ANTIQUES.CO.UK
P.o. Box 77
Leeds
LS25 9AH
www.antiques.co.uk
email: mail@antiques.co.uk
Tel: 0845 260 2 260

YTM FURNITURE
Grove Road
Pontefract
West Yorkshire
WF8 1EE
www.ytmfurniture.com
email: sales@ytmfurniture.com
Tel: 01977 703271
Fax: 01977 701882

BESPOKE & SPECIALIST FURNITURE

21ST CENTURY ANTIQUES
Tel: 01306 881029
Fax: 01306 888855

2D:3D
263 Abbeydale Road
Wembley
London
HA0 1TW
www.2d3d.co.uk
email: rob@2d3d.co.uk
Tel: 0208 998 3199
Fax: 0208 998 7767

ACRES FARM CLUB FENDERS
Acres Farm
Bradfield
Nr Reading
RG7 6JH
www.acresfarm.co.uk
email: enquiries@acresfarm.co.uk
Tel: 01189 744305
Fax: 01189 744012

ACT FURNITURE MANUFACTURERS LTD
Salop Street
Bradley
Bilston
WV14 0TQ
www.actfurniture.com
email: sales@actfurniture.com
Tel: 01902 490273
Fax: 01902 490275

AMS GROUP
20/21 Padgets Lane
South Moons Moat
Redditch, Worcestershire
B98 0RA
www.ams-group.co.uk
email: info@ams-group.co.uk
Tel: 01527 517171
Fax: 01527 510002

ANDREW CRACE
Bourne Lane, Much Hadham, Hertfordshire
SG10 6ER
www.andrewcrace.com
email: sales@andrewcrace.com
Tel: 01279 842685
Fax: 01279 843646

ANTIQUE CHURCH FURNISHINGS
Rivernook Farm
Sunnyside
Walton On Thames, Surrey
KT12 2ET
www.churchantiques.com
email: info@churchantiques.com
Tel: 01932 252736
Fax: 01932 252736

ARBORA DESIGN CONTEMPORARY FURNITURE
23 Lodge Lane
Gowdall Goole
East Yorkshire
DN14 0AR
www.arboradesign.co.uk
email: info@arboradesign.co.uk
Tel: 01405 860685
Fax: 01405 860685

ART FURNITURE
20 Century Road
London
E17 6JB
www.artfurniture.co.uk
email: arts-and-crafts@artfurniture.co.uk
Tel: 020 8527 0676

ARYMA
Tel: 01597 825505
Fax: 01597 824484

ATELIER GAGNIÈRE CRÈATEUR DE MEUBLES
Zone Artisanale De Lecheraine
Lanslebourg Mont-Cenis
France Alpes
73480
www.atelier-gagniere.com
email: contact@atelier-gagniere.com
Tel: +33 (0)479 563 570
Fax: +33 (0)479 563 570

BELVEDERE
11 Dove Street
Ipswich
IP4 1NG
www.belvederereproductions.co.uk†
Tel: 01473 214573

BENCHMARK
Bath Road
Kintbury
Hungerford
RG17 9SA
www.benchmarkfurniture.com
email: sales@benchmarkfurniture.com
Tel: 01488 608020
Fax: 01488 608030

BLUE LINE
Endeavour House
Stansted Airport
Essex
CM23 4HR
www.blueline.uk.com
email: sales@blueline.uk.com
Tel: 01279 669470
Fax: 01279 669471

BRABIN & FITZ
22 Bridge Street Row
Chester
CH1 1NN
www.brabinandfitz.co.uk
Tel: 01244 314 838
Fax: 01244 349 756

BRETFORD MANUFACTURING LTD
2 Etongate, 110 Windsor Rd
Slough
Berkshire
SL1 2JA
www.bretforduk.com
email: sales@bretforduk.com
Tel: 01753 539955
Fax: 01753 539478

BROOMLEY FURNITURE LTD
West Broomley Farm
Stocksfield, NE43 7HR
www.broomleyfurniture.co.uk
email: enquiries@broomleyfurniture.co.uk
Tel: 01434 682226
Fax: 01434 682576

CASAGUA
82 Mallard Crescent
Poynton, Cheshire, SK12 1HT
www.casagua.com
email: info@casagua.com
Tel: 01625 897508
Fax: 07006017725

CLASSIC UPHOLSTERY
Estate Yard,
Upper Harlestone,
Northampton, NN7 4EH
email: classic.upholstery@btintermet.com
Tel: 01604 584556

COLLINS & HAYES FURNITURE LTD
Menzies Road, Ponswood
St Leonards-On-Sea, Hastings
East Sussex
TN38 9XF
www.collinsandhayes.com
email: mcreedy@collinsandhayes.com
Tel: 01424 720027
Fax: 01424 720270

CHRISTOPHER CLARK WORKSHOPS
Sovereign Way,
Trafalgar Industrial Estate,
Downham Market, Norfolk, PE38 9SW
Tel: 01366 389400
Christopher@christopherclark.co.uk
www.christopherclark.co.uk

Specialists in solid timber, painted & veneered pieces, with established links to affiliates in glass, metal, stone & textiles, no detail is impossible for us to realise. Our flexibility allows us to initiate designs in house or to interpret your requirements. With contracts completed worldwide we have an international reputation & are very proud of our continuing work for many of the top interior designers.

COTSWOLD BESPOKE KITCHENS
Riverside House,
Bridgend Works,Stonehouse,
Gloucestershire
GL10 2BA
www.bespokekitchendesign.co.uk
email: info@bespokekitchendesign.co.uk
Tel: 01453 791222
Fax: 01453 825254

DAEDALIAN LTD
Tel: 01535 640860
Fax: 01535 640861

DOUGLAS HOSKING OAK FURNITURE
33 High Street
Ipswich
Suffolk
IP1 3QH
douglashosking.com
email: sales@douglashosking.com
Tel: 01473 631644
Fax: 01473 631655

DRAKS INTERIOR DOOR SYSTEMS LIMITED
Unit 221 -225 Heyford Park
Upper Heyford
Oxon
OX25 5HA
www.draksonline.co.uk
email: info@draksonline.co.uk
Tel: 01869 232989
Fax: 01869 232979

EMBARK DESIGN
Sunbeam House
Pontefract Lane
Leeds
LS9 0DX
www.embarkdesign.co.uk
email: tim.kiernan@embarkdesign.co.uk
Tel: 0800 138 6688
Fax: 0113 235 9900

ESM
Liberty House
Unit C5
West Mill, Gravesend
DA11 0DL
www.esm-uk.com
email: mail@esm-uk.com
Tel: 01474 536360
Fax: 01474 535822

FAULD TOWN & COUNTRY FURNITURE
email: enquiries@fauld.com
Tel: 01432 851 992

FEEK BVBA
Fao Sofie Couwenberg
Klapdorp 52, B-2000
Antwerp, Belgium
B-2000
www.feek.be
email: info@feek.be
Tel: 0032 3475 1765

FELICITY THORPE INTERIOR DESIGN LTD.
Allfrey's House
Bolney Road
Cowfold
RH13 8AZ
www.felicitythorpeinteriors.co.uk
email: enquiries@felicitythorpeinteriors.co.uk
Tel: 01403 864 784
Fax: 01403 865 035

FERCO SEATING SYSTEMS LTD
Unit 28
Atcham Business Park, Atcham
Shrewsbury, Shropshire
SY4 4UG
www.fercoseating.co.uk
email: info@fercoseating.co.uk
Tel: 0845 8123100
Fax: 0845 8123101

GRANTCF
The Lodge, Holdenhurst
Park Lane, Snitterfield
Stratford Upon Avon
CV37 0LS
www.grantcf.co.uk
email: sales@grantcf.co.uk
Tel: 01789 730380
Fax: 01789 731109

GRANTS MARBLE MANUFACTORY LTD
And Scagliola Workshop
Bradley Mill
Newton Abbot
TQ12 1LZ
www.grantsmarble.com
email: mark@grantsmarble.co.uk
Tel: 01626 331699
Fax: 01626 331699

HATFIELDS RESTORATION
Scholars House
49 Clapham High St
London
SW4 7TL
www.hatfieldsrestoration.com
email: info@hatfieldsrestoration.com
Tel: 0207 622 8169
Fax: 0207 622 2009

HATFIELDS RESTORATION
Scholars House
49 Clapham High St
London
SW4 7TL
www.hatfieldsrestoration.com
email: info@hatfieldsrestoration.com
Tel: 0207 622 8169
Fax: 0207 622 2009

HIGHLY SPRUNG LTD
310 Battersea Park Road London Sw11 3bu
www.highlysprung.net
email: bpr@highlysprung.co.uk
Tel: 02079 241124
Fax: 02072 285476

HOSSACK & GRAY
Studio 10, 9e Queens Yard
Whitepost Lane
London
E9 5EN
hossackandgray.co.uk
email: hossackanggray@hotmail.com
Tel: 02089 863345
Fax: 02089 863345

HOWE
93 Pimlico Road
Belgravia
London
SW1W 8PH
www.howelondon.com
email: design@howelondon.com
Tel: 02(0) 7730 7987
Fax: 02(0) 7730 0157

HYDE HOUSE BESPOKE FURNITURE
289 Lower High Street
Watford
Herts, WD17 2HY
www.hydehouse.co.uk
email: sales@hydehouse.co.uk
Tel: 01284 330 098
Fax: 01923 262 670

I TRE FURNITURE
Sladers Yard
West Bay
Bridport, Dorset, DT6 4EL
www.itre.co.uk
email: info@itrefurniture.co.uk
Tel: 01308 459511

I-DESK SOLUTIONS LTD
11 Ivanhoe Road
Finchampstead
Berkshire, RG40 4QQ
www.i-desk.co.uk
email: info@i-desk.co.uk
Tel: 01189 739700
Fax: 01189 8731058

INEX SERVICE LTD
152 Franciscan Road
London, SW17 8HH
www.inexgroup.com
email: sales@inexgroup.com
Tel: 020 868 22604
Fax: 020 868 22641

J. ROBERT SCOTT
500 North Oak Street
Inglewood
California, 90302
www.jrobertscott.com
email: london@jrobertscott.com
Tel: 001 310 680 4380
Fax: 001 310 680 4323

ISIS FURNITURE
Marches House, 47 Ennerdale Rd,
Shrewsbury, Shropshire, SY1 3LD
Tel: 01743 464 080
Fax: 01743 464 090
Email: info@isis-furniture.co.uk
Website: www.isis-furniture.co.uk
Contact: Oliver Davies / Greg Shaw

Isis manufactures cabinet work and
joinery for high specification interiors.
Typically, this includes bedrooms,
dressing rooms, libraries and kitchens, in
addition to commercial projects for retail
and hotels. Extensive modern
workshops are supported by a strong
design and technical department, to
develop close working relationships with
architects and designers.

JALI HOME DESIGN LIMITED
Albion Works
Church Lane, Barham,
Canterbury
CT4 6QS
www.jali.co.uk
email: sales@jali.co.uk
Tel: 01227 833333
Fax: 01227 831950

JAN CAVELLE FURNITURE COMPANY
Units A&B
25 Rookwood Way
Haverhill
CB9 8PB
www.jancavelle.com
email: sales@jancavelle.com
Tel: 01440 704253
Fax: 01440 761 023

JASPER & CO
The Valdoe
Goodwood
Chichester
PO180PJ
www.jasperco.co.uk
email: info@jasperco.co.uk
Tel: 0844 858 4084
Fax: 0844 858 4085

JMCK LTD
Blaen-Nos
Henllan Amgoed
Whitland
SA34 0SE
email: jmck@btconnect.com
Tel: 01994-448885
Fax: 01994-448885

JOHN BARNARD FURNITURE LTD
60 St. Giles Street
Norwich
Norfolk
NR2 1LW
www.johnbarnard.co.uk
email: design@johnbarnard.co.uk
Tel: 01603 613390
Fax: 01603 761805

JOHN SANKEY
Meadowmead House
Milner Road
Long Eaton
NG10 1LB
www.johnsankey.co.uk†
email: enquiries@johnsankey.co.uk
Tel: 01159 462121
Fax: 01159 460030

KATIE WALKER FURNITURE
Cox Farm Studios
Warnham
West Sussex
RH12 3RZ
www.katiewalkerfurniture.com
email: katie@kwf.biz
Tel: 01403 211323
Fax: 01403 211323

KEMBO
The Horseshoes
Tonbridge Road
Bough Beech
TN8 7AT
www.kembo.co.uk
email: david-goodman@btconnect.com
Tel: 01892 871444
Fax: 01892 871 675

KNOWLES & CHRSITOU
116 Lots Road
Chelsea
London
SW10 0RN
www.knowles-christou.com
email: info@knowles-christou.com
Tel: 02073 527000
Fax: 02073 528877

KUSCH & CO
48/50 St John Street
London
EC1M 4DG
www.kusch.com
email: info-uk@kusch.com
Tel: 02073 367561
Fax: 02073 367562

LAWRENCE WALSH LTD
7 St Clare Business Park
Holly Road
Hampton Hill
TW12 1PZ
www.lawrencewalsh.co.uk
email: info@lawrencewalsh.co.uk
Tel: 02089 418181
Fax: 02089 418101

LITTON FURNITURE
White Lane Close
Sturminster
Dorset
DT10 1EJ
www.littonfurniture.com
email: info@littonfurniture.com
Tel: 01258 472359
Fax: 01258 473542

LOWTHER FINE FURNITURE
East Sessacott Farm
Putford
Devon
EX22 7XG
www.lowtherfinefurniture.co.uk
email: suzi@lowtherfinefurniture.co.uk
Tel: 01409 241 583

MARTIN MOORE & COMPANY
Altrincham
Old Amersham
Esher, Halifax And Fulham
www.martinmoore.com
Tel: 0161 928 2643

MARTIN OAKLEY
43 Sandfield Road
Oxford
OX3 7RN
www.martinoakley.co.uk
email: sales@martinoakley.co.uk
Tel: 01865 742111

MATTHEW BURT
Matthew Burt Showroom
High Street
Hindon, Salisbury
BA12 0SP
www.matthewburt.com
email: furniture@matthewburt.com
Tel: 01747 820511
Fax: 01747 820176

MICHAEL REED DESIGN
Arch 12
Kingsdown Close
London
W10 6SW
www.arch12.com
email: info@arch12.com
Tel: 020 72295391

MARK BRAZIER-JONES
Hyde Hall Barn, Sandon,
Buntingford, Herts, SG9 0RU
Tel: 01763 273599
Fax: 01763 273410
Web: www.brazier-jones.com
Email: studio@brazier-jones.com

Mark Brazier-Jones has been creating
furniture and lighting for over 20
years. Working with precious metals
such as bronze and aluminium, and
glass lenses and crystals on his
lighting, Mark's design has influenced
many. As well as bespoke pieces
unique to individual clients
requirements, Mark has a collection of
work that can be made to order.

MARTIN OAKLEY
43 Sandfield Road, Oxford, OX3 7RN
Contact: Martin Oakley
Tel: 01865 742 111
Email: sales@martinoakley.co.uk
Web: www.martinoakley.co.uk

Martin Oakley has over thirty years
experience in the design and
manufacture of studies, libraries,
bookcases, panelled rooms and
furniture. We work in any timber and
any finish, specialising in 18th and 19th
century styles but also covering earlier
and more contemporary styles.
Please call or email.

ME DESIGN
Unit 2 Period Works
Lammas Road
Leyton
London, E10 7QT
Tel: 0208 988 3814
Email: info@matteltondesign.com
www.matteltondesign.com

ME Design has been successfully
established since 2002. We specialise
in the design and manufacture of
high end furniture and custom
joinery. We also work with architects
and designers on many different
projects. Ranging from restaurants to
bespoke furniture. All our projects are
hand made from our workshop in
East London.

MICKUS PROJECTS
17 Monroe Place
#5a, Brooklyn, Ny, 11201
www.mickusprojects.com
email: info@mprojects.com
Tel: 001 917 843 2285

MIVAN LTD
Newpark
Greystone Road
Antrim, BT41 2QN
www.mivan.com
email: hq@mivan.com
Tel: 02894 481000
Fax: 02894 466338

N E J STEVENSON LTD
Church Lawford Business Centre
Limestone Hall Lane
Church Lawford, CV23 9HD
www.nejstevenson.co.uk
email: neil@nejstevenson.co.uk
Tel: 02476 544662
Fax: 02476 545345

NEST DESIGN
Lassalle
Pessoulens
France
32380
www.nest-design.com
email: info@nest-design.com
Tel: 0033 5 62 67 79 03

NEW FROM OLD
The Engine House
White House Road
Little Ouse
CB7 4TG
www.newfromold.co.uk
email: rick.forward@newfromold.co.uk
Tel: 01353 676227

NIRVANA CHAIRS
Trippet Villa, Sunnyway, Bosham, W.sussex.
United Kingdom.
PO18 8HQ
www.nirvanachairs.com
email: sales@nirvanachairs.com
Tel: 01243 575446
Fax: 01243 575446

NORDPLAN LTD
Sheddingdean Business Park
Marchants Way
Burgess Hill
RH15 8QY
www.nordplan.com
email: sales@nord-plan.co.uk
Tel: 01444 237220
Fax: 01444 237221

NOWY STYL
Walkers Ind Est
Ollerton Road
Tuxford
NG22 0PQ
www.nowystylgroup.co.uk
email: info@nowystylgroup.co.uk
Tel: 01777 872882
Fax: 01777 872885

ODEON DESIGN LTD
76-78 St Edward Street
Leek
Staffordshire
ST13 5 DL
odeonantiques.co.uk
email: odeonantiques@hotmail.com
Tel: 01538 378188
Fax: 01538 384235

OPM FURNITURE LTD
219a, No7 Aldington Road
Woolwich
London
SE18 5TS
Tel: 0208 316 6080
Fax: 0208 316 6079

OPTIONS FITTED FURNITURE
37 Grace Business Centre
Willow Lane
Mitcham
CR4 4TU
www.optionsfit.com
email: optionsfit@btinternet.com
Tel: 02086 851525
Fax: 02086 465261

PARADIGM OFFICE INTERIORS LTD
Unit 1, Wilnecote Lane
Belgrave, Tamworth
Staff's
B77 2LE
www.paradigm-interiors.co.uk
email: info@paradigm-interiors.co.uk
Tel: 0845 434 9717
Fax: 01827 261597

PARMAR AND PARMAR
9 Beechcroft Road
Bushey
Herts
WD23 2JU
www.parmarandparmar.com
email: info@parmarandparmar.com
Tel: 0845 450 3714

PAUL FERGUSON WORKSHOP
Tel: 01525 851594

PERCEVAL DESIGNS

PERCEVAL DESIGNS specialises in antique and new individual pieces. The new pieces all designed by the owner Michael Hilliard and made by local craftspeople incorporate classic form with contemporary artistic flair. Visit **www.percevaldesigns.co.uk** to view the collection or call **01277 354717**.

Pictured and made to order 'The Painted and Parcel Gilt Commode'

PELLFOLD PARTHOS LTD
1 The Quadrant
Howarth Road
Maidenhead, SL6 1AP
www.designs4space.com
email: sales@pellfoldparthos.co.uk
Tel: 01628 773353
Fax: 01628 773363

PIETERSEN
11b Woodway Farm
Bicester Road
Long Crendon, HP18 9EP
www.pietersen.co.uk
email: furniture@pietersen.co.uk
Tel: 01844 201661

POSTURITE LTD
The Mill, Berwick,
East Sussex, BN26 6SZ
www.posturite.co.uk
email: support@posturite.co.uk
Tel: 0845 345 0010
Fax: 0845 345 0020

PW LTD
1 Church Street
Pewsey
Wilts, SN9 5DL
www.pwlimited.co.uk
email: johnny@pwlimited.co.uk
Tel: 01672 562878
Fax: 01672 563043

REAL WOOD STUDIOS LTD
Monteviot Nurseries
Ancrum
Jedburgh
TD8 6TU
www.realwoodstudios.com
email: info@realwoodstudios.com
Tel: 01835 830767

RICHARD BAKER FURNITURE
Wimbledon Studios
257 Burlington Road
New Malden, KT3 4NE
www.richardbakerfurniture.co.uk
email: sales@richardbakerfurniture.co.uk
Tel: 0208 336 1777
Fax: 0208 336 1666

ROBERT MORLEY & CO LTD
34 Engate Street
Lewisham
London, SE13 7HA
morleypianos.co.uk
email: sales@morleypianos.co.uk
Tel: 0208 318 5838

ROSEHILL FURNITURE GROUP
Brooke Court, Handforth,
Wilmslow, SK9 3ND
www.rosehill.co.uk
email: sales@rosehill.co.uk
Tel: 0161 485 1717
Fax: 0161 485 2727

ROSJOHN FURNITURE LTD INC WILLIAM BARTLETT
Unit 8 Abbeymead Ind Estate
Brooker Road
Waltham Abbey, Essex, EN9 1HU
www.rosjohn.com
email: sales@rosjohn.com
Tel: 01992 767353
Fax: 01992 763568

SANT STUDIO
64 Thoroughfare, Woodbridge,
Suffolk, IP12 1AL
www.santstudio.co.uk
email: georginadavid@btinternet.com
Tel: 07791 576786
Fax: 02075 867742

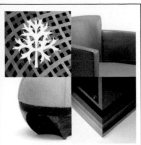

SOMERVILLE SCOTT & COMPANY
Leeder House
6 Erskine Road
London, NW3 3AJ
Tel +44 (0) 207 586 2211
Fax +44 (0) 207 586 2214
Email studio@somervillescott.com
Web www.somervillescott.com

Somerville Scott & Company specialise
in strong contemporary furniture
design made the traditional way in
England. We offer a made-to-measure
collection and work with individuals
and interior designers on bespoke
commissions for both residential and
commercial projects. Our showroom in
Primrose Hill is open by
appointment Monday to Friday.

SAXON CONTRACT FURNITURE
Manchester Road
Bolton
BL3 2NZ
Tel: 01204 365377
Fax: 01204 387554

SHADES OF JAPAN
www.shadesofjapan.net
email: glennjoachim@ntlworld.com
Tel: 01476 594603

SOFA WORKSHOP
122 Hawley Lane
Farnborough
Hampshire
GU14 9AX
www.sofaworkshop.com/information/trade-accounts
email: claire.white@sofaworkshop.com
Tel: 0208 7890793

SPACEOASIS
Grosvenor House
Central Park
Telford
TF2 9TW
www.spaceoasis.co.uk
email: sales@spaceoasis.co.uk
Tel: 01952 210197
Fax: 01952 201303

SPRINGVALE LEATHER
Foundry Street
Rawtenstall
Rossendale
BB4 6HQ
www.springvaleleather.co.uk
email: sarah.foulds@springvaleleather.co.uk
Tel: 01706 211830
Fax: 01706 229170

STUART MELROSE
81 Hangar Rd
Tadley
Hampshire
RG26 4QQ
www.stuartmelrose.com
email: info@stuartmelrose.com
Tel: 0118 982 0239

THE COAT HANGER COMPANY
Awb Ltd
Padholme Road Fast
Peterborough, Cambs, Uk
PE1 5XL
www.thecoathangercompany.com
email: sales@thecoathangercompany.com
Tel: 01733 555646
Fax: 01733 555887

THE CUBE COLLECTION
Po Box 188,
TQ9 9AY
www.thecube.uk.com
email: info@thcube.uk.com
Tel: 01803 712388
Fax: 01803 712388

The Hidden TV Company

Discover more at www.thehiddentvcompany.com
T: 01743 351120   M: 07974015755

Unique bespoke design service of traditional and contemporary tv cabinets, bed end ottomans and furniture.

THE DINING ROOM SHOP
62 White Hart Lane
London SW 130PZ
Tel: 020 8878 1020
Fax: 020 8876 2367
enquiries@thediningroomshop.co.uk
www.thediningroomshop.co.uk

Antique or bespoke furniture in formal
and informal styles for dining rooms and
kitchens is supplied, also dining
accessories, china, cutlery, glass, lighting
and linen. Tablecloths made to order.
Furniture, china, silver and glass
restoration and interior decorating
services a speciality. Established 1985...
well-known destination shop.

THE DAVID KNIGHT COLLECTION & GREENSMITH UPHOLSTERY LIMITED
Greenbank
Coach Drive
Quarndon, Derby, DE22 5JX
www.davidknightcollection.co.uk
thedavidknightcollection@btinternet.com
Tel: 01332 551818
Fax: 01332 557775

THE DESIGN NET LTD
8 Rudolf Place
Miles Street
London, SW8 1RP
www.thedesignnet.co.uk
email: info@thedesignnet.co.uk
Tel: 02078 207771
Fax: 02078 201820

THE HIDDEN TV COMPANY
Coleham Head
Shrewsbury, SY3 7BJ
www.theantiquedealers.com
Tel: 01743 351 120
Fax: 01743 271 047

THE SCAGLIOLA COMPANY
Chapeltown Business Centre
231 Chapeltown Road
Leeds, LS7 3DX
www.scagliolaco.com
email: info@scagliolaco.com
Tel: 01132 626811
Fax: 0113 2626811

THOMAS INTERIORS
Madges Farm House, Chearsley Road,
Long Crendon, HP18 9AW
www.thomasinteriors.co.uk
email: info@thomasinteriors.co.uk
Tel: 01844 201 254
Fax: 01844 208 533

TIM WOOD LTD
29a Niton Street
Fulham
London
SW6 6NH
www.timwood.com
Tel: 020 7385 7228
Fax: 0870 063 5139

TIMOTHY MARK LTD
20 New Quebec Street
London
W1H 7RZ
www.timothymark.co,uk
email: info@timothymark.co.uk
Tel: 020 7616 9390
Fax: 020 7616 9389

TOBY WINTERINGHAM
Whitehouse
Bawsey
King's Lynn
PE32 1EY
www.tobywinteringham.co.uk
email: info@tobywinteringham.co.uk
Tel: 01553 841829
Fax: 01553 841829

TWIN DESIGN
1-2 Legge Lane
Jewellery Quarter
Birmingham
B1 3LD
www.twin-design.co.uk
email: info@twin-design.co.uk
Tel: 0121 258 2574
Fax: 0121 258 2594

USKEN FURNITURE
The Coach House
138 Wingfield Road
Plymouth, Devon
PL3 4ER
www.usken.co.uk
email: info@usken.co.uk
Tel: 0870 067 7807

WANT STUDIO
Unit 5a
Randswood Farm
West Wratting, Cambs
CB21 5LR
www.wantstudio.co.uk
email: info@wantstudio.co.uk
Tel: 01223 290 022

WESLEY-BARRELL
Ducklington Mill
Standlake Road
Ducklington
OX29 7YR
www.wesley-barrell.co.uk
email: furniture@wesley-barrell.co.uk
Tel: 01993 893 100
Fax: 01993 702720

WOODCHESTER KITCHENS & INTERIORS LTD
Unit 18a
Chalford Industrial Estate
Chalford, Glos
GL6 8NT
www.woodchesterkitchens.co.uk
email: chris@woodchesterkitchens.co.uk
Tel: 01453 886411
Fax: 01453 886411

WOODTEAM LTD
Unit 7 Falcon Business Park
Meadow Lane
Loughborough
LE11 1HL
www.woodteam.co.uk
email: sales @woodteam.co.uk
Tel: 01509 262000
Fax: 01509 260718

BUILT-IN & FITTED FURNITURE

BLUE LINE
Endeavour House
Stansted Airport
Essex
CM23 4HR
www.blueline.uk.com
email: sales@blueline.uk.com
Tel: 01279 669470
Fax: 01279 669471

ESM
Liberty House
Unit C5
West Mill, Gravesend
DA11 ODL
www.esm-uk.com
email: mail@esm-uk.com
Tel: 01474 536360
Fax: 01474 535822

HOG PLC
14 West Place, West Road
Harlow
Essex
CM20 2GY
www.hogdirect.co.uk
email: sales@hogplc.com
Tel: 01279 638250
Fax: 01279 641904

INSIDE OUT CONTRACTS
13 Nelson Road
Greenwich
London
SE10 9JB
www.insideoutcontracts.com
email: mail@insideoutcontracts.com
Tel: 020 8305 3130
Fax: 020 8305 3131

JASPER & CO
The Valdoe
Goodwood
Chichester
PO180PJ
www.jasperco.co.uk
email: info@jasperco.co.uk
Tel: 0844 858 4084
Fax: 0844 858 4085

JRO DESIGN KITCHENS WORKS
220 Great Western Road
Glasgow
G4 9EJ
www.kitchenworksglasgow.co.uk
email: jrokitworks@aol.com
Tel: 01413 339602
Fax: 01413 339604

LAWRENCE WALSH LTD
7 St Clare Business Park
Holly Road
Hampton Hill, TW12 1PZ
www.lawrencewalsh.co.uk
email: info@lawrencewalsh.co.uk
Tel: 02089 418181
Fax: 02089 418101

NEATSMITH
Unit D
The Apsley Centre
Apsley Way
London
NW2 7LZ
Tel: 0800 1956 595
Web: www.neatsmith.co.uk

Neatsmith specialise in the manufacture, supply and installation of Bespoke Luxury Sliding Door Wardrobes and Walk-In Dressing Rooms. All our products can be viewed in our North London Showroom. Supply, Delivery or Full Installation service available.

OPTIONS FITTED FURNITURE
37 Grace Business Centre
Willow Lane
Mitcham, CR4 4TU
www.optionsfit.com
email: optionsfit@btinternet.com
Tel: 02086 851525
Fax: 02086 465261

PIETERSEN
11b Woodway Farm
Bicester Road
Long Crendon, HP18 9EP
www.pietersen.co.uk
email: furniture@pietersen.co.uk
Tel. 01844 201661

SHUTTER FRONTIER LTD
2 Rosemary Farmhouse, Rosemary Lane,
Flimwell, East Sussex, Tn5 7pt
TN5 7PT
www.shutterfrontier.co.uk
email: jane@shutterfrontier.co.uk
Tel: 01580 879761 / 07708 229 295

SIMPLY SCANDINAVIAN
70 Flaxman Road
London
SE5 9DH
www.simply-scandinavian.co.uk
Tel: 0207 095 8400
Fax: 07766 663960

SOLOMON'S SEAL (KKM) LTD
45 High Street
Odiham
Hampshire
RG29 1LF
www.solomonsseal.co.uk
email: info@solomonsseal.co.uk
Tel: 01256 703833
Fax: 01256 703962

SPACESLIDE
Tel: 01922 743211
Email: sales@porticomidlands.co.uk
Web: www.spaceslide.co.uk

Spaceslide offers the biggest range of sliding wardrobe doors and storage systems in the UK and has featured on TV design shows including "The Home Show" and "60 Minute Makeover". Products include stylish and versatile sliding wardrobe and internal doors, and matching home delivered made-to-measure bedside draws and cabinet units.

TIM WOOD LTD
29a Niton Street
Fulham
London
SW6 6NH
www.timwood.com
Tel: 020 7385 7228
Fax: 0870 063 5139

TIMOTHY MARK LTD
20 New Quebec Street
London
W1H 7RZ
www.timothymark.co.uk
email: info@timothymark.co.uk
Tel: 020 7616 9390
Fax: 020 7616 9389

USKEN FURNITURE
The Coach House
138 Wingfield Road
Plymouth, Devon, PL3 4ER
www.usken.co.uk
email: info@usken.co.uk
Tel: 0870 067 7807

WANT STUDIO
Unit 5a Randswood Farm
West Wratting, Cambs, CB21 5LR
www.wantstudio.co.uk
email: info@wantstudio.co.uk
Tel: 01223 290 022

WOODCHESTER KITCHENS & INTERIORS LTD
Unit 18a
Chalford Industrial Estate
Chalford, Glos, GL6 8NT
www.woodchesterkitchens.co.uk
email: chris@woodchesterkitchens.co.uk
Tel: 01453 886411
Fax: 01453 886411

CHILDREN'S FURNITURE

COSATTO LTD
Bentinck Mill, Bentinck Street
Farnworth
Bolton
BL4 7EP
www.cosatto.com
email: enquiry@cosatto.com
Tel: +44 (0)870 050 5900
Fax: +44 (0)870 050 5903

FLEXA
Bjornkjaervej 16
Hornsyld
Denmark
8783
www.flexa.dk
email: flexa@flexa.dk
Tel: +45 7668 8055
Fax: +45 7668 8069

ONE CALL FURNITURE
www.1cfl.com†
Iel: 08451 084 084

PROJEKTER INDUSTRIAL DESIGN
Springwall 4
47051 Duisburg
Germany
www.projekter.de
email: contact@playzzle.de
Tel: 0049 203 728 1827

STEENS FURNITURE
Unit 5 Berrywood Business Village
Hedge End
Southampton, SO30 2UN
www.steens.dk
email: sales@steens.dk
Tel: 01489 778890
Fax: 01489 796408

PLACES AND SPACES
30 Old Town,
Clapham,
London, SW4 0LB
Tel: 02074980998
Email: contact@placesandspaces.com
Web: www.placesandspaces.com

Nurseries through to teenage rooms - we offer rugs, lighting, storage, tables, beds, wall decoration and toys. Places and Spaces is a retail shop with a shopping service to help you source the right products for your home. Pictured – Stones can make a space come alive! A collection of pebbles that can work individually or as a cluster of seats or scatter cushions.

INTERIOR DESIGN TODAY

THE TRADE ONLY MAGAZINE FOR INTERIOR DESIGN PROFESSIONALS   NOV/DEC 2009 £5.95

PRODUCT DESIGNS

LIGHTING

BATHROOMS

DECOREX
CHELSEA WAS
CHARMED BY THE
STUNNING CREATIVITY
ON DISPLAY

100% DESIGN
THE COMPANIES AT THE TOP OF
OUR LIST ARE REVEALED IN LIGHT
OF THE RECENT SHOW

A HISTORY OF
GOOD DESIGN
BRINTON'S STEPS BACK IN TIME TO
REVEAL OUR MOST POWERFUL
DESIGN INFLUENCES

IDTMAGAZINE.CO.UK

it's a personal experience   VADO

STICKYUPS
1-6 Clay Street
London, W1U 6DA
www.stickyups.com
email: sales@stickyups.com
Tel: 0845 257 0642

CONTRACT FURNITURE

ACT FURNITURE MANUFACTURERS LTD
Salop Street
Bradley
Bilston, WV14 0TQ
www.actfurniture.com
email: sales@actfurniture.com
Tel: 01902 490273
Fax: 01902 490275

ALLERMUIR
Altham Business Park
Accrington
Lancashire, BB5 5YE
email: sales@allermuir.com
Tel: 01254 682421
Fax: 01254 673793

ATTIC 2
Unit 1
127 Bute Street
Cardiff Bay, CF10 5LE
www.attic2.co.uk
email: lynsey@attic2.co.uk
Tel: 02920 490498

BARLOW TYRIE LTD
Springwood Industrial Estate
Braintree
Essex
CM7 2RN
www.teak.com
email: devans@teak.com
Tel: 01376 557 600
Fax: 0870 460 1100

BURGESS FURNITURE LTD
Hanworth Trading Estate
Feltham
Middlesex
TW13 6EH
www.burgessfurniture.com
email: sales@burgessfurniture.com
Tel: 020 8894 9231
Fax: 020 8894 2943

CLASSIC FURNITURE GROUP LTD
Audley Avenue
Newport
Shropshire, TF10 7BX
www.classicfurniture.co.uk
email: sales@classicfurniture.co.uk
Tel: 01952 825000
Fax: 01952 811948

CONNECTION SEATING LTD
15 Great Sutton Street
Clerkenwell
London, EC1V 0BX
www.connection.uk.com
email: sales@connection.uk.com
Tel: 0207 2539877
Fax: 01484 600125

DINING CHAIRS U K
Unit 7
Oxton Road
Epperstone
NG14 6AT
www.diningchairsuk.com
email: sales@diningchairsuk.com
Tel: 01159 655302
Fax: 01159 656189

DOVETAIL CONTRACT FURNITURE LTD
8 St Johns Lane
Clerkenwell
London
EC1M 4BF
www.dovetailfurniture.com
email: iweddell@dovetaillondon.com
Tel: 02078 689000
Fax: 02078 689009

EDEN CONTRACT FURNITURE
Unit 12 Weights Farm Business Park
Weights Lane
Redditch
B97 6RG
www.edencontractfurniture.co.uk
email: sales@edencontractfurniture.co.uk
Tel: 01527 592455
Fax: 08450 536001

EFFEZETA S.P.A
Via Manzano 70/1
Premariacco (Ud)
Italy
33040
www.effezeta.it
email: info@effezeta.it
Tel: 0039 0432 706501
Fax: 0039 0432 706533

EME FURNITURE
Blackaddie Road
Sanquhar
Dumfriesshire
DG4 6DE
www.emefurniture.co.uk
email: info@emefurniture.co.uk
Tel: 01659 50404
Fax: 01659 50107

FEBLAND GROUP
Ashworth Road, Marton,
Blackpool, Lancs, FY4 4UN
www.febland.co.uk
email: info@febland.co.uk
Tel: 01253 600 600
Fax: 01253 792211

FERCO SEATING SYSTEMS LTD
Unit 28
Atcham Business Park, Atcham
Shrewsbury, Shropshire, SY4 4UG
www.fercoseating.co.uk
email: info@fercoseating.co.uk
Tel: 0845 8123100
Fax: 0845 8123101

FIGUERAS SEATING UK
www.figueras.com
email: info@figueras.com
Tel: +34 93 844 50 50
Fax: +34 93 844 50 61

FRAMES FURNITURE
Cockaynes Orchard
Cockaynes Lane
Alresford, CO7 8BZ
www.framesuk.com
email: enquiries@framesuk.com
Tel: 01206 820301
Fax: 01206 820221

HITCH MYLIUS LTD
301 Alma Road
Enfield
Middlesex
EN3 7BB
www.hitchmylius.co.uk
email: info@hitchmylius.co.uk
Tel: 020 8443 2616
Fax: 020 8443 2617

INDIGO FURNITURE LTD
22 Dale Road
Matlock
Derbyshire
DE4 3LT
www.indigofurniture.co.uk
email: sales@indigofurniture.co.uk
Tel: 01629 581800

INFORM FURNITURE LIMITED
99 St John's Hill
London
SW11 1SY
www.informfurniture.co.uk
email: info@informfurniture.co.uk
Tel: 020 7228 3335
Fax: 020 7924 5955

INOVA FURNITURE CONTRACTS
75b Great Eastern St
London, EC2A 3HN
www.inovafurniture.com
email: brent@inovafurniture.com
Tel: 02077 392300
Fax: 02077 392336

INSIDE OUT CONTRACTS
13 Nelson Road
Greenwich
London, SE10 9JB
www.insideoutcontracts.com
email: mail@insideoutcontracts.com
Tel: 020 8305 3130
Fax: 020 8305 3131

JAN CAVELLE FURNITURE COMPANY
Units A&B
25 Rookwood Way
Haverhill, CB9 8PB
www.jancavelle.com
email: sales@jancavelle.com
Tel: 01440 704253
Fax: 01440 761 023

JT CONTRACT MARKETING LTD
46 Anhalt Road
London
SW11 4NX
www.parridesign.it
email: jtcontract@waitrose.com
Tel: 02078 010206
Fax: 02078 010207

KESTERPORT LTD
Kestrel House
Hanworth Lane
Chertsey, Surrey
KT16 9JX
www.kesterport.com
email: contractsales@kesterport.com
Tel: 01932 573 600
Fax: 01932 573 698

KNIGHTSBRIDGE FURNITURE
191 Thornton Rd
Bradford
BD1 2JT
Tel: 01274 731900
Fax: 01274 - 736641

KOEHL UK LTD
5 Coopers Drive
Bexley Grange
Dartford
DA2 7WS
www.koehl.co.uk
email: sales@koehl.co.uk
Tel: 01322 551082
Fax: 01322 310302

KUSCH & CO
48/50 St John Street
London
EC1M 4DG
www.kusch.com
email: info-uk@kusch.com
Tel: 02073 367561
Fax: 02073 367562

MHF CONTRACT FURNITURE LTD
The Hollins, Merrington,
Shrewsbury, SY4 3QF
www.mhf-furniture.co.uk
email: info@mhf-furniture.co.uk
Tel: 01939 290280
Fax: 01939 291173

MODUS FURNITURE
5 Westcombe Trading Estate
Station Road
Ilminster, SOMERSET
www.modusfurniture.co.uk
email: info@modusfurniture.co.uk
Tel: 01460 258590
Fax: 01460 57004

MOMENTUM
31 Charles Street
Cardiff, CF10 2GA
www.momentumcardiff.com
email: info@momentumcardiff.com
Tel: 02920 236266
Fax: 02920 236311

MOVISI GMBH
Burghaldenweg 62-64
70469 Stuttgart, Germany
www.movisi.com
email: info@movisi.com
Tel: 0049 711 505 5485
Fax: 0049 711 505 1368

NORTHCROFT LIMITED
Argall Works
Argall Avenue
London, E10 7QE
www.michaelnorthcroft.com
email: info@michaelnorthcroft.com
Tel: 0208 558 6919
Fax: 0208 558 1097

NOWY STYL
Walkers Ind Est
Ollerton Road, Tuxford, NG22 0PQ
www.nowystylgroup.co.uk
email: info@nowystylgroup.co.uk
Tel: 01777 872882
Fax: 01777 872885

ONE CALL FURNITURE
www.1cfl.com†
Tel: 08451 084 084

OPTIONS FITTED FURNITURE
37 Grace Business Centre
Willow Lane
Mitcham, CR4 4TU
www.optionsfit.com
email: optionsfit@btinternet.com
Tel: 02086 851525
Fax: 02086 465261

PROTOCOL LTD
2-3 Bankside Park, 28 Thames Road
Barking
Essex, IG11 0HZ
www.protocoluk.com
email: sales@protocoluk.com
Tel: 0208 5916770
Fax: 0208 5917913

PTT DESIGN LTD
Bleachers Yard
Radford Road
Nottingham
NG7 7EF
www.pttdesign.com
email: info@pttdesign.com
Tel: 01159 420014
Fax: 01159 422155

PURVES & PURVES CONTRACTS
7 Mill Farm Business Park
Millfield Road
Hounslow, TW4 5PY
www.purves-contracts.co.uk
email: contracts@purves.co.uk
Tel: 020 8898 2318
Fax: 020 8893 4024

SAXON CONTRACT FURNITURE
Manchester Road
Bolton
BL3 2NZ
Tel: 01204 365377
Fax: 01204 387554

SICO EUROPE LTD
The Link Park
Lympne Industrial Estate
Lympne, Kent
CT21 4LR
www.sico-europe.com
email: sales@sico-europe.com
Tel: 01303 234000
Fax: 01303 234001

SPACEOASIS
Grosvenor House
Central Park
Telford
TF2 9TW
www.spaceoasis.co.uk
email: sales@spaceoasis.co.uk
Tel: 01952 210197
Fax: 01952 201303

SPATIAL FURNITURE
272 Bath Street,
Glasgow, G2 4JR
www.spatialfurniture.co.uk
email: info@spatialfurniture.co.uk
Tel: 0141 353 9553
Fax: 0141 353 9555

SPRINGVALE LEATHER
Foundry Street
Rawtenstall
Rossendale
BB4 6HQ
www.springvaleleather.co.uk
email: sarah.foulds@springvaleleather.co.uk
Tel: 01706 211830
Fax: 01706 229170

SWANKY DESIGN
Po Box 6786
Kettering
Northamptonshire
NN16 8ZS
www.swankydesign.com
email: info@swankydesign.com
Tel: 01536 524240
Fax: 01536 520689

THE MARBLE FURNITURE COMPANY
Unit 7
Peel Park Works
Peel Park View, Bradford
BD3 0JY
www.marblefurnitureco.com
email: contracts@marblefurnitureco.com
Tel: 01274 638811

THOMAS INTERIORS
Madges Farm House
Chearsley Road
Long Crendon
HP18 9AW
www.thomasinteriors.co.uk
email: info@thomasinteriors.co.uk
Tel: 01844 201 254
Fax: 01844 208 533

TWIN DESIGN
1-2 Legge Lane
Jewellery Quarter
Birmingham
B1 3LD
www.twin-design.co.uk
email: info@twin-design.co.uk
Tel: 0121 258 2574
Fax: 0121 258 2594

VICCARBE
Trav. Camí El Racú 1 P.i Norte Beniparrell.
Valencia
46469
www.viccarbe.com
email: info@viccarbe.com
Tel: 0034 961201010
Fax: 0034 961211211

WESTMINSTER
Westminster House
Bellbrook Business Park
Uckfield, East Sussex
TN221QZ
www.westminsterfurniture.eu
email: sales@westminsterfurniture.eu
Tel: +44 (0)1825 764222
Fax: +44 (0)1825 749444

WILKHAHN LTD
Morelands
5-23 Old Street
London
EC1V 9HL
www.wilkhahn.com
email: greg@wilkhahn.co.uk
Tel: 02073 242900
Fax: 02073 242901

WILLIS & GAMBIER
Kingston Park
Flaxley Road
Peterborough
PE2 9EN
www.wguk.com
Tel: 0845 606 7004

WRIGHTS FINE FURNITURE LTD
Stretton Heath
Yockleton
Shrewsbury
SY5 9QQ
www.wrightsfinefurniture.com
email: margo@wrightsfinefurniture.com
Tel: 01743 821800
Fax: 01743 821333

DESIGNER FURNITURE

56 FW635 FW629 FW596 FW594 FW591 FW590 FW455 FW416 FW414 FU287 FGC09

68 FW663 FW655 FW654 FW653 FW637C FW634 FW622 FW636

W639 FW638 FW628 FW627 FW570 FU127 FU145 FW541

U58 FGU313 FGU226

FEBLAND GROUP LTD
ASHWORTH ROAD
BLACKPOOL
LANCS, FY4 4UN
TEL: 01253 600600
INFO@FEBLAND.CO.UK
WWW.FEBLAND.CO.UK

FGU56 FGU72 FGU160LR

LM75G LST10 LW368T/3 LW368C/3 LW365S/4

637 FM639 FM633 FM638 FM635 FM632 FM410 FM629

W642 FW666 FW644 FW646 FW648

DINING FURNITURE

4 FRONT FURNITURE
1a Valley House, 9 Harbet Road
(Entrance On Blackwood Avenue)
London
N18 3QP
www.4ff.co.uk
email: info@4ff.co.uk
Tel: 020 8803 6446
Fax: 020 8803 6556

BELVEDERE
11 Dove Street
Ipswich
IP4 1NG
www.belvederereproductions.co.uk†
Tel: 01473 214573

BLUE BONE IMPORTS LIMITED
River Mill 2
Park Road
Dukinfield
SK16 5PD
www.bluebone.co.uk
email: manchester@bluebone.co.uk
Tel: 0161 330 8959
Fax: 0161 330 8949

BRETZ
Alexander-Bretz-Street 2
55116 Gensingen
Germany
55116
www.bretz.com
email: cultsofa@bretz.de
Tel: 0049 672 78 950
Fax: 0049 676 21 030

CAPRICORN IMPORTS LTD
Unit 1
Greendale Business Park
Woodbury Salterton
EX5 1EW
www.capricornimports.co.k
email: sales@capricornimports.co.uk
Tel: 01395 233320
Fax: 01395 233554

CHARLES PAGE FURNITURE & INTERIOR DESIGN
61 Fairfax Road
Swiss Cottage
London
NW6 4EE
www.charlespage.co.uk
email: info@charlespage.co.uk
Tel: 02073 289851
Fax: 02073 287240

DOUGLAS HOSKING OAK FURNITURE
33 High Street
Ipswich
Suffolk
IP1 3QH
douglashosking.com
email: sales@douglashosking.com
Tel: 01473 631644
Fax: 01473 631655

ERCOL FURNITURE LTD
Summerleys Road
Princes Risborough
Bucks
HP27 9PX
www.ercol.com
email: edward.tadros@ercol.com
Tel: 01844 271 800
Fax: 01844 271887

ETHNICRAFT
Scheldeweg 5
Boom
Belgium
2850
www.ethnicraft.com
email: alf@ethnicraft.com
Tel: 00323 443 0126
Fax: 00323 443 0127

FAULD TOWN & COUNTRY FURNITURE
email: enquiries@fauld.com
Tel: 01432 851 992

GURU
www.guru-design.com†
email: info@guru-design.com
Tel: 020 8960 6655

GUSTAVIAN
59 Lancaster Avenue
Hadley Wood
EN4 0ER
www.gustavian.com
email: info@gustavian.com
Tel: 0208 440 8043
Fax: 020 8216 3640

H. J. BERRY
Kirk Mills
Chipping
Preston
PR3 2RA
www.hjberry.co.uk
email: sales@hjberry.co.uk
Tel: 01995 61226
Fax: 01995 61512

HAMMEL FURNITURE
Anbaekvej 111
Dk - Hammel
8450
hammel-furniture.dk
email: sales@hammel-furniture.dk
Tel: 045 8963 1577
Fax: 045 8963 1588

HULSTA FURNITURE U K LTD
5th Floor
2 Conduit Street
London
W1S 2XB
www.hulsta.co.uk
email: sales@huelsta.co.uk
Tel: 02073 188000
Fax: 02074 092417

I TRE FURNITURE
Sladers Yard
West Bay
Bridport, Dorset
DT6 4EL
www.itre.co.uk
email: info@itrefurniture.co.uk
Tel: 01308 459511

INEX SERVICE LTD
152 Franciscan Road
London
SW17 8HH
www.inexgroup.com
email: sales@inexgroup.com
Tel: 020 868 22604
Fax: 020 868 22641

INSIDE OUT CONTRACTS
13 Nelson Road
Greenwich
London
SE10 9JB
www.insideoutcontracts.com
email: mail@insideoutcontracts.com
Tel: 020 8305 3130
Fax: 020 8305 3131

JAMES ADAM FURNITURE LTD
26, Quayside
Woodbridge
Suffolk
IP12 1BH
www.jamesadam.com
email: sales@jamesadam.com
Tel: 01394 384471
Fax: 01394 384520

JEREMY LOXTON & COMPANY
P O Box 5588
Thatcham
RG19 8XY
Tel: 0870 385 1086
Fax: 0870 385 1086

JMCK LTD
Blaen-Nos
Henllan Amgoed
Whitland
SA34 0SE
email: jmck@btconnect.com
Tel: 01994-448885
Fax: 01994-448885

KNIGHTSBRIDGE FURNITURE
191 Thornton Rd
Bradford
BD1 2JT
Tel: 01274 731900
Fax: 01274 - 736641

LCF (LAMATA CONTRACT FURNITURE) LTD
The Barlands
London Road
Cheltenham
GL52 6UT
www.lamata.co.uk
email: info@lamata.co.uk
Tel: 01242 524777
Fax: 01242 233031

MAKASIHOME
138 Oatlands Drive
Weybridge
Surrey
KT13 9HJ
www.makasihome.co.uk
email: info@makasihome.co.uk
Tel: 01932 860841
Fax: 01932 860841

MARK STODDART INTERNATIONAL DESIGNER
Ladybank House
Ladybank
Turnberry
KA26 9JJ
www.markstoddart.com
email: info@markstoddart.com
Tel: 01292 443 103

MYAKKA LTD
Tythings Commercial Centre
Wincanton
Somerset BA9 9EQ
www.myakka.co.uk
email: sales@myakka.co.uk
Tel: 0845 460 3122

NORTHCROFT LIMITED
Argall Works
Argall Avenue
London E10 7QE
www.michaelnorthcroft.com
email: info@michaelnorthcroft.com
Tel: 0208 558 6919
Fax: 0208 558 1097

PAVILLION RATTAN
The Ulvers Building
Budby Road
Notts, NG20 - 9JP
www.pavilionrattan.co.uk
email: sales@pavilionrattan.co.uk
Tel: 01623 847030
Fax: 0870 706 2159

RACK AND RUIN
Pump House
Kirkby Malzeard
Ripon, North Yorkshire
HG4 3RY
www.rackandruin.com
email: info@rackandruin.com
Tel: 0845 330 8897

ROCHE BOBOIS UK
Smugglers Way
By Wandsworth Bridge
London
SW18 1AZ
www.roche-bobois.com
email: info.uk@roche-bobois.com
Tel: 0208 874 9818
Fax: 0208 874 9798

STEENS FURNITURE
Unit 5 Berrywood Business Village
Hedge End
Southampton, SO30 2UN
www.steens.dk
email: sales@steens.dk
Tel: 01489 778890
Fax: 01489 796408

SYLVAWOOD FURNITURE
The Old Workshops
Longbridge Deverill
Wiltshire BA12 7DP
www.sylvawoodfurniture.co.uk
email: sales@sylvawoodfurniture.co.uk
Tel: 01985 840012
Fax: 01985 840781

THE MARBLE FURNITURE COMPANY
Unit 7
Peel Park Works
Peel Park View, Bradford, BD3 0JY
www.marblefurnitureco.com
email: contracts@marblefurnitureco.com
Tel: 01274 638811

TOM FAULKNER
Chelsea Reach
79/89 Lots Rd
London, SW10 0RN
www.tomfaulkner.co.uk
email: info@tomfaulkner.co.uk
Tel: 020 7351 7272
Fax: 020 7352 7620

VINCENT SHEPPARD
Industriepark 5
Spiere - Belgium 8587
www.vincentsheppard.com
email: uk@vincentsheppard.com
Tel: 0032 5646 1111
Fax: 0032 56461112

WESLEY-BARRELL
Ducklington Mill
Standlake Road
Ducklington, OX29 7YR
www.wesley-barrell.co.uk
email: furniture@wesley-barrell.co.uk
Tel: 01993 893 100
Fax: 01993 702720

WILLIS & GAMBIER
Kingston Park, Flaxley Road,
Peterborough, PE2 9EN
www.wguk.com
Tel: 0845 606 7004

YP FUNITURE LTD
Corringham Road Industrial Estate
Gainsborough
Lincs, DN21 1QB
Tel: 01664 434 188

FENDER SEATS

ROCKINGHAM FENDER SEATS
Grange Farm
Thorney
Peterborough, PE6 0PJ
Tel: 01733 270233
Evening Tel: 01780 444391
Mob: 07860 361323
Fax: 01733 270512
E-mail: info@fenderseats.com
www.rockingham-fenderseats.com

Rockingham Fender Seats make bespoke
fireside surrounds for both period and
contemporary properties. They provide
extra seating around the fireplace taking
up very little valuable space. They are
made in many different designs and
materials, including antiqued or polished
brass, bronze and copper, burnished or
polished steel, woods (oak / mahogany),
or any combination of these.

ACRES FARM CLUB FENDERS
Acres Farm
Bradfield
Nr Reading
RG7 6JH
www.acresfarm.co.uk
email: enquiries@acresfarm.co.uk
Tel: 01189 744305
Fax: 01189 744012

FURNITURE DESIGNERS
AQUA CREATIONS
Ben Zvi Road,
Tel Aviv, 68103
email: albi@aquagallery.com
Tel: 0097 23551227
Fax: 00972 35151223

ATELIER GAGNIÈRE CRÈATEUR DE MEUBLES
Zone Artisanale De Lecheraine
Lanslebourg Mont-Cenis
France Alpes
73480
www.atelier-gagniere.com
email: contact@atelier-gagniere.com
Tel: +33 (0)479 563 570
Fax: +33 (0)479 563 570

ATTIC 2
Unit 1
127 Bute Street
Cardiff Bay, CF10 5LE
www.attic2.co.uk
email: lynsey@attic2.co.uk
Tel: 02920 490498

BOWLES & LINARES
www.bowlesandlinares.co.uk
email: info@bowlesandlinares.co.uk
Tel: 0207 229 9886

BROOMLEY FURNITURE LTD
West Broomley Farm
Stocksfield, NE43 7HR
www.broomleyfurniture.co.uk
email: enquiries@broomleyfurniture.co.uk
Tel: 01434 682226
Fax: 01434 682576

COURTNEY CONTRACT FURNISHERS LTD
J&K Enterprise Centre
Paycocke Road
Basildon
SS14 3DY
www.courtney-contracts.co.uk
email: info@courtney-contracts.co.uk
Tel: 01268 531771
Fax: 01268 271299

CHRISTOPHER CLARK WORKSHOPS
Sovereign Way,
Trafalgar Industrial Estate,
Downham Market, Norfolk, PE38 9SW
Tel: 01366 389400
Christopher@christopherclark.co.uk
www.christopherclark.co.uk

Highly skilled team of experienced
furniture designers, manufacturers &
finishers offering a complete design to
manufacture service of exceptional
quality made bade furniture. Unique
pieces can include collaboration with
specialists in glass, metal, stone &
textiles. We can handle individual pieces
or production runs for commercial or
residential projects.

DAEDALIAN LTD
Tel: 01535 640860
Fax: 01535 640861

DAVID COLWELL DESIGN
Trannon Studio, Llawr Y Glyn, Caersws, Powys.
SY17 5RH
www.davidcolwell.com
email: info@davidcolwell.com
Tel: 01686 430434

DECORATIVE LIVING
The Studio
CHISWICK LONDON W4
www.decorativeliving.co.uk
email: info@decorativeliving.co.uk
Tel: 020 89950037

DRAWING OFFICE FURNITURE LTD
1 Kinkell
St Johns Road
New Milton
BH25 5SD
www.art-drawingoffice.co.uk
email: sales@drawingoffice.org.uk
Tel: 01425 625160
Fax: 01425 625161

GIRSBERGER
Invicta House
4th Floor
108-114 Golden Lane, London
EC1Y 0TG
www.girsberger.com
email: infouk@girsberger.com
Tel: 0207 490 3223
Fax: 0207 490 5665

GUILLAUME PIECHAUD
2, Rue De La Libert
93600 Aulnay Sous Bois
France
www.guillaumepiechaud.com
email: contact@guillaumepiechaud.com
Tel: 0033 1486 61504

I TRE FURNITURE
Sladers Yard
West Bay
Bridport, Dorset
DT6 4EL
www.itre.co.uk
email: info@itrefurniture.co.uk
Tel: 01308 459511

JOE EARLEY DESIGN
Mallards Cottage, South Gren Road
Fingringhoe, Colchester
Essex
CO5 DR
www.earleybrothers.com
email: joe@earleybrothers.com
Tel: 07909994860

JOHN SANKEY
Meadowmead House
Milner Road
Long Eaton
NG10 1LB
www.johnsankey.co.uk†
email: enquiries@johnsankey.co.uk
Tel: 01159 462121
Fax: 01159 460030

KABILJO INC.
Gonzagagasse 5, Vienna, Austria
1010
www.kabiljo.com
email: wisdom@kabiljo.com
Tel: +43 1 5321094

KATIE WALKER FURNITURE
Cox Farm Studios
Warnham
West Sussex
RH12 3RZ
www.katiewalkerfurniture.com
email: katie@kwf.biz
Tel: 01403 211323
Fax: 01403 211323

KNIGHTSBRIDGE FURNITURE
191 Thornton Rd
Bradford
BD1 2JT
Tel: 01274 731900
Fax: 01274 - 736641

LOWTHER FINE FURNITURE
East Sessacott Farm
Putford
Devon
EX22 7XG
www.lowtherfinefurniture.co.uk
email: suzi@lowtherfinefurniture.co.uk
Tel: 01409 241 583

LP FURNITURE
The Old Brewery
Short Acre Street
Walsall West Midlands
WS2 8HW
www.lpfurniture.net†
email: frenchfurniture@btconnect.com
Tel: 01922 746764
Fax: 01922 611316

MARK STODDART INTERNATIONAL DESIGNER
Ladybank House
Ladybank
Turnberry
KA26 9JJ
www.markstoddart.com
email: info@markstoddart.com
Tel: 01292 443 103

MATTHEW BURT
Matthew Burt Showroom
High Street
Hindon, Salisbury
BA12 0SP
www.matthewburt.com
email: furniture@matthewburt.com
Tel: 01747 820511
Fax: 01747 820176

N E J STEVENSON LTD
Church Lawford Business Centre
Limestone Hall Lane
Church Lawford
CV23 9HD
www.nejstevenson.co.uk
email: neil@nejstevenson.co.uk
Tel: 02476 544662
Fax: 02476 545345

NEO DESIGN
Herdeckerstr. 26
58453 WITTEN
www.neo-studios.de
email: info@neo-studios.de
Tel: 0049 2302 202 76 28
Fax: 0049 2302 202 76 28

NEST DESIGN
Lassalle
Pessoulens
France
32380
www.nest-design.com
email: info@nest-design.com
Tel: 0033 5 62 67 79 03

PINCH DESIGN
www.pinchdesign.com
email: studio@pinchdesign.com
Tel: 020 7501 9262

REAL WOOD STUDIOS LTD
Monteviot Nurseries
Ancrum
Jedburgh
TD8 6TU
www.realwoodstudios.com
email: info@realwoodstudios.com
Tel: 01835 830767

REINHARD DESIGN
Kyffhaeuserstrasse 7
Koeln
D- 50674
www.claasreinhard.de
email: buero@claasreinhard.de
Tel: 0049 221 721 2366

RICHARD BAKER FURNITURE
Wimbledon Studios
257 Burlington Road
New Malden
KT3 4NE
www.richardbakerfurniture.co.uk
email: sales@richardbakerfurniture.co.uk
Tel: 0208 336 1777
Fax: 0208 336 1666

SAND & BIRCH DESIGN
Viale Xxi Aprile, 10 04100 Latina (Lt) Italy
4100
www.sandbirch.com
email: info@sandbirch.com
Tel: 0039 (0)773 1762584
Fax: 0039 (0)773 1760684

STUA
Poligono 26 Bidebitarte
Astigarraga
Spain
E20115
www.stua.com
email: stua@stua.com
Tel: 0034 94333 0188
Fax: 0034 943 556002

STUART MELROSE
81 Hangar Rd
Tadley
Hampshire
RG26 4QQ
www.stuartmelrose.com
email: info@stuartmelrose.com
Tel: 0118 982 0239

T BAC DESIGN
AUSTRALIA
www.tbacdesign.com
email: troy@tbacdesign.com
Tel: 0061 39417 6595

IMOTHY MARK LTD
O New Quebec Street
ondon
V1H 7RZ
www.timothymark.co,uk
mail: info@timothymark.co.uk
el: 020 7616 9390
ax: 020 7616 9389

OBY WINTERINGHAM
Vhitehouse
awsey
ing's Lynn
E32 1EY
www.tobywinteringham.co.uk
mail: info@tobywinteringham.co.uk
el: 01553 841829
ax: 01553 841829

OM FAULKNER
helsea Reach
9/89 Lots Rd
ondon
V10 ORN
www.tomfaulkner.co.uk
mail: info@tomfaulkner.co.uk
el: 020 7351 7272
ax: 020 7352 7620

WENTYTWENTYONE
Bc River Street
ondon
C1R 1XN
www.twentytwentyone.com
mail: mail@twentytwentyone.com
el: 02078 371900
ax: 02078 371908

YE3D
nit 8 Block A
Fawe Street
ondon
4 6PD
www.tye3d.com
mail: mail@tye3d.com
l: 020 7536 9291

WAMBAMBOO
4 Swan Terrace
Vindsor Qld
ustralia
030
www.wambamboo.com.au
mail: info@wambamboo.com.au
l: 0061 73315 6605

WANT STUDIO
nit 5a
andswood Farm
'est Wratting, Cambs
321 5LR
www.wantstudio.co.uk
mail: info@wantstudio.co.uk
l: 01223 290 022

OME FURNITURE

FRONT FURNITURE
Valley House, 9 Harbet Road
ntrance On Blackwood Avenue)
ndon
8 3QP
ww.4ff.co.uk
mail: info@4ff.co.uk
l: 020 8803 6446
x: 020 8803 6556

4 LIVING FURNITURE
24-26 Berwick Court Farm
Berwick
Polegate
BN26 5QS
www.4living.co.uk
email: office@4living.co.uk
Tel: 0800 75 65 199
Fax: 0800 75 65 199

BLUE BONE IMPORTS LIMITED
River Mill 2
Park Road
Dukinfield, SK16 5PD
www.bluebone.co.uk
email: manchester@bluebone.co.uk
Tel: 0161 330 8959
Fax: 0161 330 8949

**CHESHIRE CURTAINS & INTERIORS
LIMITED**
Stanley Studio
Stanley Street
Macclesfield
SK11 6AU
www.cheshirecurtains.co.uk
email: mail@cheshirecurtains.co.uk
Tel: 01625 434121
Fax: 01625 618857

CONSORZIO AX ARTIGIANEXPORT
email: consorzioax@libero.it
Tel: 0039 0759 72240
Fax: 0039 0759711757

CONTAINERS DIRECT LTD
214 Western Rd
Kilmarnock
Ka3 1nj
www.containersdirect.co.uk
Tel: 01563 559799
Fax: 01563 528790

BENCHMARK
Bath Road, Kintbury,
Hungerford, RG17 9SA
Tel: 01488 608020
sales@benchmarkfurniture.com
www.benchmarkfurniture.com

Handmade English furniture in certified
timbers sold direct from the workshops
to both the trade and general public.
The designs are exclusive to Benchmark
and have been developed with
well-known designers including Terence
Conran, Russell Pinch and Kay+
Stemmer among others. Bespoke sizes
and finishes made to order. Visit the
showroom 9.00am – 5.30pm Monday
to Friday and 10.00am-4pm on
Saturdays or call for a brochure.

DINING CHAIRS U K
Unit 7
Oxton Road
Epperstone
NG14 6AT
www.diningchairsuk.com
email: sales@diningchairsuk.com
Tel: 01159 655302
Fax: 01159 656189

EFFEZETA S.P.A
Via Manzano 70/1
Premariacco (Ud)
Italy
33040
www.effezeta.it
email: info@effezeta.it
Tel: 0039 0432 706501
Fax: 0039 0432 706533

ERCOL FURNITURE LTD
Summerleys Road
Princes Risborough
Bucks
HP27 9PX
www.ercol.com
email: edward.tadros@ercol.com
Tel: 01844 271 800
Fax: 01844 271887

ETHNICRAFT
Scheldeweg 5
Boom
Belgium
2850
www.ethnicraft.com
email: alf@ethnicraft.com
Tel: 00323 443 0126
Fax: 00323 443 0127

FLAMERITE FIRES
Greenhough Road
Lichfield
Staffs
WS13 7AU
www.flameritefires.com
email: info@flameritefires.com
Tel: 01543 251 122
Fax: 01543 251 133

FLEXA
Bjornkjaervej 16
Hornsyld
Denmark
8783
www.flexa.dk
email: flexa@flexa.dk
Tel: +45 7668 8055
Fax: +45 7668 8069

FORNHAM HALL FURNITURE
Tel: 01359 271078
Fax: 01359 271355

FRAMES FURNITURE
Cockaynes Orchard
Cockaynes Lane
Alresford
CO7 8BZ
www.framesuk.com
email: enquiries@framesuk.com
Tel: 01206 820301
Fax: 01206 820221

GRANDFATHER CLOCKS
Billib
Norwich Road
Bournemouth
BH2 5QZ
www.billib.co.ukt
Tel: 01202 290917

GRAHAM AND GREEN
Capital Interchange Way
Brentford
TW8 0EX
Tel: 0845 130 6622
Email: info@grahamandgreen.co.uk
Web: www.grahamandgreen.co.uk

Graham and Green are interior design
and lifestyle product specialists with a
reputation that spans over 35 years.
With our unique sense of style we offer a
collection of fabulous and exotic interior
products for a truly inspirational look.

GUILLAUME PIECHAUD
2, Rue De La Libert
93600 Aulnay Sous Bois, France
www.guillaumepiechaud.com
email: contact@guillaumepiechaud.com
Tel: 0033 1486 61504

GUSTAVIAN
59 Lancaster Avenue, Hadley Wood, EN4 0ER
www.gustavian.com
email: info@gustavian.com
Tel: 0208 440 8043
Fax: 020 8216 3640

HERITAGE TABLES
Tel: 01580 852316

HJELLEGJERDE UK LTD
5 Heron Gate, Hankridge Way,
Taunton , Somerset TA1 2LR
www.hjellegjerde.com
email: uk@hjellegjerde.com
Tel: 01823 444027
Fax: 0182 344 4033

ISOKON PLUS
Turnham Green Terrace Mews
Chiswick
London, W4 1QU
www.isokonplus.com
email: ply@isokonplus.com
Tel: 020 8994 7032
Fax: 020 8994 5635

JALI HOME DESIGN LIMITED
Albion Works
Church Lane, Barham,
Canterbury, CT4 6QS
www.jali.co.uk
email: sales@jali.co.uk
Tel: 01227 833333
Fax: 01227 831950

JAMES ADAM FURNITURE LTD
26, Quayside
Woodbridge
Suffolk, IP12 1BH
www.jamesadam.com
email: sales@jamesadam.com
Tel: 01394 384471
Fax: 01394 384520

JAN CAVELLE FURNITURE COMPANY
Units A&B
25 Rookwood Way
Haverhill, CB9 8PB
www.jancavelle.com
email: sales@jancavelle.com
Tel: 01440 704253
Fax: 01440 761 023

JYSK
Melford Road
Hazel Grove
Stockport, SK3 0JD
www.jysk.co.uk
email: dgoo@jysk.com
Tel: 0845 389 3089

KENDO MOBILIARIO S.L
C/Gibraltar,8
46930 Quart De Poblet, Valencia
www.kendomobiliario.com
email: kendo@kendomobiliario.com
Tel: 0034 961 530 330
Fax: 0034 961 520510

KOMFI UK
Fao Phillip Whittell
Units 60/70 Bmk Industrial Estate
Wakefield Road, Liversedge, WF15 6BS
www.komfi.com
email: sales@komfi.com
Tel: 0800 6524445
Fax: 01924 408541

KARAVAN
The Courtyard, 74 Church Road,
London, SW13 0DO
Tel: 020 8748 2266
Web: www.karavaninteriors.co.uk

KARAVAN is one of the most innovative
and elegant home interior shops with
branches in Barnes & Reigate.
KARAVAN is an oasis of delights, and is
sure to inspire you with products
carefully chosen from some of Europe's
most stylish manufacturers & design
studios, displayed in stunning room
settings. Chic furniture, soft furnishings
& luxurious bed linens together with
beautiful crystal, casual & formal
tableware, cutlery & table linens are
combined with elegant lighting and
lamps. A stunning new garden range
offers the ultimate in a' fresco 'dining,
and a wedding and interior design
service make this a one stop destination.

LOFT INTERNATIONAL
22 Dock Street
Simpsons Fold
Leeds
LS10 1JF
www.loftinternational.com
email: info@loftinternational.com
Tel: 01132 3466 60
Fax: 01133 051500

MAKASIHOME
138 Oatlands Drive
Weybridge
Surrey
KT13 9HJ
www.makasihome.co.uk
email: info@makasihome.co.uk
Tel: 01932 860841
Fax: 01932 860841

MARK STODDART INTERNATIONAL DESIGNER
Ladybank House
Ladybank
Turnberry
KA26 9JJ
www.markstoddart.com
email: info@markstoddart.com
Tel: 01292 443 103

MICKUS PROJECTS
17 Monroe Place
#5a
Brooklyn, Ny
11201
www.mickusprojects.com
email: info@mprojects.com
Tel: 001 917 843 2285

MYAKKA LTD
Tythings Commercial Centre
Wincanton
Somerset
BA9 9EQ
www.myakka.co.uk
email: sales@myakka.co.uk
Tel: 0845 460 3122

NEIL ROGERS INTERIORS
18 Main Street
Goadby Marwood
Melton Mowbray
LE14 4LN
www.neilrogersinteriors.co.uk
email: neil@neilrogersinteriors.co.uk
Tel: 01664 464000
Fax: 01664 464111

NEST DESIGN
Lassalle
Pessoulens
France
32380
www.nest-design.com
email: info@nest-design.com
Tel: 0033 5 62 67 79 03

NEW FROM OLD
The Engine House
White House Road
Little Ouse
CB7 4TG
www.newfromold.co.uk
email: rick.forward@newfromold.co.uk
Tel: 01353 676227

GRAHAM *and* GREEN

Exceptional interiors and gifts

With our unique sense of style we offer a collection of fabulous
and exotic interior products for a truly inspirational look.

www.grahamandgreen.co.uk

Orderline 0845 130 6622

PIET HEIN EEK
Nuenenseweg 167
NL-5667 KP GELDROP
www.pietheineek.nl
email: info@pietheineek.nl
Tel: 0031 40-285 6610
Fax: 0031 40285 9460

PINCH DESIGN
www.pinchdesign.com
email: studio@pinchdesign.com
Tel: 020 7501 9262

RACK AND RUIN
Pump House
Kirkby Malzeard
Ripon, North Yorkshire
HG4 3RY
www.rackandruin.com
email: info@rackandruin.com
Tel: 0845 330 8897

REAL WOOD STUDIOS LTD
Monteviot Nurseries
Ancrum
Jedburgh
TD8 6TU
www.realwoodstudios.com
email: info@realwoodstudios.com
Tel: 01835 830767

REINHARD DESIGN
Kyffhaeuserstrasse 7
Koeln
D- 50674
www.claasreinhard.de
email: buero@claasreinhard.de
Tel: 0049 221 721 2366

ROBERT MORLEY & CO LTD
34 Engate Street
Lewisham
London
SE13 7HA
morleypianos.co.uk
email: sales@morleypianos.co.uk
Tel: 0208 318 5838

SCOTTISH ANTIQUE & ARTS CENTRE
Abernyte Ph14 9sj
Doune Fk16 6hg
www.scottish-antiques.com
email: margaret@scottish-antiques.com
Tel: 01828 686401 / 01786 841203

STUA
Poligono 26 Bidebitarte
Astigarraga
Spain
E20115
www.stua.com
email: stua@stua.com
Tel: 0034 94333 0188
Fax: 0034 943 556002

SYLVAWOOD FURNITURE
The Old Workshops
Longbridge Deverill
Wiltshire
BA12 7DP
www.sylvawoodfurniture.co.uk
email: sales@sylvawoodfurniture.co.uk
Tel: 01985 840012
Fax: 01985 840781

TECNO GB LTD
309 Harbour Yard
Chelsea Harbour
London
SW10 0XD
www.tecnospa.com
email: agency.uk@tecnospa.com
Tel: 020 7349 1100
Fax: 02074 7351 1805

THE CONRAN SHOP
81 Fulham Road
London
SW3 6RD
www.conranshop.co.uk
Tel: 02075 897401
Fax: 02078 237015

VITSÚ
Centric Close
London
NW1 7EP
www.vitsoe.com
email: email@vitsoe.com
Tel: 020 7428 1606
Fax: 020 7424 9591

WITHIN4WALLS LTD
Stratford Lodge
29 Leam Terrace
Royal Leamington Spa
CV31 1BQ
www.within4walls.co.uk
email: info@within4walls.co.uk
Tel: 01926 772217

YP FUNITURE LTD
Corringham Road Industrial Estate
Gainsborough
Lincs
DN21 1QB
Tel: 01664 434 188

HOME OFFICE FURNITURE

21ST CENTURY ANTIQUES
Tel: 01306 881029
Fax: 01306 888855

ACT FURNITURE MANUFACTURERS LTD
Salop Street
Bradley
Bilston
WV14 0TQ
www.actfurniture.com
email: sales@actfurniture.com
Tel: 01902 490273
Fax: 01902 490275

AZZURRO LTD
32 Viking Road
Brownsburn Estate
Airdre
ML6 9SE
www.azzurro-ltd.com
email: info@azzurro-ltd.com
Tel: 01236 762262
Fax: 01236 747428

BRETFORD MANUFACTURING LTD
2 Etongate, 110 Windsor Rd
Slough
Berkshire
SL1 2JA
www.bretforduk.com
email: sales@bretforduk.com
Tel: 01753 539955
Fax: 01753 539478

CARLETON FURNITURE GROUP
Tel: 01977 700770
Fax: 01977 792322

CONNECTION SEATING LTD
15 Great Sutton Street
Clerkenwell
London
EC1V 0BX
www.connection.uk.com
email: sales@connection.uk.com
Tel: 0207 2539877
Fax: 01484 600125

DAUPHIN UK
12-16 Clerkenwell Road
Clerkenwell
London
EC1M 5PQ
www.dauphin-group.com
email: info@dauphinuk.com
Tel: 020 73246 210
Fax: 020 73246 211

DOVETAIL CONTRACT FURNITURE LTD
8 St Johns Lane
Clerkenwell
London
EC1M 4BF
www.dovetailfurniture.com
email: iweddell@dovetaillondon.com
Tel: 02078 689000
Fax: 02078 689009

DRAWING OFFICE FURNITURE LTD
1 Kinkell
St Johns Road
New Milton
BH25 5SD
www.art-drawingoffice.co.uk
email: sales@drawingoffice.org.uk
Tel: 01425 625160
Fax: 01425 625161

EME FURNITURE
Blackaddie Road
Sanquhar
Dumfriesshire
DG4 6DE
www.emefurniture.co.uk
email: info@emefurniture.co.uk
Tel: 01659 50404
Fax: 01659 50107

FANTONI
1 The Mews
Wharf St
Godalming, Surrey
GU7 1NN
Tel: 01483 527 997
Fax: 01483 527 991

FORNHAM HALL FURNITURE
Tel: 01359 271078
Fax: 01359 271355

G.G.I OFFICE FURNITURE (U K) LTD
Global Way
Darwen
Lancashire
BB3 0RW
www.globaltotaloffice.com
email: sales@ggieurope.com
Tel: 01254 778500
Fax: 01254 778519

GIRSBERGER
Invicta House
4th Floor
108-114 Golden Lane, London
EC1Y 0TG
www.girsberger.com
email: infouk@girsberger.com
Tel: 0207 490 3223
Fax: 0207 490 5665

GRANTCF
The Lodge, Holdenhurst
Park Lane, Snitterfield
Stratford Upon Avon
CV37 0LS
www.grantcf.co.uk
email: sales@grantcf.co.uk
Tel: 01789 730380
Fax: 01789 731109

HARTS OF MAIDSTONE
11-17 Upper Stone Street
Maidstone
Kent
ME15 6EU
www.hartsofmaidstone.co.uk
email: contact@hartsofmaidstone.co.uk
Tel: 01622 673063
Fax: 01622 200057

HEATON OFFICE INTERIORS
Campbeltown Road
Lairdside Technology Park
Birkenhead
CH41 9HP
www.heatons.net
email: sales@heatons.net
Tel: 01516 496000
Fax: 01516 496031

HERITAGE TABLES
Tel: 01580 852316

HOG PLC
14 West Place, West Road
Harlow
Essex
CM20 2GY
www.hogdirect.co.uk
email: sales@hogplc.com
Tel: 01279 638250
Fax: 01279 641904

I-DESK SOLUTIONS LTD
11 Ivanhoe Road
Finchampstead
Berkshire
RG40 4QQ
www.i-desk.co.uk
email: info@i-desk.co.uk
Tel: 01189 739700
Fax: 01189 8731058

INOVA FURNITURE CONTRACTS
75b Great Eastern St
London
EC2A 3HN
www.inovafurniture.com
email: brent@inovafurniture.com
Tel: 02077 392300
Fax: 02077 392336

KEMBO
The Horseshoes
Tonbridge Road
Bough Beech
TN8 7AT
www.kembo.co.uk
email: david-goodman@btconnect.com
Tel: 01892 871444
Fax: 01892 871 675

KOEHL UK LTD
5 Coopers Drive
Bexley Grange
Dartford
DA2 7WS
www.koehl.co.uk
email: sales@koehl.co.uk
Tel: 01322 551082
Fax: 01322 310302

KUSCH & CO
48/50 St John Street
London
EC1M 4DG
www.kusch.com
email: info-uk@kusch.com
Tel: 02073 367561
Fax: 02073 367562

LEE AND PLUMPTON LTD
Bunns Bank
Attleborough
Norfolk
NR17 1QD
www.leeandplumpton.co.uk
email: sales@leeandplumpton.co.uk
Tel: 01953 453830
Fax: 01953 456349

LOFT INTERNATIONAL
22 Dock Street
Simpsons Fold
Leeds
LS10 1JF
www.loftinternational.com
email: info@loftinternational.com
Tel: 01132 3466 60
Fax: 01133 051500

MAINE
Home Park
Kings Langley
Hertfordshire
WD4 8LZ
www.maine.co.uk
email: sales@maine.co.uk
Tel: 01923 260411
Fax: 01923 267136

MCFEGGAN BROWN LTD
2 Farleigh Court
Old Weston Road
Flax Bourton
B S48 1UR
www.mcfegganbrown.co.uk
email: tony@mcfegganbrown.co.uk
Tel: 01275 464220
Fax: 01275 463133

MICHAEL REED DESIGN
Arch 12
Kingsdown Close
London
W10 6SW
www.arch12.com
email: info@arch12.com
Tel: 020 72295391

NEIL ROGERS INTERIORS
18 Main Street
Goadby Marwood
Melton Mowbray
LE14 4LN
www.neilrogersinteriors.co.uk
email: neil@neilrogersinteriors.co.uk
Tel: 01664 464000
Fax: 01664 464111

NORDPLAN LTD
Sheddingdean Business Park
Marchants Way
Burgess Hill
RH15 8QY
www.nordplan.com
email: sales@nord-plan.co.uk
Tel: 01444 237220
Fax: 01444 237221

NOWY STYL
Walkers Ind Est
Ollerton Road
Tuxford
NG22 0PQ
www.nowystylgroup.co.uk
email: info@nowystylgroup.co.uk
Tel: 01777 872882
Fax: 01777 872885

OCEE DESIGN LTD
Tel: 01604 674674

OSMOND GROUP LIMITED
21 Johnson Road
Ferndown Industrial Estate
Wimborne
BH21 7SE
www.osmondoffice.com
email: info@osmondoffice.com
Tel: 01202 850550
Fax: 01202 850560

PARADIGM OFFICE INTERIORS LTD
Unit 1, Wilnecote Lane
Belgrave, Tamworth
Staff's
B77 2LE
www.paradigm-interiors.co.uk
email: info@paradigm-interiors.co.uk
Tel: 0845 434 9717
Fax: 01827 261597

PORRO
Via per Cantù 35
22060 Montesolaro, CO Italy
Tel: +39 031 783266
E-mail: info@porro.com
Web: www.porro.com

H.Chair is the comfortable and wrap-around chair by Christopher Pillet, consisting of a light tubular structure in chromium-plated metal, and a synthetic core, covered with padded leather. Available in white or black leather, for 2009 this family is enriched with two new types, the office chair on spokes and the model covered in fabric.

PIET HEIN EEK
Nuenenseweg 167
NL-5667 KP GELDROP
www.pietheineek.nl
email: info@pietheineek.nl
Tel: 0031 40-285 6610
Fax: 0031 40285 9460

POSTURITE LTD
The Mill
Berwick
East Sussex
BN26 6SZ
www.posturite.co.uk
email: support@posturite.co.uk
Tel: 0845 345 0010
Fax: 0845 345 0020

PROCOL LTD
New Hall
Market Place
Melksham
SN12 6EX
www.procol.ltd.uk
email: nick@procol.ltd.uk
Tel: 01225 701701
Fax: 01225 701702

RONIS-DOM LTD
Unit 1 Junction 2 Industrial Estate
Demuth Way
Oldbury
B69 4LT
www.ronis-dom.co.uk
email: sales@ronis-dom.co.uk
Tel: 0800 988 4348
Fax: 0800 988 4349

SICO EUROPE LTD
The Link Park
Lympne Industrial Estate
Lympne, Kent
CT21 4LR
www.sico-europe.com
email: sales@sico-europe.com
Tel: 01303 234000
Fax: 01303 234001

SMARTSTREETS
94 Sutton Court
Chiswick
London
W4 3JF
www.smartstreets.co.uk
email: sales@smartstreets.co.uk
Tel: 020 8742 3210
Fax: 0208 742 3226

SPACEOASIS
Grosvenor House
Central Park
Telford
TF2 9TW
www.spaceoasis.co.uk
email: sales@spaceoasis.co.uk
Tel: 01952 210197
Fax: 01952 201303

TECNO GB LTD
309 Harbour Yard
Chelsea Harbour
London
SW10 0XD
www.tecnospa.com
email: agency.uk@tecnospa.com
Tel: 020 7349 1100
Fax: 02074 7351 1805

TORASEN OFFICE FURNITURE
Newhouse Road
Huncoat Business Park
Accrington, Lancs
BB5 6NA
email: gbird@torasen.co.uk
Tel: 01254 306000
Fax: 01254 306010

TRADEMARK INTERIORS LTD
8 Marchmont Gate
Boundary Way
Hemel Hempstead, Herts
HP27BF
www.tmark.co.uk
email: barrycollins@tmark.co.uk
Tel: 01442 260022
Fax: 01442 232244

VICCARBE
Trav. Camì El Racû 1 P.i Norte Beniparrell.
Valencia
46469
www.viccarbe.com
email: info@viccarbe.com
Tel: 0034 961201010
Fax: 0034 961211211

WILKHAHN LTD
Morelands
5-23 Old Street
London
EC1V 9HL
www.wilkhahn.com
email: greg@wilkhahn.co.uk
Tel: 02073 242900
Fax: 02073 242901

MODERN FURNITURE

ASHLEY MANOR UPHOLSTERY LTD
Unit 1 Woodside Ind. Estate
Pedmore Road
Dudley, West Midlands
DY20RL
www.ashleymanor.co.uk
email: info@ashleymanor.co.uk
Tel: 01384 486800
Fax: 01384 473070

BENTLEY DESIGNS (UK) LTD
Unit 1, Tera 40
Auriol Drive
Greenford
UB6 0TP
www.bentleydesigns.com†
email: emma@bentleydesigns.com
Tel: 020 8833 7500
Fax: 020 8578 2696

BLUE MARMALADE LTD
32-36 Dalmeny Street
Edinburgh
EH6 8RG
www.bluemarmalade.co.uk
email: info@bluemarmalade.co.uk
Tel: 0131 5537766
Fax: 0131 5536659

CASAGUA
82 Mallard Crescent
Poynton
Cheshire
SK12 1HT
www.casagua.com
email: info@casagua.com
Tel: 01625 897508
Fax: 07006017725

CATERINA FADDA STUDIO
201b Saga Centre,
326 Kensal Rd
London, W10 5BZ
www.caterinafadda.com
email: info@caterinafadda.com
Tel: 0208 9643725

CHAPLINS FURNITURE LTD
477-507 Uxbridge Rd
Hatch End
Middlesex, HA5 4JS
www.chaplins.co.uk
email: sales@chaplins.co.uk
Tel: 020 84211779
Fax: 020 84213872

COLONY FABRICS LTD
2/14 Chelsea Harbour Design Centre
Chelsea Harbour
London, SW10 0XE
www.colonyfabrics.com
email: colonyfabrics@aol.com
Tel: 0207 3513232
Fax: 020 73512242

DAVID & JANE PAINE FURNITURE COLLECTION
4 Devereaux Court
Ipswich
Suffolk, IP4 2BF
www.dandjpainefurniturecollection.co.uk
info@dandjpainefurniturecollection.co.uk
Tel: 07989 027656
Fax: 01473 232253

DAVID COLWELL DESIGN
Trannon Studio, Llawr Y Glyn, Caersws,
Powys.SY17 5RH
www.davidcolwell.com
email: info@davidcolwell.com
Tel: 01686 430434

DIPLOMAT DESIGN
www.diplomatdesign.com
email: info@diplomatdesign.com
Tel: 02083 425285

DO SHOP LIMITED
G/F And Basement
47 Beak Street
London
W1F 9SE
www.do-shop.com
email: info@do-shop.com
Tel: 020 7494 9090
Fax: 020 7494 9090

DOVETAIL CONTRACT FURNITURE LTD
8 St Johns Lane
Clerkenwell
London
EC1M 4BF
www.dovetailfurniture.com
email: iweddell@dovetaillondon.com
Tel: 02078 689000
Fax: 02078 689009

DREAM DESIGN
A35 Lyndhurst Road
Christchurch
Dorset
BH23 7DU
www.dream-design.co.uk
email: sales@dream-design.co.uk
Tel: 01425 279525
Fax: 01425 273550

EFFEZETA S.P.A
Via Manzano 70/1
Premariacco (Ud)
Italy
33040
www.effezeta.it
email: info@effezeta.it
Tel: 0039 0432 706501
Fax: 0039 0432 706533

EMBARK DESIGN
Sunbeam House
Pontefract Lane
Leeds
LS9 0DX
www.embarkdesign.co.uk
email: tim.kiernan@embarkdesign.co.uk
Tel: 0800 138 6688
Fax: 0113 235 9900

FEBLAND GROUP
Ashworth Road
Marton
Blackpool, Lancs
FY4 4UN
www.febland.co.uk
email: info@febland.co.uk
Tel: 01253 600 600
Fax: 01253 792211

FIGUERAS SEATING UK
www.figueras.com
email: info@figueras.com
Tel: +34 93 844 50 50
Fax: +34 93 844 50 61

GILLMORESPACE LTD
22 Torbay Business Park
Woodview Road
Paignton
TQ4 7HP
www.gillmorespace.com
email: info@gillmorespace.com
Tel: 0845 373 2763
Fax: 0845 373 2764

GUILLAUME PIECHAUD
2, Rue De La Libert
93600 Aulnay Sous Bois
France
www.guillaumepiechaud.com
email: contact@guillaumepiechaud.com
Tel: 0033 1486 61504

HAMMEL FURNITURE
Anbaekvej 111
Dk - Hammel
8450
hammel-furniture.dk
email: sales@hammel-furniture.dk
Tel: 045 8963 1577
Fax: 045 8963 1588

HIGHLY SPRUNG LTD
310 Battersea Park Road London Sw11 3bu
www.highlysprung.net
email: bpr@highlysprung.co.uk
Tel: 02079 241124
Fax: 02072 285476

HITCH MYLIUS LTD
301 Alma Road
Enfield
Middlesex
EN3 7BB
www.hitchmylius.co.uk
email: info@hitchmylius.co.uk
Tel: 020 8443 2616
Fax: 020 8443 2617

HYDE HOUSE BESPOKE FURNITURE
289 Lower High Street
Watford
Herts
WD17 2HY
www.hydehouse.co.uk
email: sales@hydehouse.co.uk
Tel: 01284 330 098
Fax: 01923 262 670

INOVA FURNITURE CONTRACTS
75b Great Eastern St
London
EC2A 3HN
www.inovafurniture.com
email: brent@inovafurniture.com
Tel: 02077 392300
Fax: 02077 392336

INTERDESIGN (U K) LTD
G30 Design Centre Chelsea Harbour
London
SW10 0XE
www.interdesignuk.com
Tel: 02073 765272
Fax: 02073 763020

INTERIOR SUPPLY LTD
2/15 Chelsea Harbour Design Centre
London
SW10 0XE
www.interiorsupply.co.uk
email: info@interiorsupply.co.uk
Tel: 0207 352 0502
Fax: 0207 352 2026

JENNIFER NEWMAN
Worlds End Studio
132-134 Lots Road
Chelsea
SW10 0RJ
www.jennifernewman.com
email: studio@jennifernewman.com
Tel: 0207 349 7222

JOE EARLEY DESIGN
Mallards Cottage, South Gren Road
Fingringhoe, Colchester
Essex
CO5 DR
www.earleybrothers.com
email: joe@earleybrothers.com
Tel: 07909994860

JT CONTRACT MARKETING LTD
46 Anhalt Road
London
SW11 4NX
www.parridesign.it
email: jtcontract@waitrose.com
Tel: 02078 010206
Fax: 02078 010207

KEMBO
The Horseshoes
Tonbridge Road
Bough Beech
TN8 7AT
www.kembo.co.uk
email: david-goodman@btconnect.com
Tel: 01892 871444
Fax: 01892 871 675

KENDO MOBILIARIO S.L
C/Gibraltar,8
46930 Quart De Poblet
Valencia
www.kendomobiliario.com
email: kendo@kendomobiliario.com
Tel: 0034 961 530 330
Fax: 0034 961 520510

LATERA SHELVING
Unit 9
Brunswick Way
London
N11 1JL
www.laterashelving.com
email: enquiries@laterashelving.com
Tel: 020 8362 8515
Fax: 020 8362 8525

LOWTHER FINE FURNITURE
East Sessacott Farm
Putford
Devon
EX22 7XG
www.lowtherfinefurniture.co.uk
email: suzi@lowtherfinefurniture.co.uk
Tel: 01409 241 583

MATTHEW BURT
Matthew Burt Showroom
High Street
Hindon, Salisbury
BA12 0SP
www.matthewburt.com
email: furniture@matthewburt.com
Tel: 01747 820511
Fax: 01747 820176

MHF CONTRACT FURNITURE LTD
The Hollins
Merrington
Shrewsbury
SY4 3QF
www.mhf-furniture.co.uk
email: info@mhf-furniture.co.uk
Tel: 01939 290280
Fax: 01939 291173

"Conformism is an enemy of creativity..."

MICKUS PROJECTS
17 Monroe Place
#5a
Brooklyn, Ny
11201
www.mickusprojects.com
email: info@mprojects.com
Tel: 001 917 843 2285

MODUS FURNITURE
5 Westcombe Trading Estate
Station Road
Ilminster
SOMERSET
www.modusfurniture.co.uk
email: info@modusfurniture.co.uk
Tel: 01460 258590
Fax: 01460 57004

MOMENTUM
31 Charles Street
Cardiff
CF10 2GA
www.momentumcardiff.com
email: info@momentumcardiff.com
Tel: 02920 236266
Fax: 02920 236311

NEIL ROGERS INTERIORS
18 Main Street
Goadby Marwood
Melton Mowbray
LE14 4LN
www.neilrogersinteriors.co.uk
email: neil@neilrogersinteriors.co.uk
Tel: 01664 464000
Fax: 01664 464111

NORMANN COPENHAGEN
Osterbrogade 70
Copenhagen
Denmark
2100
www.normann-copenhagen.com
email: normann@normann-copenhagen.com
Tel: 0045 35 554 459
Fax: 0045 35 554 439

NORTHCROFT LIMITED
Argall Works
Argall Avenue
London
E10 7QE
www.michaelnorthcroft.com
email: info@michaelnorthcroft.com
Tel: 0208 558 6919
Fax: 0208 558 1097

ONE CALL FURNITURE
www.1cfl.com†
Tel: 08451 084 084

PAVILION RATTAN LTD
The Ulvers Building
Budby Road
Cuckney, Nr. Mansfield
NG20 9JP
www.pavilionrattan.co.uk
email: sales@pavilionrattan.co.uk
Tel: 01623 847030
Fax: 0870 706 2159

PICTURE HOUSE CABINETS
Po Box 421
Surrey
KT14 6YR
www.picturehouse.eu
email: info@picturehouse.eu
Tel: 01932 345 184
Fax: 01932 402128

PIET HEIN EEK
Nuenenseweg 167
NL-5667 KP GELDROP
www.pietheineek.nl
email: info@pietheineek.nl
Tel: 0031 40-285 6610
Fax: 0031 40285 9460

PINCH DESIGN
www.pinchdesign.com
email: studio@pinchdesign.com
Tel: 020 7501 9262

PREMIER HOUSEWARES LLP
Premier Business Park
55 Jordanvale Avenue
Glasgow
G14 0QP
www.premierhousewares.co.uk
email: info@premierhousewares.co.uk
Tel: 0141 579 2000
Fax: 0141 579 2005

PURVES & PURVES CONTRACTS
7 Mill Farm Business Park
Millfield Road
Hounslow
TW4 5PY
www.purves-contracts.co.uk
email: contracts@purves.co.uk
Tel: 020 8898 2318
Fax: 020 8893 4024

RASMUS
12-13 Royal Parade
Harrogate
North Yorkshire
HG1 2SZ
www.rasmusdesign.co.uk
email: info@rasmusdesign.co.uk
Tel: 01423 560050
Fax: 01423 875087

ROCHE BOBOIS UK
Smugglers Way
By Wandsworth Bridge
London
SW18 1AZ
www.roche-bobois.com
email: info.uk@roche-bobois.com
Tel: 0208 874 9818
Fax: 0208 874 9798

ROSJOHN FURNITURE LTD INC WILLIAM BARTLETT
Unit 8 Abbeymead Ind Estate
Brooker Road
Waltham Abbey, Essex
EN9 1HU
www.rosjohn.com
email: sales@rosjohn.com
Tel: 01992 767353
Fax: 01992 763568

SILVERMOON STYLES LTD
14 Holmwood Court
Keymer Road
Hassocks
BN6 8AS
www.silvermoonstyles.com
email: info@silvermoonstyles.com
Tel: 01273 844413
Fax: 01273 844413

SPATIAL FURNITURE
272 Bath Street
Glasgow, G2 4JR
www.spatialfurniture.co.uk
email: info@spatialfurniture.co.uk
Tel: 0141 353 9553
Fax: 0141 353 9555

SKANDIUM
247 Brompton Road,
London, SW3 2EP
Tel: 020 7584 2066
&
86 Marylebone High Street,
London, W1U 4QS
Tel: 020 7935 2077

Contract sales
Interior design
Wedding list
Gift service
Tel: 020 7823 8874

www.skandium.com
We Supply Good Ideas

STUART MELROSE
81 Hangar Rd
Tadley
Hampshire
RG26 4QQ
www.stuartmelrose.com
email: info@stuartmelrose.com
Tel: 0118 982 0239

THE CUBE COLLECTION
Po Box 188,
TQ9 9AY
www.thecube.uk.com
email: info@thcube.uk.com
Tel: 01803 712388
Fax: 01803 712388

TOBY WINTERINGHAM
Whitehouse
Bawsey
King's Lynn, PE32 1EY
www.tobywinteringham.co.uk
email: info@tobywinteringham.co.uk
Tel: 01553 841829
Fax: 01553 841829

TOM FAULKNER
Chelsea Reach
79/89 Lots Rd
London, SW10 0RN
www.tomfaulkner.co.uk
email: info@tomfaulkner.co.uk
Tel: 020 7351 7272
Fax: 020 7352 7620

TWENTYTWENTYONE
18c River Street
London, EC1R 1XN
www.twentytwentyone.com
email: mail@twentytwentyone.com
Tel: 02078 371900
Fax: 02078 371908

GetaStyle elements

The new Polymer glass element

WESTAG & GETALIT AG

le.export@westag-getalit.de
www.westag-getalit.de

AINTED FURNITURE

· SASHA · WADDELL ·
FURNITURE
LONDON

SASHA WADDELL FURNITURE
1 Thames Street, Hampton,
Middlessex, TW12 2EW
Tel: +44 (0) 20 8979 9189
Fax: +44 (0) 20 8979 0804
Web: www.sashawaddell.com
Email: info@sashawaddell.com

The home of beautiful, hand crafted
furniture inspired by classic Swedish,
French and East Coast American
designs.
Uncluttered, with simple, subtly
painted pieces, our elegant furniture
is designed to mesh perfectly with
modern, pared down living.

REPAIRING & RESTORATION

ALBERT E. CHAPMAN LTD
17 Crouch Hill
London
N4 4AP
albertechapman.co.uk
Tel: 020 7272 2536
Fax: 020 7263 1033

ASHBURN UPHOLSTERY
Unit 3 Western Units
Pottery Road
Bovey Tracey, Devon
TQ13 9DS
www.ashburn-upholstery.co.uk
email: mail@ashupohl.plus.com
Tel: 01626 832532
Fax: 01626 832532

BLUE LINE
Endeavour House
Stansted Airport
Essex
CM23 4HR
www.blueline.uk.com
email: sales@blueline.uk.com
Tel: 01279 669470
Fax: 01279 669471

CARVERS & GILDERS LTD
Unit 44 Spaces Business Centre
Ingate Place
London
SW8 3NS
www.carversandgilders.com
email: info@carversandgilders.com
Tel: 0207 498 5070
Fax: 0207 498 1221

CLASSIC UPHOLSTERY
Estate Yard,
Upper Harlestone,
Northampton.
NN7 4EH
email: classic.upholstery@btintermet.com
Tel: 01604 584556

DANIEL NEWLYN UPHOLSTERY
The Old Forge, Lock Farm House
Dell Lane, Spellbrook
Hertfordshire
CM22 7SG
www.danielnewlyn.com
email: daniel@newlyn.biz
Tel: 01279 600 686

HATFIELDS RESTORATION
Scholars House
49 Clapham High St
London
SW4 7TL
www.hatfieldsrestoration.com
email: info@hatfieldsrestoration.com
Tel: 0207 622 8169
Fax: 0207 622 2009

HOSSACK & GRAY
Studio 10, 9e Queens Yard
Whitepost Lane
London
E9 5EN
hossackandgray.co.uk
email: hossackanggray@hotmail.com
Tel: 02089 863345
Fax: 02089 863345

LFS
Unit 1, Autumn Yard, 39 Autumn Street
London
E3 2TT
email: sales@lfsuk.com
Tel: 020 8983 9111
Fax: 020 8983 9222

MARK HORNAK
email: hornax@hotmail.com
Tel: 07930 205 350

OPTIMUM BRASSES
Castle Street
Bampton
Nr. Tiverton, Devon
EX16 9NS
www.optimumbrasses.co.uk
email: brass@optimumbrasses.co.uk
Tel: 01398 331515
Fax: 01398 331164

PAUL FERGUSON WORKSHOP
Tel: 01525 851594

THE CHAIR WORKSHOP
99 Main Street
Sedbergh
Cumbria
LA10 5AD
www.chairworkshop.co.uk
email: info@chairworkshop.co.uk
Tel: 01539 621489

WHITEHEAD DESIGNS
Atlas Mills
Birchwood Road
Long Eaton
NG10 3ND
www.whiteheads.co.uk†
email: info@whiteheaddesigns.com
Tel: 0115 972 5056
Fax: 0115 946 1044

WILDWOOD ANTIQUES
Manor Farm, Heyshott
Midhurst
West Sussex
GU29 0DR
www.wildwoodwood.co.uk
Tel: 01730 816880/ 07989815355

REPRODUCTION

AEL HEATING SOLUTIONS
4 Berkeley Court
Manor Park
Runcorn , Cheshire
WA7 1TQ
www.aelheating.com
email: sales@aelheating.com
Tel: 01928 579 068
Fax: 01928 579 523

ATELIER GAGNIÈRE CRÈATEUR DE MEUBLES
Zone Artisanale De Lecheraine
Lanslebourg Mont-Cenis
France Alpes
73480
www.atelier-gagniere.com
email: contact@atelier-gagniere.com
Tel: +33 (0)479 563 570
Fax: +33 (0)479 563 570

BYLAW THE FURNITURE MAKERS
The Workshop
Norwich Road
Lenwade
NR9 5SH
www.bylaw.co.uk
email: info@bylaw.co.uk
Tel: 01603 30 80 90
Fax: 01603 872 122

DOUGLAS HOSKING OAK FURNITURE
33 High Street
Ipswich
Suffolk, IP1 3QH
douglashosking.com
email: sales@douglashosking.com
Tel: 01473 631644
Fax: 01473 631655

FAULD TOWN & COUNTRY FURNITURE
email: enquiries@fauld.com
Tel: 01432 851 992

FORNHAM HALL FURNITURE
Tel: 01359 271078
Fax: 01359 271355

GRANDFATHER CLOCKS
Billib
Norwich Road
Bournemouth, BH2 5QZ
www.billib.co.uk†
Tel: 01202 290917

GST-GLOBAL SOURCING & TRADING LIMITED
22 Dalston Gardens, Stanmore,
Middlesex, HA7 1BU
www.gstuk.com
email: anna@papillonuk.com
Tel: 0208 2061818
Fax: 0208 2061218

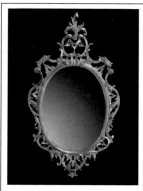

ELG LONDON LTD.
210 South Dome, The Design Centre,
Chelsea Harbour, London, SW10 0XE
Tel: 0207 351 4433
E-mail: info@elglondon.com
Web: www.elglondon.com

Now fully established in the Design
Centre, Chelsea Harbour London, ELG
London, has rapidly gained an
international reputation for supplying
the finest hand carved mirrors and
furniture. Find us on the 2nd Floor in
the South Dome.

JEREMY LOXTON & COMPANY
P O Box 5588
Thatcham
RG19 8XY
Tel: 0870 385 1086
Fax: 0870 385 1086

LP FURNITURE
The Old Brewery
Short Acre Street
Walsall West Midlands
WS2 8HW
www.lpfurniture.net†
email: frenchfurniture@btconnect.com
Tel: 01922 746764
Fax: 01922 611316

OPTIMUM BRASSES
Castle Street
Bampton
Nr. Tiverton, Devon
EX16 9NS
www.optimumbrasses.co.uk
email: brass@optimumbrasses.co.uk
Tel: 01398 331515
Fax: 01398 331164

ROSJOHN FURNITURE LTD INC WILLIAM BARTLETT
Unit 8 Abbeymead Ind Estate
Brooker Road
Waltham Abbey, Essex
EN9 1HU
www.rosjohn.com
email: sales@rosjohn.com
Tel: 01992 767353
Fax: 01992 763568

WILDWOOD ANTIQUES
Manor Farm, Heyshott
Midhurst
West Sussex
GU29 0DR
www.wildwoodwood.co.uk
Tel: 01730 816880/ 07989815355

SHELVING & STORAGE

21ST CENTURY ANTIQUES
Tel: 01306 881029
Fax: 01306 888855

3D DISPLAYS LTD
Upper Brents Industrial Estate
ME13 7DZ
email: info@3ddisplays.co.uk
Tel: 01795 532947
Fax: 01795 539934

ECONOWALL
Joyces Farm Buildings
Southminster Road
Mayland
CM3 6EB
www.econowall.co.uk
email: sales@econowall.co.uk
Tel: 0845 0942 751
Fax: 0845 0942 761

EMBARK DESIGN
Sunbeam House
Pontefract Lane
Leeds
LS9 0DX
www.embarkdesign.co.uk
email: tim.kiernan@embarkdesign.co.uk
Tel: 0800 138 6688
Fax: 0113 235 9900

GILLMORESPACE LTD
22 Torbay Business Park
Woodview Road
Paignton
TQ4 7HP
www.gillmorespace.com
email: info@gillmorespace.com
Tel: 0845 373 2763
Fax: 0845 373 2764

GURU
www.guru-design.com†
email: info@guru-design.com
Tel: 020 8960 6655

HAMMEL FURNITURE
Anbaekvej 111
Dk - Hammel
8450
hammel-furniture.dk
email: sales@hammel-furniture.dk
Tel: 045 8963 1577
Fax: 045 8963 1588

HULSTA FURNITURE U K LTD
5th Floor
2 Conduit Street
London
W1S 2XB
www.hulsta.com
email: sales@huelsta.co.uk
Tel: 02073 188000
Fax: 02074 092417

J-ME
Unit 1.15
Oxo Tower Wharf
London
SE1 9PH
www.j-me.co.uk
email: info@j-me.co.uk
Tel: 020 7928 8828
Fax: 020 7928 8846

KENDO MOBILIARIO S.L
C/Gibraltar,8
46930 Quart De Poblet
Valencia
www.kendomobiliario.com
email: kendo@kendomobiliario.com
Tel: 0034 961 530 330
Fax: 0034 961 520510

LATERA SHELVING
Unit 9
Brunswick Way
London
N11 1JL
www.laterashelving.com
email: enquiries@laterashelving.com
Tel: 020 8362 8515
Fax: 020 8362 8525

MARTIN OAKLEY
43 Sandfield Road
Oxford
OX3 7RN
www.martinoakley.co.uk
email: sales@martinoakley.co.uk
Tel: 01865 742111

MOVISI GMBH
Burghaldenweg 62-64
70469 Stuttgart
Germany
www.movisi.com
email: info@movisi.com
Tel: 0049 711 505 5485
Fax: 0049 711 505 1368

NORDPLAN LTD
Sheddingdean Business Park
Marchants Way
Burgess Hill
RH15 8QY
www.nordplan.com
email: sales@nord-plan.co.uk
Tel: 01444 237220
Fax: 01444 237221

POSTURITE LTD
The Mill
Berwick
East Sussex
BN26 6SZ
www.posturite.co.uk
email: support@posturite.co.uk
Tel: 0845 345 0010
Fax: 0845 345 0020

REDLAKE GROUP
Park Road
Faringdon
Oxfordshire
SN7 7BP
www.redlakegroup.xcom
email: njones@redlakegroup.com
Tel: 01367 241507
Fax: 01367 241705

SLIMLINE SYSTEMS LIMITED
Woodwards Road
Walsall
WS2 9SL
www.slimline.co.uk
email: sales@slimlinesystems.co.uk
Tel: 01922 748860
Fax: 01922 748869

SODEM SYSTEM UK LIMITED
Units 2 - 4 Maylan Court
Corby
NN17 4DR
www.sodemsystem.com
email: sales@sodem.co.uk
Tel: 01536 408686
Fax: 01536 408687

STORAGE CONCEPTS LTD
Gate Road , Leicester Road Industrial Estate ,
Melton Mowbray , Leicestershire
LE13 ORG
www.storageconcepts.co.uk
Tel: 01664 410414
Fax: 01664 569969

VITSÚ
Centric Close
London
NW1 7EP
www.vitsoe.com
email: email@vitsoe.com
Tel: 020 7428 1606
Fax: 020 7424 9591

SOFAS

4 FRONT FURNITURE
Sofa Valley House, 9 Harbet Road
(Entrance On Blackwood Avenue)
London
N18 3QP
www.4ff.co.uk
email: info@4ff.co.uk
Tel: 020 8803 6446
Fax: 020 8803 6556

ALSTONS UPHOLSTERY LTD
Albro Works
Gosbecks Road
Colchester
ESSEX
www.alstons.co.uk
Tel: 01206 765343
Fax: 01206 763 401

ATTIC 2
Unit 1
127 Bute Street
Cardiff Bay
CF10 5LE
www.attic2.co.uk
email: lynsey@attic2.co.uk
Tel: 02920 490498

BRETZ
Alexander-Bretz-Street 2
55116 Gensingen
Germany
55116
www.bretz.com
email: cultsofa@bretz.de
Tel: 0049 672 78 950
Fax: 0049 676 21 030

BURGESS FURNITURE LTD
Hanworth Trading Estate
Feltham
Middlesex
TW13 6EH
www.burgessfurniture.com
email: sales@burgessfurniture.com
Tel: 020 8894 9231
Fax: 020 8894 2943

CELEBRITY MOTION FURNITURE
Celebrity Motion Furniture
Winsey Way, Alfreton Trading Estate,
Somercotes, Derbyshire De55 4ls
WIMSEY WAY, ALFRETON TRADING ESTATE,
SOMERCOTES, DERBYSHIRE DE55 4LS
www.celebrity-furniture.co.uk
Tel: 01773 604607
Fax: 01773 540 141

**CHARLES PAGE FURNITURE & INTERIOR
DESIGN**
61 Fairfax Road
Swiss Cottage
London
NW6 4EE
www.charlespage.co.uk
email: info@charlespage.co.uk
Tel: 02073 289851
Fax: 02073 287240

COLLINS & HAYES FURNITURE LTD
Menzies Road, Ponswood
St Leonards-On-Sea, Hastings
East Sussex
TN38 9XF
www.collinsandhayes.com
email: mcreedy@collinsandhayes.com
Tel: 01424 720027
Fax: 01424 720270

CONNECTION SEATING LTD
15 Great Sutton Street
Clerkenwell
London
EC1V 0BX
www.connection.uk.com
email: sales@connection.uk.com
Tel: 0207 2539877
Fax: 01484 600125

**DAVID & JANE PAINE FURNITURE
COLLECTION**
4 Devereaux Court
Ipswich
Suffolk
IP4 2BF
www.dandjpainefurniturecollection.co.uk
email:
info@dandjpainefurniturecollection.co.uk
Tel: 07989 027656
Fax: 01473 232253

ETHOS
G Plan Upholstery Ltd
Hampton Park West
Melksham, Wiltshire
SN12 6GU
www.ethosfurniture.co.uk
email: info@ethosfurniture.co.uk
Tel: 01225 700880
Fax: 01225 792397

FRAMES FURNITURE
Cockaynes Orchard
Cockaynes Lane
Alresford
CO7 8BZ
www.framesuk.com
email: enquiries@framesuk.com
Tel: 01206 820301
Fax: 01206 820221

G PLAN UPHOLSTERY
Hampton Park West
Melksham
Wiltshire
SN12 6GU
www.gplan.co.uk†
email: info@gplan.co.uk
Tel: 01225 700880
Fax: 01225 792397

THE SOFA COLLECTION
www.thesofacollection.co.uk
info@thesofacollection.co.uk

The Sofa Collection showcases a
selection of the highest quality
handmade settees and armchairs.
The range is produced by one of the
country's leading upholstery
manufacturers and is available
exclusively from a selection of retailers
throughout the UK. Please visit our
website to view the range and for
details of your nearest stockist.

GURU
www.guru-design.com†
email: info@guru-design.com
Tel: 020 8960 6655

HEATON OFFICE INTERIORS
Campbeltown Road
Lairdside Technology Park
Birkenhead
CH41 9HP
www.heatons.net
email: sales@heatons.net
Tel: 01516 496000
Fax: 01516 496031

INTERIOR SUPPLY LTD
2/15 Chelsea Harbour Design Centre
London
SW10 0XE
www.interiorsupply.co.uk
email: info@interiorsupply.co.uk
Tel: 0207 352 0502
Fax: 0207 352 2026

JAMES ADAM FURNITURE LTD
26, Quayside
Woodbridge
Suffolk
IP12 1BH
www.jamesadam.com
email: sales@jamesadam.com
Tel: 01394 384471
Fax: 01394 384520

KESTERPORT LTD
Kestrel House
Hanworth Lane
Chertsey, Surrey
KT16 9JX
www.kesterport.com
email: contractsales@kesterport.com
Tel: 01932 573 600
Fax: 01932 573 698

OCEE DESIGN LTD
Tel: 01604 674674

PROTOCOL LTD
2-3 Bankside Park, 28 Thames Road
Barking
Essex
IG11 0HZ
www.protocoluk.com
email: sales@protocoluk.com
Tel: 0208 5916770
Fax: 0208 5917913

ROCHE BOBOIS UK
Smugglers Way
By Wandsworth Bridge
London
SW18 1AZ
www.roche-bobois.com
email: info.uk@roche-bobois.com
Tel: 0208 874 9818
Fax: 0208 874 9798

SCAN-THOR
35a Keighley Road
Silsden
West Yorkshire
BD20 0EB
Tel: 01535 656 002

WESLEY-BARRELL
Ducklington Mill, Standlake Road,
Ducklington, Witney,
Oxfordshire, OX29 7YR
Tel: 01993 893100
furniture@wesley-barrell.co.uk

In their Oxfordshire family workshops
Wesley-Barrell hand make an exclusive
range of classic sofas armchairs and
footstools. Natural materials and
traditional upholstery methods are used
and sofas can be finished with a range
of bespoke options. The collection
includes dining, occasional furniture and
home accessories. Wesley-Barrell also
offer an Interiors Advisory Service.

Visit one of the 15 nationwide
Wesley-Barrell showrooms or visit
www.wesley-barrell.co.uk

SOFA WORKSHOP
122 Hawley Lane
Farnborough
Hampshire, GU14 9AX
www.sofaworkshop.com/information/trade-accounts
email: claire.white@sofaworkshop.com
Tel: 0208 7890793

THE DAVID KNIGHT COLLECTION & GREENSMITH UPHOLSTERY LIMITED
Greenbank
Coach Drive
Quarndon, Derby
DE22 5JX
www.davidknightcollection.co.uk
email:
thedavidknightcollection@btinternet.com
Tel: 01332 551818
Fax: 01332 557775

WHITEHEAD DESIGNS
Atlas Mills
Birchwood Road
Long Eaton
NG10 3ND
www.whiteheads.co.uk†
email: info@whiteheaddesigns.com
Tel: 0115 972 5056
Fax: 0115 946 1044

UPHOLSTERED FURNITURE

ALBERT E. CHAPMAN LTD
17 Crouch Hill
London
N4 4AP
albertechapman.co.uk
Tel: 020 7272 2536
Fax: 020 7263 1033

ALEXANDER MILES
68 Welbeck Street
London, W1G 0AS
www.alexandermiles.co.uk
email: office@alexandermiles.co.uk
Tel: 0207 486 4545
Fax: 0207 935 2684

ALSTONS UPHOLSTERY LTD
Albro Works
Gosbecks Road
Colchester, ESSEX
www.alstons.co.uk
Tel: 01206 765343
Fax: 01206 763 401

ASHLEY MANOR UPHOLSTERY LTD
Unit 1 Woodside Ind. Estate
Pedmore Road
Dudley, West Midlands, DY20RL
www.ashleymanor.co.uk
email: info@ashleymanor.co.uk
Tel: 01384 486800
Fax: 01384 473070

BURGESS FURNITURE LTD
Hanworth Trading Estate
Feltham, Middlesex, TW13 6EH
www.burgessfurniture.com
email: sales@burgessfurniture.com
Tel: 020 8894 9231
Fax: 020 8894 2943

CELEBRITY MOTION FURNITURE
Celebrity Motion Furniture
Winsey Way, Alfreton Trading Estate,
Somercotes, Derbyshire De55 4ls
WIMSEY WAY, ALFRETON TRADING ESTATE,
SOMERCOTES, DERBYSHIRE DE55 4LS
www.celebrity-furniture.co.uk
Tel: 01773 604607
Fax: 01773 540 141

BEAUMONT & FLETCHER
Showroom, 261 Fulham Road,
London, SW3 6HY
Tel: 020 7352 5594
sales@beaumontandfletcher.com
www.beaumontandfletcher.com

Beaumont & Fletcher have an
international reputation as makers
of the finest English handmade furniture.
Each piece is made to order by skilled
craftsmen, using only the finest
traditional materials: seasoned timber
frames, horsehair stuffing and hand-tied
coil springs. Meticulous finishing and
stitching ensure an unequalled quality
that will last for generations.

sinclair matthews

TRADITIONAL VALUES   CONTEMPORARY STYLE

Shown here is the new Charlbury Sofa. Combining traditional comfort
with a contemporary twist with the chrome nailing. Available in six
sofa sizes with a matching armchair.

Ferry Yacht Station. Ferry Road. Thames Ditton. Surrey KT7 0YB
phone. 020 8398 5694 fax. 020 8398 6709
web. www.sinclairmatthews.co.uk

CLASSIC UPHOLSTERY
Estate Yard,
Upper Harlestone,
Northampton.
NN7 4EH
email: classic.upholstery@btintermet.com
Tel: 01604 584556

COLLINS & HAYES FURNITURE LTD
Menzies Road, Ponswood
St Leonards-On-Sea, Hastings
East Sussex
TN38 9XF
www.collinsandhayes.com
email: mcreedy@collinsandhayes.com
Tel: 01424 720027
Fax: 01424 720270

COURTNEY CONTRACT FURNISHERS LTD
J&K Enterprise Centre
Paycocke Road
Basildon
SS14 3DY
www.courtney-contracts.co.uk
email: info@courtney-contracts.co.uk
Tel: 01268 531771
Fax: 01268 271299

DAVID & JANE PAINE FURNITURE COLLECTION
4 Devereaux Court
Ipswich
Suffolk
IP4 2BF
www.dandjpainefurniturecollection.co.uk
email:
info@dandjpainefurniturecollection.co.uk
Tel: 07989 027656
Fax: 01473 232253

DAVID SEYFRIED LTD
1/5 Chelsea Harbour Design Centre
London
SW10 0XE
www.davidseyfried.com
email: info@davidseyfried.com
Tel: 020 7823 3848
Fax: 020 7823 3221

ELAINE PHILLIPS ANTIQUES LTD
2 Royal Parade
Harrogate
North Yorkshire
HG1 2SZ
www.elainephillipsantiques.co.uk
email: info@elainephillipsantiques.co.uk
Tel: 01423 569745

EME FURNITURE
Blackaddie Road
Sanquhar
Dumfriesshire
DG4 6DE
www.emefurniture.co.uk
email: info@emefurniture.co.uk
Tel: 01659 50404
Fax: 01659 50107

ERCOL FURNITURE LTD
Summerleys Road
Princes Risborough
Bucks
HP27 9PX
www.ercol.com
email: edward.tadros@ercol.com
Tel: 01844 271 800
Fax: 01844 271887

FERCO SEATING SYSTEMS LTD
Unit 28
Atcham Business Park, Atcham
Shrewsbury, Shropshire
SY4 4UG
www.fercoseating.co.uk
email: info@fercoseating.co.uk
Tel: 0845 8123100
Fax: 0845 8123101

G.G.I OFFICE FURNITURE (U K) LTD
Global Way
Darwen
Lancashire
BB3 0RW
www.globaltotaloffice.com
email: sales@ggieurope.com
Tel: 01254 778500
Fax: 01254 778519

GST-GLOBAL SOURCING & TRADING LIMITED
22 Dalston Gardens
Stanmore
Middlesex
HA7 1BU
www.gstuk.com
email: anna@papillonuk.com
Tel: 0208 2061818
Fax: 0208 2061218

GUARDSMAN FURNITURE SOLUTIONS GROUP
Valspar Industries (Uk) Ltd
152 Milton Park
Abingdon, Oxfordshire
OX14 4SD
www.guardsman.co.uk
email: marketing@valspareurope.com
Tel: 01235 444700
Fax: 01235 862730

GUSTAVIAN
59 Lancaster Avenue
Hadley Wood
EN4 0ER
www.gustavian.com
email: info@gustavian.com
Tel: 0208 440 8043
Fax: 020 8216 3640

HIGHLY SPRUNG LTD
310 Battersea Park Road London Sw11 3bu
www.highlysprung.net
email: bpr@highlysprung.co.uk
Tel: 02079 241124
Fax: 02072 285476

HITCH MYLIUS LTD
301 Alma Road
Enfield
Middlesex
EN3 7BB
www.hitchmylius.co.uk
email: info@hitchmylius.co.uk
Tel: 020 8443 2616
Fax: 020 8443 2617

HOSSACK & GRAY
Studio 10, 9e Queens Yard
Whitepost Lane
London
E9 5EN
hossackandgray.co.uk
email: hossackanggray@hotmail.com
Tel: 02089 863345
Fax: 02089 863345

**ICONIC FURNITURE:
CONTEMPORARY CLASSICS,
DESIGNED AND BUILT TO LAST
Tel: + 44 (0)1159 469 900
Web: www.iconicfurniture.com
Email: iconicdesign@hotmail.co.uk**

A new range of beautifully
proportioned and solidly built pieces,
individually crafted using traditional
upholstery techniques: sofas, sofa beds,
armchairs, stools, banquettes,
upholstered headboards, bed units.
Full custom design service and
comprehensive range of upholstery
fabrics. Complete interiors service.

HYDE HOUSE BESPOKE FURNITURE
289 Lower High Street
Watford
Herts
WD17 2HY
www.hydehouse.co.uk
email: sales@hydehouse.co.uk
Tel: 01284 330 098
Fax: 01923 262 670

INTERIOR SUPPLY LTD
2/15 Chelsea Harbour Design Centre
London
SW10 0XE
www.interiorsupply.co.uk
email: info@interiorsupply.co.uk
Tel: 0207 352 0502
Fax: 0207 352 2026

JACK AND ROSE
Unit 1, Solhamptom Farm Business Park
Astley
Stourport On Severn
DY13 0RR
www.jackandrose.co.uk
email: info@jackandrose.co.uk
Tel: 01299 828930
Fax: 01299 829786

JEFFREYS INTERIORS
8 North West Circus Place
Edinburgh
EH3 6ST
www.jeffreys-interiors.co.uk
email: info@jeffreys-interiors.co.uk
Tel: 0131 247 8010
Fax: 0845 882 2656

KINGCOME SOFAS

KINGCOME SOFAS
114 Fulham Road
London SW3 6HU
Tel: 020 7244 7747
Email: sales@kingcomesofas.co.uk
Web: www.kingcomesofas.co.uk

Kingcome Sofas, known for its exceptional quality, comfort and workmanship, is owned by the fabric and wallpaper company, Colefax and Fowler.

Kingcome furniture is designed exclusively in England, using only the finest materials. Every piece is meticulously hand–finished to meet the exacting demands of each Kingcome client.

LFS
Unit 1, Autumn Yard, 39 Autumn Street
London, E3 2TT
email: sales@lfsuk.com
Tel: 020 8983 9111
Fax: 020 8983 9222

LP FURNITURE
The Old Brewery
Short Acre Street
Walsall West Midlands, WS2 8HW
www.lpfurniture.net†
email: frenchfurniture@btconnect.com
Tel: 01922 746764
Fax: 01922 611316

MARGARET SHERIDAN
36 Market Place
Hingham
Norwich, NR9 4AF
www.margaretsheridan.co.uk
email: enquiries@margaretsheridan.co.uk
Tel: 01953 850691
Fax: 01953 851447

MODUS FURNITURE
5 Westcombe Trading Estate
Station Road
Ilminster, SOMERSET
www.modusfurniture.co.uk
email: info@modusfurniture.co.uk
Tel: 01460 258590
Fax: 01460 57004

MOVISI GMBH
Burghaldenweg 62-64
70469 Stuttgart
Germany
www.movisi.com
email: info@movisi.com
Tel: 0049 711 505 5485
Fax: 0049 711 505 1368

NATUZZI

Natuzzi Stores:
London - Finchley Road, Selfridges and Harrods, Thurrock, Croydon, Manchester, Cardiff and selected House of Fraser stores across the UK.
www.natuzzi.co.uk

Natuzzi is Italy's largest furniture manufacturer and the world's leading producer of leather sofas. Many of its products are made to order and customers can choose from hundreds of compositions, colours and finishes. Natuzzi's range also includes stylish furnishing and accessories to provide a "total look" for the home.

OCEE DESIGN LTD
Tel: 01604 674674

PROJEKTER INDUSTRIAL DESIGN
Springwall 4
47051 Duisburg, Germany
www.projekter.de
email: contact@playzzle.de
Tel: 0049 203 728 1827

ROSEHILL FURNITURE GROUP
Brooke Court
Handforth
Wilmslow, SK9 3ND
www.rosehill.co.uk
email: sales@rosehill.co.uk
Tel: 0161 485 1717
Fax: 0161 485 2727

SANDLER SEATING
58 - 64 Three Colts Lane, London, E2 6JR
Tel: 0207 749 3000
Fax: 0207 729 2843

SAXON CONTRACT FURNITURE
Manchester Road
Bolton, BL3 2NZ
Tel: 01204 365377
Fax: 01204 387554

SCAN-THOR
35a Keighley Road
Silsden, West Yorkshire, BD20 0EB
Tel: 01535 656 002

SILVERMOON STYLES LTD
14 Holmwood Court
Keymer Road, Hassocks, BN6 8AS
www.silvermoonstyles.com
email: info@silvermoonstyles.com
Tel: 01273 844413
Fax: 01273 844413

SINCLAIR MATTHEWS LTD
Ferry Yacht Station
Ferry Road
Thames Ditton
Surrey, KT7 0XZ
Tel: 020 8398 5694
Fax: 020 8398 6709
showroom@sinclairmatthews.co.uk
www.sinclairmatthews.co.uk

Sinclair Matthews design and manufacture bespoke sofas and chairs in their factories in Sussex. They have a large showroom in Surrey where the majority of their designs can be viewed. Shown here is the 'Frome' All designs can be adapted to suite your design wishes. They also have a large fabric library to choose from or you can supply your own fabric.

SOFA WORKSHOP
122 Hawley Lane
Farnborough
Hampshire, GU14 9AX
www.sofaworkshop.com/information/trade-accounts
email: claire.white@sofaworkshop.com
Tel: 0208 7890793

SPRINGVALE LEATHER
Foundry Street
Rawtenstall
Rossendale, BB4 6HQ
www.springvaleleather.co.uk
email: sarah.foulds@springvaleleather.co.uk
Tel: 01706 211830
Fax: 01706 229170

THE CAMPBELL GROUP
Units 1-3, Block 1
Alva Industrial Estate
Alva, FK12 5JA
www.thecampbellgroup.co.uk
email: info@thecampbellgroup.co.uk
Tel: 01259 760572
Fax: 01259 769434

THE CONRAN SHOP
81 Fulham Road
London, SW3 6RD
www.conranshop.co.uk
Tel: 02075 897401
Fax: 02078 237015

THE DAVID KNIGHT COLLECTION & GREENSMITH UPHOLSTERY LIMITED
Greenbank, Coach Drive,
Quarndon, Derby, DE22 5JX
www.davidknightcollection.co.uk
thedavidknightcollection@btinternet.com
Tel: 01332 551818
Fax: 01332 557775

THOMAS INTERIORS
Madges Farm House
Chearsley Road
Long Crendon
HP18 9AW
www.thomasinteriors.co.uk
email: info@thomasinteriors.co.uk
Tel: 01844 201 254
Fax: 01844 208 533

WESLEY-BARRELL
Ducklington Mill
Standlake Road
Ducklington
OX29 7YR
www.wesley-barrell.co.uk
email: furniture@wesley-barrell.co.uk
Tel: 01993 893 100
Fax: 01993 702720

WHITEHEAD DESIGNS
Atlas Mills
Birchwood Road
Long Eaton
NG10 3ND
www.whiteheads.co.uk†
email: info@whiteheaddesigns.com
Tel: 0115 972 5056
Fax: 0115 946 1044

WILKHAHN LTD
Morelands
5-23 Old Street
London
EC1V 9HL
www.wilkhahn.com
email: greg@wilkhahn.co.uk
Tel: 02073 242900
Fax: 02073 242901

Heating & Ventilation

BAXI GROUP
Brooks House
Coventry Road
Warwick
CV34 4LL
www.baxigroup.com/uk
email: enquiries@baxigroup.com
Tel: 0844 871 1555
Fax: 01772 646449

CAMINOS STOVES, LANDY VENT LTD
Foster House
2 Redditich Rd
Studley, Warwickshire
B80 7AX
www.caminosstoves.co.uk
email: sales@caminosstoves.co.uk
Tel: 01527 857814
Fax: 01527 854101

CHARTERED INSTITUTE OF PLUMBING AND HEATING ENGINEERING
64 Station Lane
Hornchurch
Essex
RM12 6NB
www.ciphe.org.uk
email: info@ciphe.org.uk
Tel: 01708 472791
Fax: 01708 448987

COPPER DEVELOPMENT ASSOCIATION
5 Grovelands Business Centre
Boundary Way
Hemel Hempstead, Herts
HP2 7TE
www.copperinfo.co.uk
email: mail@copperdev.co.uk
Fax: 01442 275716

JETMASTER FIRES
Unit 2 Peacock Trading Estate
Goodwood Road
Eastleigh, Hants
SO50 4NT
www.jetmaster.co.uk
email: jetmastersales@aol.com
Tel: 0870 727 0105
Fax: 0870 727 0106

THE RADIATOR COMPANY
Trc House
13 - 14 Charlwoods Road
East Grinstead
RH19 2HU
www.theradiatorcompany.co.uk
email: sales@theradiatorcompany.co.uk
Tel: 01342 302250
Fax: 01342 302260

TROX UK LTD
Caxton Way
Thetford
Norfolk
IP24 3SQ
www.troxuk.co.uk
email: info@troxuk.co.uk
Tel: 01842 754545
Fax: 01842 763051

WORCESTER BOSCH GROUP
Cotswold Way
Warndon
Worcester
WR4 9SW
www.worcester-bosch.co.uk
Tel: 01905 754 624
Fax: 01905 754 619

AIR CONDITIONING

BDC
Bdc Head Office
550 White Hart Lane
London
N17 7RQ
www.bdc.co.uk
email: sales@bdc.co.uk
Tel: 0844 811 0040
Fax: 0844 811 0041

DIFFUSION / ET ENVIRONMENTAL
47 Central Avenue
West Molesey
KT8 2QZ
www.diffusion-group.co.uk
email: diffusion@etenv.co.uk
Tel: 02087 830033
Fax: 0208 783 0140

LAWTON IMPORTS
Fanton Barn 2
Fanton Hall Farm
Wickford, Essex
SS12 9JF
www.lawton-imports.com
email: sales@lawton-imports.co.uk
Tel: 01268 769444
Fax: 01268 560271

RAPID CLIMATE CONTROL LTD
423 Becontree Avenue
Dagenham
Essex
RM8 3UH
www.rapidclimatecontrol.com
email: info@rapidclimatecontrol.com
Tel: 0208 598 4000
Fax: 0808 590 8303

SPACE AIR
Willway Court
1 Opus Park
Guildford
GU1 1SZ
www.spaceair.co.uk
email: info@spaceair.co.uk
Tel: 01483 504883
Fax: 01483 574835

STORAGE CONCEPTS LTD
Pate Road , Leicester Road Industrial Estate ,
Melton Mowbray , Leicestershire
LE13 ORG
www.storageconcepts.co.uk
Tel: 01664 410414
Fax: 01664 569969

CENTRAL HEATING

ARISTON THERMO UK LTD
Ariston Building
Hughenden Avenue
High Wycombe
HP13 5FT
www.ariston.co.uk
email: info@uk.aristonthermo.com
Tel: 01494 755600
Fax: 01494 535551

BAXI GROUP
Brooks House
Coventry Road
Warwick
CV34 4LL
www.baxigroup.com/uk
email: enquiries@baxigroup.com
Tel: 0844 871 1555
Fax: 01772 646449

CALOR GAS
Athena Drive
Tachbrook Park
Warwick
CV34 6RL
www.calor.co.uk
email: askcalor@calor.co.uk
Tel: 0800 626 626

ELECTRIC HEATING COMPANY (EHC)
Unit 40, Block 5
Third Road, Blantyre Ind. Est.
Blantyre, Glasgow
G72 0UP
www.electric-heatingcompany.co.uk
email: bill@electric-heatingcompany.co.uk
Tel: 01698 820533
Fax: 01698 825697

HORTSMANN CONTROLS LTD
South Bristol Business Park
Roman Farm Road
Bristol
BS4 1UP
www.horstmann.co.uk
email: sales@horstmann.co.uk
Tel: 01179 978 8700
Fax: 01179 978 8701

KERMI UK LTD
7 Brunel Road
Corby
Northants
NN17 4JW
www.kermi.co.uk
email: marketing@kermi.co.uk
Tel: 01536 400 004
Fax: 01536 446 614

LEEMICK UNDERFLOOR HEATING LTD
70 London Road
Newington
Sittingbourne
ME9 7 NR
www.leemick.co.uk
email: ml@leemick.co.uk
Tel: 01795 841249
Fax: 01795 841249

SMITH'S ENVIRONMENTAL PRODUCTS
Units 1-2 Blackall Industrial Estate
South Woodham Ferriers
Chelmsford, Essex
CM3 5UW
www.smiths-env.com
email: info@smiths-env.com
Tel: 01245 324900
Fax: 01245 324422

TRIANCO HEATING PRODUCTS LTD
Thornncliffe Industrial Estate
Chapeltown
Sheffield
S35 2PH
www.trianco.co.uk
email: info@trianco.co.uk
Tel: 0114 257 2300
Fax: 0114 257 1419

GAS FIRES

BRILLIANT FIRES
Thwaites Close
Shadsworth Business Park
Blackburn
BB1 2QQ
www.brilliantfires.co.uk
email: info@brilliantfires.co.uk
Tel: 01254 682384
Fax: 01254 672647

BURLEY APPLIANCES
Tel: 01572 756956
Fax: 01572 724 390

CALOR GAS
Athena Drive
Tachbrook Park
Warwick
CV34 6RL
www.calor.co.uk
email: askcalor@calor.co.uk
Tel: 0800 626 626

CAPITAL FIREPLACES LTD
Units 12-17 Henlow Trading Estate
Henlow
Bedfordshire
SG16 6DS
www.capitalfireplaces.co.uk
email: alex.shaw@capitalfireplaces.co.uk
Tel: 01462 813138
Fax: 08009 804847

FIREGROUP
5 Stenhouse Mill Wynd
Edinburgh
EH11 3LR
www.firegroup.co.uk
email: sales@firegroup.co.uk
Tel: 0131 444 2262
Fax: 0131 444 1726

LAWTON IMPORTS
Fanton Barn 2
Fanton Hall Farm
Wickford, Essex
SS12 9JF
www.lawton-imports.com
email: sales@lawton-imports.co.uk
Tel: 01268 769444
Fax: 01268 560271

MAGIGLO LTD
Lysander Close
Broadstairs, Kent, CT10 2YJ
www.magiglo.co.uk
email: sales@magiglo.co.uk
Tel: 01843 602863
Fax: 01843 86 0108

MARBLE HILL FIREPLACES
70-72 Richmond Road
Twickenham, TW1 3BE
www.marblehill.co.uk
Tel: 0208 892 1488
Fax: 0208 891 6591

SPIRIT FIRES LIMITED
4 Beaumont Square
Aycliffe Industrial Park
Newton Aycliffe, Co Durham
DL5 6SW
www.spiritfires.co.uk
Tel: 01325 327221
Fax: 01325 327929

RADIATORS

ACOVA
Unit 4, Watchmoor Point
Camberley
Surrey
GU15 3AD
www.acova.co.uk
email: pam.hay@acova.co.uk
Tel: 01252 531207
Fax: 01252 531201

AEL HEATING SOLUTIONS
4 Berkeley Court, Manor Park,
Runcorn , Cheshire, WA7 1TQ
www.aelheating.com
email: sales@aelheating.com
Tel: 01928 579 068
Fax: 01928 579 523

BISQUE
23 Queen Square, Bath, BA1 2HX
www.bisque.co.uk
email: mail@bisque.co.uk
Tel: 01225 47 8500
Fax: 0122 547 8586

AEON
Unit 7 & 8, 7 Grovebury Road,
Leighton Buzzard, Beds LU7 4SR
Tel: 01525 379505
Email: info@pitacs.com
Web: www.aeon.uk.com

Aeon epitomises stylish, sculptural heating for contemporary homes available from a nationwide network of accredited retailers. Made from high-quality stainless steel, Aeon designer radiators look fabulous and deliver exceptional performance. The 40-strong collection (including Twister above) is engineered to exacting standards and each hand-finished product carries a 20-year guarantee.

MARBLE HEATING COMPANY
Po Box 51292
London, SE17 3AA
www.marbleheating.co.uk
email: sales@marbleheating.co.uk
Tel: 0845 230 0877
Fax: 0845 230 0878

MHS RADIATORS
3 Juniper West, Fenton Way, Southfields
Business Park, Basildon,
Essex, SS15 6SJ
www.mhsradiators.co.uk
email: kbandey@mhsradiators.co.uk
Tel: 01268 546 700
Fax: 01268 888 250

SMR BATHROOMS
Unit Q, Fishers Grove
Farlington, Portsmouth, PO6 1RN
www.smrbathrooms.co.uk
email: general-enquiry@smrbathrooms.co.uk
Tel: 08452 255045
Fax: 08452 255046

THE CAST IRON RECLAMATION COMPANY
The White House
8a Burgh Heath Road
Epsom, Surrey, KT17 4LJ
perfect-irony.com
email: enquiries@perfect-irony.com
Tel: 02089 775977
Fax: 01372 726845

THE RADIATOR COMPANY
Trc House, 13 - 14 Charlwoods Road,
East Grinstead, RH19 2HU
www.theradiatorcompany.co.uk
email: sales@theradiatorcompany.co.uk
Tel: 01342 302250
Fax: 01342 302260

TIVOLIS
SP Heating Ltd, Unit A,
Hight Street, Didcot,
Oxon, OX11 7LW
Tel: 01235 515 340
Fax: 01235 515 348
E-mail: sales@tivolisdesign.com
Web: www.tivolisdesign.com

We are a leading manufacturing and distribution company of heated towel rails and compact panel radiators with over five years experience in the UK market and offering the widest choices for our customers.

The Glass Radiator Co.

THE GLASS RADIATOR COMPANY
Unit 7, Devizes Trade Centre,
Hopton Park Industrial Estate, Devizes,
Wiltshire, SN10 2EH
Tel: 01380 738840
Email: info@glassradiators.co.uk
Web: www.glassradiators.co.uk

Glass radiators for electric or plumbed
heating systems are available. Our
exceptional radiators have now been
joined by innovative electrically
controlled glass systems including
Switchable Privacy Glass which
changes from clear to opaque, Solar
Control Glass which controls the suns
glare and heated windows used as a
complete central heating system.

WALNEY RADIATORS
Tel: 0870 733 0011
E-mail: info@walneyuk.com
Web: www.walneyuk.com

Walney Radiators supplier of high
quality radiators for over 30 years has
now opened a showroom in St
Albans.
The radiator range is carefully selected
from high-quality manufacturers
across Europe. Bringing together a
comprehensive range of radiators in
over 100 colours and finishes, the
collection includes aluminium, cast
iron, steel, contemporary, tubular and
heated towel rails.

TUSCAN FOUNDRY PRODUCTS
Unit 8 Tamar Business Units
River Tamar Way
Holsworthy
EX22 6HL
www.tuscanfoundry.co.uk
email: info@tuscanfoundry.co.uk
Tel: 01409 255120
Fax: 0845 3450215

RENEWABLE ENERGY PRODUCTS

ARISTON THERMO UK LTD
Ariston Building
Hughenden Avenue
High Wycombe
HP13 5FT
www.ariston.co.uk
email: info@uk.aristonthermo.com
Tel: 01494 755600
Fax: 01494 535551

BAXI GROUP
Brooks House
Coventry Road
Warwick
CV34 4LL
www.baxigroup.com/uk
email: enquiries@baxigroup.com
Tel: 0844 871 1555
Fax: 01772 646449

LEEMICK UNDERFLOOR HEATING LTD
70 London Road
Newington
Sittingbourne
ME9 7 NR
www.leemick.co.uk
email: ml@leemick.co.uk
Tel: 01795 841249
Fax: 01795 841249

MORLEY STOVE COMPANY LTD
Marsh Lane
Ware
Herts
SG12 9QB
www.morley-stoves.co.uk
email: info@morley-stoves.co.uk
Tel: 01920 468001
Fax: 01920 463893

MORLEY STOVE COMPANY LTD
Marsh Lane
Ware
Herts
SG12 9QB
www.morley-stoves.co.uk
email: info@morley-stoves.co.uk
Tel: 01920 468001
Fax: 01920 463893

NU-HEAT UNDERFLOOR & RENEWABLES
Heathpark House, Devonshire Road
Heathpark Industrial Estate
Honiton, Devon
EX14 1SD
www.nu-heat.co.uk
email: info@nu-heat.co.uk
Tel: 01404 549 770
Fax: 01404 549 771

SMITH'S ENVIRONMENTAL PRODUCTS
Units 1-2 Blackall Industrial Estate
South Woodham Ferriers
Chelmsford, Essex
CM3 5UW
www.smiths-env.com
email: info@smiths-env.com
Tel: 01245 324900
Fax: 01245 324422

SPACE AIR
Willway Court
1 Opus Park
Guildford
GU1 1SZ
www.spaceair.co.uk
email: info@spaceair.co.uk
Tel: 01483 504883
Fax: 01483 574835

THE UNDERFLOOR HEATING MANUFACTURERS' ASSOCIATION UHMA
39 Ethelbert Road
Birchington
Kent
CT7 9PX
www.uhma.org.uk
email: uhma410@aol.com
Tel: 01843 842241

TRIANCO HEATING PRODUCTS LTD
Thornncliffe Industrial Estate
Chapeltown
Sheffield
S35 2PH
www.trianco.co.uk
email: info@trianco.co.uk
Tel: 0114 257 2300
Fax: 0114 257 1419

UNDERFLOOR HEATING

EBECO UK LTD
Unit N
Kingsfield Business Centre
Redhill , Surrey
RH1 4DP
www.ebeco.com
email: uksales@ebeco.com
Tel: 01737 761767
Fax: 01737 507907

FANSKI GROUP INC
M&E Industrial Zone, Yuhuan County, Zhejiang
Provice, 317600 Pr China
317600
www.fanski.com
email: fanski@fanski.com
Tel: 86 576 87276781
Fax: 86 576 87276797

FLOWCRETE UK LTD
The Flooring Technology Centre
Booth Lane
Sandbach, Cheshire
CW11 3QF
www.flowcrete.com
email: uk@flowcrete.com
Tel: 01270 753 000
Fax: 01270 753 333

KARELIA WOOD FLOORING
Highfield Drive
Churchfields Industrial Estate
St Leonards On Sea
TN38 9TG
www.kareliaparketti.com
email: enquiries@kareliawoodflooring.co.uk
Tel: 01424 856805
Fax: 01424 856855

LEEMICK UNDERFLOOR HEATING LTD
70 London Road
Newington
Sittingbourne
ME9 7 NR
www.leemick.co.uk
email: ml@leemick.co.uk
Tel: 01795 841249
Fax: 01795 841249

MARBLE HEATING COMPANY
Po Box 51292
London
SE17 3AA
www.marbleheating.co.uk
email: sales@marbleheating.co.uk
Tel: 0845 230 0877
Fax: 0845 230 0878

MARMOX UK LTD
Unit 3, Forward Way
Laker Road
Rochester
ME1 3QX
www.marmox.co.uk
email: sales@marmox.co.uk
Tel: 01634 862277
Fax: 01634 864223

NU-HEAT UNDERFLOOR & RENEWABLES
Heathpark House, Devonshire Road
Heathpark Industrial Estate
Honiton, Devon
EX14 1SD
www.nu-heat.co.uk
email: info@nu-heat.co.uk
Tel: 01404 549 770
Fax: 01404 549 771

SPEEDHEAT
Iona House
Stratford Rd
Wicken , Milton Keynes
MK19†6DF
www.speedheat.co.uk
email: info@speedheat.co.uk
Tel: 01908 562 211
Fax: 01908 562 205

THE UNDERFLOOR HEATING MANUFACTURERS' ASSOCIATION UHMA
39 Ethelbert Road
Birchington
Kent
CT7 9PX
www.uhma.org.uk
email: uhma410@aol.com
Tel: 01843 842241

THERMOTECH
Dolphin House
Gorseinon Road
Swansea
SA4 9GE
www.thermotech-underfloorheating.co.uk
email: info@thermotech-underfloorheating.co.uk
Tel: 0845 224 8938
Fax: 0845 224 0932

TRIANCO HEATING PRODUCTS LTD
Thornncliffe Industrial Estate
Chapeltown
Sheffield
S35 2PH
www.trianco.co.uk
email: info@trianco.co.uk
Tel: 0114 257 2300
Fax: 0114 257 1419

WAXMAN CERAMICS LTD
Grove Mills
Elland
West Yorkshire
HX5 9DZ
www.waxmanceramics.co.uk
email: sales@waxmanceramics.co.uk
Tel: 01422 311331
Fax: 01422 310654

VENTILATION

DIFFUSION / ET ENVIRONMENTAL
47 Central Avenue
West Molesey
KT8 2QZ
www.diffusion-group.co.uk
email: diffusion@etenv.co.uk
Tel: 02087 830033
Fax: 0208 783 0140

RAPID CLIMATE CONTROL LTD
423 Becontree Avenue
Dagenham
Essex
RM8 3UH
www.rapidclimatecontrol.com
email: info@rapidclimatecontrol.com
Tel: 0208 598 4000
Fax: 0808 590 8303

SPACE AIR
Willway Court
1 Opus Park
Guildford
GU1 1SZ
www.spaceair.co.uk
email: info@spaceair.co.uk
Tel: 01483 504883
Fax: 01483 574835

Interior Design Services

CONNECTIONS INTERIORS LTD
286 -288 Leigh Road
Leigh-On-Sea
Essex
SS9 1BW
www.connectionsinteriors.co.uk
email: sales@connectionsinteriors.co.uk
Tel: 01702 470 939
Fax: 01702 480 238

DECORATIVE LIVING
The Studio
CHISWICK LONDON W4
www.decorativeliving.co.uk
email: info@decorativeliving.co.uk
Tel: 020 89950037

ELAINE PHILLIPS ANTIQUES LTD
2 Royal Parade
Harrogate
North Yorkshire
HG1 2SZ
www.elainephillipsantiques.co.uk
email: info@elainephillipsantiques.co.uk
Tel: 01423 569745

FIONA CAMPBELL LTD
259 New Kings Road
Parsons Green
London
SW6 4RB
www.fionacampbelldesign.co.uk
email: info@fionacampbelldesign.co.uk
Tel: 0207 731 3681
Fax: 0207 736 7436

G & H INTERIORS
The Chantry
Combe Raleigh
Honiton
EX14 4TQ
www.gandhinteriors.co.uk
email: info@gandhinteriors.co.uk
Tel: 01404 42063
Fax: 01404 45112

GILES COOK DESIGN
The Dove House
Astwood, Newport Pagnell
Bucks
MK16 9JX
www.gilescookdesign.co.uk
email: info@gilescookdesign.co.uk
Tel: 01234 391156
Fax: 01234 391156

GREEN COMMERCIAL
88
Gillespie Road
Highbury
N5 1LN
www.interior4u.co.uk
email: james@interior4u.co.uk
Tel: 0207 359 7924
Fax: 0207 354 0077

HARROW GREEN DESIGN & BUILD
16 Bastwick Street
London
EC1V 3PS
www.hgdb.co.uk
email: hgdb@harrowgreen.com
Tel: 020 014 3088
Fax: 020 014 3089

HELEN GREEN DESIGN
29 Milner Street
London
SW3 3QD
www.helengreendesign.com
email: mail@helengreendesign.com
Tel: 020 7352 3344
Fax: 020 7352 5544

JACK AND ROSE
Unit 1, Solhamptom Farm Business Park
Astley
Stourport On Severn
DY13 0RR
www.jackandrose.co.uk
email: info@jackandrose.co.uk
Tel: 01299 828930
Fax: 01299 829786

LEFA PRINT
Enterprise Works
Lefa Business Park
Edgington Way
DA14 5BH
www.lefaprint.com
email: info@lefaprint.com
Tel: 0208 3022555
Fax: 0208 3021333

NOCHINTZ LTD
Carvers Warehouse
77 Dale Street
Manchester
M1 2HG
www.nochintz.co.uk
email: info@nochintzltd.co.uk
Tel: 0161 236 1412
Fax: 0161 880 2407

P-ARCH
Petek Mimarlik Muhendislik
Portakal Yokusu Duvarci Sok
19/2 34300 Ortakoy İStanbul
TURKEY
www.p-arch.com
email: info@p-arch.com
Tel: 0090 212 2366498
Fax: 0090 212 2599588

SAMANTHA JOHNSON DESIGN
34 Cromwell Road
Maidenhead
SL6 6BJ
www.samanthajohnsondesign.com
email: sj@samanthajohnsondesign.com
Tel: 01628 632517
Fax: 01628 632717

SAND & BIRCH DESIGN
Viale Xxi Aprile, 10 04100 Latina (Lt) Italy
4100
www.sandbirch.com
email: info@sandbirch.com
Tel: 0039 (0)773 1762584
Fax: 0039 (0)773 1760684

SASHA WADDELL FURNITURE (TEED INTERIORS LTD)
Tel: 0208 979 9189
Fax: 0208 979 0804

SHADES OF JAPAN
www.shadesofjapan.net
email: glennjoachim@ntlworld.com
Tel: 01476 594603

TAYLOR ETC
Beaufort Road
Plasmarl
Swansea
SA6 8JG
www.taylorsetc.co.uk
email: info@taylortiles.co.uk
Tel: 01792 797712
Fax: 01792 791103

TH:2 DESIGNS LTD
Studio 405
The Chambers
Chelsea Harbour, London
SW10 0XF
www.th2designs.co.uk
email: info@th2designs.co.uk
Tel: 020 7349 9494

VANGUARD CONTRACTS LTD
2 Birch Court
Blackpole East
Worcester
WR3 8SG
www.vanguardcontracts.co.uk†
email: sales@vanguardcontracts.co.uk
Tel: 01905 759700
Fax: 01905 759711

VASSALLO MELLOR PARRIS
8 Plato Place
72-74 St Dionis Road
London
SW6 4TU
www.vmpdesign.co.uk
email: mail@vmpdesign.co.uk
Tel: 02077 317903

COMMERCIAL FIT-OUT
ASSOCIATION OF INTERIOR SPECIALISTS
Olton Bridge
245 Warwick Road
Solihull
B92 7AH
www.ais-interiors.org.uk
email: info@ais-interiors.org.uk
Tel: 0121 707 0077
Fax: 0121 706 1949

AXIOM DISPLAYS LTD
Mersey Road North
Failsworth
Manchester
M35 9LT
www.axiom-displays.co.uk
email: info@axiom-displays.co.uk
Tel: 0161 681 1371
Fax: 0161 683 4641

DAUPHIN UK
12-16 Clerkenwell Road
Clerkenwell
London
EC1M 5PQ
www.dauphin-group.com
email: info@dauphinuk.com
Tel: 020 73246 210
Fax: 020 73246 211

ECONOWALL
Joyces Farm Buildings
Southminster Road
Mayland
CM3 6EB
www.econowall.co.uk
email: sales@econowall.co.uk
Tel: 0845 0942 751
Fax: 0845 0942 761

ESM
Liberty House
Unit C5
West Mill, Gravesend
DA11 0DL
www.esm-uk.com
email: mail@esm-uk.com
Tel: 01474 536360
Fax: 01474 535822

FAIR TRADES LTD.
Prenton Business Park
Prenton
Wirral
L43 3EA
www.homepro.com
email: info@fairtrades.co.uk
Tel: 08707 38 48 58
Fax: 08707 38 48 68

FINESSE GROUP LTD
Cobbs Wood Estate
Brunswick Road
Ashford
TN23 1EH
www.finessegroup.com
email: info@finessegroup.com
Tel: 01233 663399
Fax: 01233 665599

HARROW GREEN DESIGN & BUILD
16 Bastwick Street
London
EC1V 3PS
www.hgdb.co.uk
email: hgdb@harrowgreen.com
Tel: 020 014 3088
Fax: 020 014 3089

HOG PLC
14 West Place, West Road
Harlow
Essex
CM20 2GY
www.hogdirect.co.uk
email: sales@hogplc.com
Tel: 01279 638250
Fax: 01279 641904

KESSLERS INTERNATIONAL LTD
International Business Park
Rick Roberts Way
Stratford, London
E15 2NF
www.kesslers.com
email: kesslers@kesslers.com
Tel: 02085 223000
Fax: 02085 223129

OVERBURY
77 Newman Street
London
W1T 3EW
www.overbury.com
email: info@overbury.com
Tel: 020 7307 9073

PARADIGM OFFICE INTERIORS LTD
Unit 1, Wilnecote Lane
Belgrave, Tamworth
Staff's
B77 2LE
www.paradigm-interiors.co.uk
email: info@paradigm-interiors.co.uk
Tel: 0845 434 9717
Fax: 01827 261597

PROCOL LTD
New Hall
Market Place
Melksham
SN12 6EX
www.procol.ltd.uk
email: nick@procol.ltd.uk
Tel: 01225 701701
Fax: 01225 701702

REDLAKE GROUP
Park Road
Faringdon
Oxfordshire
SN7 7BP
www.redlakegroup.xcom
email: njones@redlakegroup.com
Tel: 01367 241507
Fax: 01367 241705

SLIMLINE SYSTEMS LIMITED
Woodwards Road
Walsall
WS2 9SL
www.slimline.co.uk
email: sales@slimlinesystems.co.uk
Tel: 01922 748860
Fax: 01922 748869

STYLO
Attn Vicky House
Hille Business Centre
132 St Albans Road, Watford
WD24 4AJ
Tel: 01923 800777

SWIFT BLINDS & CURTAINS LTD
Aldon Works
Lockwood Rd
Huddersfield
HD1 3TG
swifttradeblinds.com
email: info@switblinds-curtains.co.uk
Tel: 01484 512741
Fax: 01484 542954

T & E DISPLAY GROUP
Mucklow Hill Halesowen, West Midlands
B62 8DL
www.te-displaygroup.com
email: sales@te-displaygroup.com
Tel: 01215 857600
Fax: 01215 857601

TRADEMARK INTERIORS LTD
8 Marchmont Gate
Boundary Way
Hemel Hempstead, Herts
HP27BF
www.tmark.co.uk
email: barrycollins@tmark.co.uk
Tel: 01442 260022
Fax: 01442 232244

VANGUARD CONTRACTS LTD
2 Birch Court
Blackpole East
Worcester
WR3 8SG
www.vanguardcontracts.co.uk†
email: sales@vanguardcontracts.co.uk
Tel: 01905 759700
Fax: 01905 759711

VASSALLO MELLOR PARRIS
8 Plato Place
72-74 St Dionis Road
London
SW6 4TU
www.vmpdesign.co.uk
email: mail@vmpdesign.co.uk
Tel: 02077 317903

VIVID INTERIORS
1-2 Berners Street
London
W1T 3LA
www.vividinteriors.com
email: info@vividinteriors.com
Tel: 0207 307 9000
Fax: 0207 307 9007

WOODTEAM LTD
Unit 7 Falcon Business Park
Meadow Lane
Loughborough
LE11 1HL
www.woodteam.co.uk
email: sales @woodteam.co.uk
Tel: 01509 262000
Fax: 01509 260718

DESIGN CONSULTANCIES

AGUSTIN OTEGUI
www.agustin-otegui.com
email: agustin@nos-id.com
Tel: 005255 44399655

ANDREA MAFLIN
44 Albert Road
Stroud Green
London
N4 3RP
www.andreamaflin.co.uk
email: design@andreamaflin.co.uk
Tel: 0207 272 7972

ASTON DISPLAY LIMITED
30 Brewery Street
Aston
Birmingham
B6 4JB
www.'astondisplay.com
email: info@astondisplay.com
Tel: 0121 333 6768
Fax: 0121 333 6769

AXIOM DISPLAYS LTD
Mersey Road North
Failsworth
Manchester
M35 9LT
www.axiom-displays.co.uk
email: info@axiom-displays.co.uk
Tel: 0161 681 1371
Fax: 0161 683 4641

DIPLOMAT DESIGN
www.diplomatdesign.com
email: info@diplomatdesign.com
Tel: 02083 425285

DZ DESIGNS
The Old Mill House
Stanwell Moor
Staines
TW19 6BQ
email: dz_designs@btconnect.com
Tel: 01753 682266
Fax: 01753 682203

EDWARD BULMER LTD
Court Of Noke
Pembridge
Herefordshire
HR6 9HW
www.edwardbulmer.co.uk
Tel: 01544 388535
Fax: 01544 388332

FELICITY THORPE INTERIOR DESIGN LTD.
Allfrey's House
Bolney Road
Cowfold
RH13 8AZ
www.felicitythorpeinteriors.co.uk
email: enquiries@felicitythorpeinteriors.co.uk
Tel: 01403 864 784
Fax: 01403 865 035

FENG SHUI WITH RÈNUKA
Tel: 07958 204916

FINESSE GROUP LTD
Cobbs Wood Estate
Brunswick Road
Ashford
TN23 1EH
www.finessegroup.com
email: info@finessegroup.com
Tel: 01233 663399
Fax: 01233 665599

GRANTCF
The Lodge, Holdenhurst
Park Lane, Snitterfield
Stratford Upon Avon
CV37 0LS
www.grantcf.co.uk
email: sales@grantcf.co.uk
Tel: 01789 730380
Fax: 01789 731109

INTERBAR LTD
Unit 2 Kings Park
Primrose Hill
Kings Langley
WD4 8ST
www.interbar.co.uk
email: design@interbar.co.uk
Tel: 0845 271 3216
Fax: 0845 271 3217

INTERIORS OF CHISWICK
454 Chiswick High Road
London
W4 5TT
www.interiorsofchiswick.co.uk
Tel: 02089 940073
Fax: 02089 944144

JAPP DECORATIVE ARTS & INTERIORS
83 Rectory Rd
Worthing
West Sussex
BN14 7PD
email: davidjapp@ntlworld.com
Tel: 01903 203491
Fax: 01903 203491

KABILJO INC.
Gonzagagasse 5, Vienna, Austria
1010
www.kabiljo.com
email: wisdom@kabiljo.com
Tel: +43 1 5321094

KARIN MOORHOUSE INTERIORS
1 School Lane
Arundel
West Sussex
BN18 9DR
www.karinmoorhousedesign.com
email: karin@karinmoorhouse.co.uk
Tel: 07801 613334

LAS VEGAS MARKET
World Market Center
495 S Grand Central Parkway
Las Vegas, Nevada
NV89106
www.lasvegasmarket.com
email: design@lasvegasmarket.com
Tel: 0208 3347077
Fax: 0208 3348100

LIGHTING DESIGN INTERNATIONAL
Tel: 020 8600 5777
Fax: 020 8600 5778

PROPORTION LONDON
9 Dallington St
London
EC1V 0LN
www.proportionlondon.com
email: info@proportionlondon.com
Tel: 020 7251 6943
Fax: 020 7250 1798

PRYKE, PAULA FLOWERS
The Flower House
Cynthia Street
London
N1 9JF
www.paula-pryke-flowers.com
email: paula@paula-pryke-flowers.com
Tel: 0207 8377336
Fax: 0207 8376766

SANT STUDIO
64 Thoroughfare
Woodbridge
Suffolk
IP12 1AL
www.santstudio.co.uk
email: georginadavid@btinternet.com
Tel: 07791 576786
Fax: 02075 867742

T & E DISPLAY GROUP
Mucklow Hill Halesowen, West Midlands
B62 8DL
www.te-displaygroup.com
email: sales@te-displaygroup.com
Tel: 01215 857600
Fax: 01215 857601

T BAC DESIGN
AUSTRALIA
www.tbacdesign.com
email: troy@tbacdesign.com
Tel: 0061 39417 6595

TH:2 DESIGNS LTD
Studio 405
The Chambers
Chelsea Harbour, London
SW10 0XF
www.th2designs.co.uk
email: info@th2designs.co.uk
Tel: 020 7349 9494

THE ART SURGERY
33-35 Tib Street
Northern Quarter
Manchester
M4 1LX
www.theartsurgery.co.uk
email: info@theartsurgery.co.uk
Tel: 0161 8192888

THE MYERS TOUCH LTD
29 Springvale Road
Kings Worthy
Winchester
SO23 7ND
www.themyerstouch.co.uk
email: info@themyerstouch.co.uk
Tel: 0800 011 2585
Fax: 0870 446 5012

TONIK DESIGN
2 Newhams Row
London
SE1 3UZ
www.tonikdesign.co.uk
email: talk@tonikdesign.co.uk
Tel: 0207 940 7150
Fax: 0207 403 3110

TYE3D
Unit 8 Block A
1 Fawe Street
London
E14 6PD
www.tye3d.com
email: mail@tye3d.com
Tel: 020 7536 9291

VAN DER MEERSCH & WESTON
The Old Truman Brewery
91 Brick Lane
London
E1 6QL
www.vdmw.co.uk
email: mail@vdmw.co.uk
Tel: 0781 4195484/07967 832927

EVENTS

ASTON DISPLAY LIMITED
30 Brewery Street
Aston
Birmingham
B6 4JB
www'astondisplay.com
email: info@astondisplay.com
Tel: 0121 333 6768
Fax: 0121 333 6769

EXMEDIA LTD
Tel: 02476 224774
Fax: 02476 224775

FINESSE GROUP LTD
Cobbs Wood Estate
Brunswick Road
Ashford
TN23 1EH
www.finessegroup.com
email: info@finessegroup.com
Tel: 01233 663399
Fax: 01233 665599

LAS VEGAS MARKET
World Market Center
495 S Grand Central Parkway
Las Vegas, Nevada
NV89106
www.lasvegasmarket.com
email: design@lasvegasmarket.com
Tel: 0208 3347077
Fax: 0208 3348100

PRYKE, PAULA FLOWERS
The Flower House
Cynthia Street
London
N1 9JF
www.paula-pryke-flowers.com
email: paula@paula-pryke-flowers.com
Tel: 0207 8377336
Fax: 0207 8376766

SAXON DESIGN GROUP LTD
Unit 40 Deykin Park Industrial Estate
Deykin Avenue
Witton Birmingham
B6 7HN
www.saxondesign.co.uk
email: bob@saxondesign.co.uk
Tel: 01213 289996
Fax: 01213 289992

WORLD MARKET CENTER LAS VEGAS
495 South Grand Central Parkway
Las Vegas
Nevada
NV89106
www.lasvegasmarket.com
email: design@lasvegasmarket.com

MAIN CONTRACTORS

FAIR TRADES LTD.
Prenton Business Park
Prenton
Wirral
L43 3EA
www.homepro.com
email: info@fairtrades.co.uk
Tel: 08707 38 48 58
Fax: 08707 38 48 68

OVERBURY
77 Newman Street
London
W1T 3EW
www.overbury.com
email: info@overbury.com
Tel: 020 7307 9073

T & E DISPLAY GROUP
Mucklow Hill Halesowen, West Midlands
B62 8DL
www.te-displaygroup.com
email: sales@te-displaygroup.com
Tel: 01215 857600
Fax: 01215 857601

VANGUARD CONTRACTS LTD
2 Birch Court
Blackpole East
Worcester
WR3 8SG
www.vanguardcontracts.co.uk†
email: sales@vanguardcontracts.co.uk
Tel: 01905 759700
Fax: 01905 759711

VASCROFT CONTRACTORS LTD
Vascroft Estate
861 Coronation Road
London
NW10 7PT
www.vascroft.com
email: info@vascroft.com
Tel: 020 8963 3400
Fax: 020 8963 3401

VIVID INTERIORS
1-2 Berners Street, London, W1T 3LA
www.vividinteriors.com
email: info@vividinteriors.com
Tel: 0207 307 9000
Fax: 0207 307 9007

PHOTOGRAPHY
**JONATHAN MOORE ARCHITECTURAL
PHOTOGRAPHER**
2 Grange Paddock
Mark, Somersetn TA9 4RW
www.jonathanmoore.co.uk
email: info@jonathanmoore.co.uk
Tel: 00 44 (0)7970 192342
Fax: 00 44 (0)7970 092702

PICTURE FRAMERS & RESTORATION

BOURLET
32 Connaught Street
London
W2 2AF
Tel/Fax: 020 7724 4837
Email: enquiries@bourlet.co.uk

Bourlet began making frames almost
200 years ago. The frames we make
today still employ the same skills,
techniques and materials of the old
master frame makers. Our clients
range from contemporary west end
dealers and artists to old master
dealers and national museums and
galleries. We carve, gild, veneer, stain
and French polish.

RESEARCH & INFORMATION
FAIR TRADES LTD.
Prenton Business Park
Prenton,
Wirral, L43 3EA
www.homepro.com
email: info@fairtrades.co.uk
Tel: 08707 38 48 58
Fax: 08707 38 48 68

SHIPPERS & PACKERS

HEDLEY'S HUMPERS
3 St Leonard's Road
North Acton
London, NW10 6SX
Tel: +44 (0) 20 8965 8733
Fax: +44 (0) 20 8965 0249
London@hedleyshumpers.com
www.hedleyshumpers.com

Hedley's Humpers offers a complete
solution to all your transportation,
installation and storage requirements.
With over thirty years' experience
Hedley's Humpers has established an
international reputation of expertise in
moving, installing and storing. With
offices in London, New York, Paris and
the south of France, we are uniquely
placed to provide a truly global service.

DESIGN HOUSE EUROPE
Design House, Balme Road,
Cleckheaton, BD19 4EW
www.prontex.co.uk
email: louisemarren@designhouseeurope.com
Tel: 01274 863747
Fax: 01274 863748

SIGNAGE
ACRYLIC DESIGN
3a 3b Shakespeare Industrial Estate
Shakespeare Street, Watford
Hertfordshire, WD24 5RS
www.acrylicdesign.co.uk
email: sales@acrylicdesign.co.uk
Tel: 01923 241122
Fax: 01923 241144

ALBION DESIGN & FABRICATION LTD
4-16 Gosforth Close
Middlefield Industrail Estate
Sandy, SG191RB
www.albion-manufacturing.com
email: info@albion-manufacturing.com
Tel: 01767 692313
Fax: 01767 683157

AUSTIN LUCE & COMPANY LTD
Elm Trees House
Effingham Road
Copthorne
RH10 3HX
www.austinluce.co.uk
email: enquiries@austinluce.co.uk
Tel: 01342 713310
Fax: 01342 718097

BLAZE NEON LTD
Pysons Road Industrial Estate
Broadstairs
Kent
CT10 2XZ
www.blazeneon.com
email: blaze@blazeneon.com
Tel: 01843 601075
Fax: 01843 867924

COLITE INTERNATIONAL
Po Box 4380
Worthing
West Sussex
BN13 2WE
www.coite.com
email: info@colite.co.uk
Tel: 01903 694925
Fax: 01803 9359003

G PRINT
Mill Lodge
Lodge Lane
Salfords, Redhill
RH1 5DS
www.g-print.co.uk
email: sales@g-print.co.uk
Tel: 01293 820861
Fax: 01293 774778

IMEX GRAFIX LTD
Whinfield Drive
Aycliffe Industrial Park
Co. Durham
DL5 6AU
www.sign-suppliers.co.uk
email: sales@imexgrafix.co.uk
Tel: 01325 321321
Fax: 01325 300838

JOHN ANTHONY SIGNS LTD
Claydons Lane
Rayleigh
Essex
SS6 7UU
www.askjas.co.uk
email: info@askjas.co.uk
Tel: 01268 777333
Fax: 01268 777193

JOHN ANTHONY SIGNS LTD
Claydons Lane
Rayleigh
Essex
SS6 7UU
www.askjas.co.uk
email: info@askjas.co.uk
Tel: 01268 777333
Fax: 01268 777193

OMC (UK) LTD.
Candela House
Cardew Industrial Estate
Redruth, Cornwall
TR15 1SS
www.omc-uk.com
email: omc-sales@omc-uk.com
Tel: 01209 215424
Fax: 01209 215197

POWERGRAPHIC DISPLAYS LTD
Unit 6, Blenheim Road
Cressex Business Park
High Wycombe
HP12 3RS
www.powergraphicdisplays.com
email: sales@powergraphicdisplays.com
Tel: 01494 450936
Fax: 01494 461975

SIGNWAVES LTD
Lefevre Way
Gapton Hall Industrial Estate
Great Yarmouth
NR31 0NW
www.signwavesgroup.com
email: enquiries@signwavesgroup.com
Tel: 01493 419300
Fax: 01493 419301

SK SIGNS & LABELS LTD
16 Brookside Centre
Temple Farm Ind Est
Southend On Sea
SS2 5RR
www.sksigns.co.uk
email: info@sksigns.co.uk
Tel: 01702 462401
Fax: 01702 462404

SNOWDONIA SLATE & STONE
North Wales
www.snowdoniaslate.co.uk
email: richard@snowdoniaslate.co.uk
Tel: 01766 832525
Fax: 01766 832404

STYLO
Attn Vicky House
Hille Business Centre
132 St Albans Road, Watford
WD24 4AJ
Tel: 01923 800777

TARA SIGNS LTD
St Peters Place
Western Road
Lancing
BN15 8SB
www.tarasigns.com
email: sales@tarasigns.com
Tel: 01903 750710
Fax: 01903 754008

VISTA SYSTEM LTD
103 High St
Waltham Cross
Herts
EN8 7AN
www.vistasystem.co.uk
email: info@vistasystem.co.uk
Tel: 0800 404 9151
Fax: 0845 280 5635

Kitchens

ALNO
Shaw Cross Court
Shaw Cross Business Park
Dewsbury
WF12 7RF
www.alno.co.uk
email: mail@alno.co.uk
Tel: 01924 487900

ANSON CONCISE LTD
1, Eagle Close
Arnold
Nottingham
NG5 7FJ
www.ansonconcise.co.uk
email: info@ansonconcise.co.uk
Tel: 01159 262102
Fax: 01159 673398

BOSCH
Grand Union House
Old Wolverton Road, Wolverton
Milton Keynes
MK12 5PT
www.boschappliances.co.uk
Tel: 01908 328 500

CLIVE CHRISTIAN
1st Floor, South Dome
Chelsea Harbour Design Centre
London
SW10 0XE
www.clive.com
email: london@clive.com
Tel: 020 73499200

COTSWOLD BESPOKE KITCHENS
Riverside House,
Bridgend Works,Stonehouse,
Gloucestershire
GL10 2BA
www.bespokekitchendesign.co.uk
email: info@bespokekitchendesign.co.uk
Tel: 01453 791222
Fax: 01453 825254

EGGERSMANN KITCHENS
33,Station Road
Sible Hedingham
Essex
CO9 3QA
email: eggersmann@btconnect.com
Tel: 01787 461788
Fax: 01787 462674

ELFIN KITCHENS LTD
Unit 3, Taber Place
Crittal Road
Witham, Essex
CM8 3YP
www.elfinkitchens.co.uk
email: enquiries@elfinkitchens.co.uk
Tel: 01376 501333
Fax: 01376 530066

IN-TOTO
Shaw Cross Court
Shaw Cross Business Park
Dewsbury
WF12 7RF
www.intoto.co.uk
email: eve@ddpr.biz
Tel: 01924 487900

LIVING IN STYLE KITCHENS.
Unit 1-162 Coles Green Road.
Staples Corner, London NW2 7HW
Tel: 020 8450 9555
Fax: 020 8450 7565
Web: www.livinginstyle.co.uk

Innovative solutions to kitchen design.

KITCHEN ITALIA LTD
Unit 4 Spring Valley Business Centre
Porterswood
St Albans, AL3 6PD
www.kitchenitalia.com
email: sales@kitchenitalia.com
Tel: 01727 843 840
Fax: 01727 843 432

MASTERPIECES LTD
St Oswalds Road
Gloucester, GL1 2SG
www.masterpieces.ltd.uk
Tel: 01452 423261
Fax: 01452 310968

PLANIT FUSION
Inca House, Eureka Scinece Park
Trinity Road
Ashford, Kent
TN25 4AB
www.2020-fusion.com
email: fusionsales@2020.net
Tel: 01233 649 700
Fax: 01233 627 855

ROMANYS LTD
104 Arlington Road
Camden Town
London
NW1 7HP
www.romanys.uk.com
Tel: 020 7424 0349
Fax: 020 7428 6465

SIGMA 3 (KITCHENS) LTD
Llantrisant Business Park
Llantrisant, Mid Glamorgan, CF72 8LF
www.sigma3.co.uk
email: sales@sigma3.co.uk
Tel: 01443 237732
Fax: 01443 237343

SOLOMON'S SEAL (KKM) LTD
45 High Street, Odiham,
Hampshire, RG29 1LF
www.solomonsseal.co.uk
email: info@solomonsseal.co.uk
Tel: 01256 703833
Fax: 01256 703962

THE NATURAL WOOD FLOOR CO.
20 Smugglers Way Wandsworth
London, SW181EG
www.naturalwoodfloor.co.uk
email: sales@naturalwoodfloor.co.uk
Tel: 020 8871 9771
Fax: 020 8877 0273

WOODCHESTER KITCHENS & INTERIORS LTD
Unit 18a, Chalford Industrial Estate,
Chalford, Glos, GL6 8NT
www.woodchesterkitchens.co.uk
email: chris@woodchesterkitchens.co.uk
Tel: 01453 886411
Fax: 01453 886411

BESPOKE KITCHENS

THE SECRET DRAWER
Showrooms at:
Main Street, Cononley, Skipton, BD20 8LJ
and
21B Brook Street, Ilkley, LS29 8AA
Tel: 01535 630072
www.secret-drawer.co.uk

Tailormade kitchens, bedrooms,
bathrooms, studies and furniture,
handmade in wood by skilled craftsmen
and installed by experienced fitters.
Cunningly hidden and with tiny
dovetailed joints, The Secret Drawer is a
signature speciality. Superior appliances
from Wolfe, Miele and Sub Zero and a
full in-house interior design service
including soft furnishings complete the
bespoke service.

BUILT-IN APPLIANCES

BUYERS & SELLERS
120 - 122 Ladbroke Grove
London
W10 5NE
www.buyersandsellersonline.co.uk
email: lowestprices@buyers-sellers.co.uk
Tel: 02072 435400
Fax: 02072 214113

DE-DIETRICH KITCHEN APPLIANCES LTD
Intec 4
Wade Road
Basingstoke RG248NE
www.dedietrich.co.uk
email: enquiries-uk@fagorbrandt.com
Tel: 01256 308 000
Fax: 01256 843 024

LIEBHERR COOLECTRIC LTD
Interchange Point
Renny Park Road
Newport Pagnell MK16 0HA
www.liebherr.co.uk
email: sales@coolectric.co.uk
Tel: 08444 122 655

SILVERLINE BUILT IN APPLIANCES
Yilanli Ayazma Yolu, Yesil Plaza No:15 Kat:10
34010 Topkapi Istanbul Turkey
www.silverlineappliances.com
Tel: 0090 212 481 8144
Fax: 0090 212 481 4008

THE MYERS TOUCH LTD
29 Springvale Road
Kings Worthy, Winchester, SO23 7ND
www.themyerstouch.co.uk
email: info@themyerstouch.co.uk
Tel: 0800 011 2585
Fax: 0870 446 5012

MIELE CO LTD
Fairacres, Abingdon, Oxon, OX14 1TW
Tel: 0845 365 6600
E-mail: info@miele.co.uk
Web: www.miele.co.uk

Premium appliance manufacturer Miele
is leading the way when it comes to
kitchen technology and has been for
over a century. An innovator in design,
Miele's Generation 5000 is a sleek and
modern collection of appliances.
Ranging from 90cm ovens, single ovens,
compact ovens, steam ovens and coffee
machines, the appliances all complement
each other in any formation.

WHIRLPOOL UK
209 Purley Way
Croydon
CR9 4RY
www.whirlpool.co.uk
email: olivia_elliot@whirlpool.com
Tel: 020 8649 5000

WS WESTIN LTD
Phoenix Mills
Leeds Road
Huddersfield
HD1 6NG
www.westin.co.uk
email: sales@westin.co.uk
Tel: 01484 421 585
Fax: 01484 432420

COMMERCIAL KITCHENS

ANSON CONCISE LTD
1, Eagle Close
Arnold
Nottingham
NG5 7FJ
www.ansonconcise.co.uk
email: info@ansonconcise.co.uk
Tel: 01159 262102
Fax: 01159 673398

CAVENDISH EQUIPMENT LTD
Unit 10 Monro Industrial Estate
Station Approach
Waltham Cross
HERTS
www.cavendishequipment.co.uk
email: sales@cavendishequipment.co.uk
Tel: 01992 767105
Fax: 01992 716927

ELFIN KITCHENS LTD
Unit 3, Taber Place
Crittal Road
Witham, Essex
CM8 3YP
www.elfinkitchens.co.uk
email: enquiries@elfinkitchens.co.uk
Tel: 01376 501333
Fax: 01376 530066

GEC ANDERSON
Oakengrove
Shire Lane
Hastoe, Tring, Hertfordshire
HP23 6LY
www.gecanderson.co.uk
email: info@gecanderson.co.uk
Tel: 01442 826 999
Fax: 01442 825 999

KITCHENS INTERNATIONAL
East Mains Industrial Estate
11 Youngs Rd
Broxburn
EH56 5LY
email: sales@kitchensinternational.co.uk
Tel: 0845 0740022

PRONORM KITCHENS
Tel: 07801 862 691

SIEMATIC UK LTD
Osprey House
Primett Road
Stevenage
SG1 3EE
www.siematic.co.uk
email: sales@siematic.co.uk
Tel: 01438 369 251
Fax: 01438 368 920

SIGMA 3 (KITCHENS) LTD
Llantrisant Business Park
Llantrisant
Mid Glamorgan
CF72 8LF
www.sigma3.co.uk
email: sales@sigma3.co.uk
Tel: 01443 237732
Fax: 01443 237343

DOMESTIC KITCHENS

ALNO
Shaw Cross Court
Shaw Cross Business Park
Dewsbury
WF12 7RF
www.alno.co.uk
email: mail@alno.co.uk
Tel: 01924 487900

ANSON CONCISE LTD
1, Eagle Close
Arnold
Nottingham
NG5 7FJ
www.ansonconcise.co.uk
email: info@ansonconcise.co.uk
Tel: 01159 262102
Fax: 01159 673398

BLANCO
1 Victor Way,
Colney Street
St.albans , Herts
AL2 2FL
www.blanco.co.uk.
email: salesdesk@blanco.co.uk
Tel: 0844 912 0100

BROOMLEY FURNITURE LTD
West Broomley Farm
Stocksfield
NE43 7HR
www.broomleyfurniture.co.uk
email: enquiries@broomleyfurniture.co.uk
Tel: 01434 682226
Fax: 01434 682576

BUYERS & SELLERS
120 - 122 Ladbroke Grove
London
W10 5NE
www.buyersandsellersonline.co.uk
email: lowestprices@buyers-sellers.co.uk
Tel: 02072 435400
Fax: 02072 214113

CAPLE
Fourth Way
Avonmouth
Bristol
BS11 8DW
www.caple.co.uk
Tel: 0117 938 1900
Fax: 0800 373 163

CARRON PHOENIX
Carron Works
Stenhouse Road
Carron, Falkirk,
FK2 8DW
www.carron.com
email: sales@carron.com
Tel: 01324 638 321
Fax: 01324 620 978

CHAMBER FURNITURE

CHAMBER FURNITURE
The Old Timber Yard
London Road
Halstead
Kent
TN14 7DZ
Tel: 01959 532553
Email: info@chamberfurniture.co.uk
Web: www.chamberfurniture.com

To truly appreciate our furniture and service, please visit our showroom.

Open: Mon-Fri: 09.00-17.30
Sat: 09.00-14.00

CAVENDISH EQUIPMENT LTD
Unit 10 Monro Industrial Estate
Station Approach
Waltham Cross
HERTS
www.cavendishequipment.co.uk
email: sales@cavendishequipment.co.uk
Tel: 01992 767105
Fax: 01992 716927

CRABTREE
17 Station Road,
London, SW13 0LF
email: design@finewoodinteriors.co.uk
Tel: 020 8392 6955
Fax: 020 8392 6944

DAEDALIAN LTD
Tel: 01535 640860
Fax: 01535 640861

DAVAL FURNITURE
Spa Fields Industrial Estate
New Street
Slaithwaite, Huddesfield, HD7 5BB
Tel: 01484 848500
Fax: 01484 848 520

DE-DIETRICH KITCHEN APPLIANCES LTD
Intec 4, Wade Road, Basingstoke, RG248NE
www.dedietrich.co.uk
email: enquiries-uk@fagorbrandt.com
Tel: 01256 308 000
Fax: 01256 843 024

DREAM DESIGN
A35 Lyndhurst Road
Christchurch, Dorset, BH23 7DU
www.dream-design.co.uk
email: sales@dream-design.co.uk
Tel: 01425 279525
Fax: 01425 273550

ELFIN KITCHENS LTD
Unit 3, Taber Place
Crittal Road
Witham, Essex
CM8 3YP
www.elfinkitchens.co.uk
email: enquiries@elfinkitchens.co.uk
Tel: 01376 501333
Fax: 01376 530066

FINESSE DESIGN
Project House
Villa Real
Consett, County Durham
DH8 6BP
www.finessedesign.com
email: sales@finessedesign.com
Tel: 01207 500050
Fax: 01207 599757

GEC ANDERSON
Oakengrove
Shire Lane
Hastoe, Tring, Hertfordshire
HP23 6LY
www.gecanderson.co.uk
email: info@gecanderson.co.uk
Tel: 01442 826 999
Fax: 01442 825 999

GIBBS AND DANDY
226 Dallow Road
Luton
LU1 1YB
email: luton@gibbsanddandy.com
Tel: 01582 798798
Fax: 01582 798799

JASPER & CO
The Valdoe
Goodwood
Chichester
PO180PJ
www.jasperco.co.uk
email: info@jasperco.co.uk
Tel: 0844 858 4084
Fax: 0844 858 4085

JMCK LTD
Blaen-Nos
Henllan Amgoed
Whitland
SA34 0SE
email: jmck@btconnect.com
Tel: 01994-448885
Fax: 01994-448885

JOHN BARNARD FURNITURE LTD
60 St. Giles Street
Norwich
Norfolk
NR2 1LW
www.johnbarnard.co.uk
email: design@johnbarnard.co.uk
Tel: 01603 613390
Fax: 01603 761805

JRO DESIGN KITCHENS WORKS
220 Great Western Road
Glasgow
G4 9EJ
www.kitchenworksglasgow.co.uk
email: jrokitworks@aol.com
Tel: 01413 339602
Fax: 01413 339604

LA CORNUE
14, rue du Bois du Pont
95310 Saint Ouen L'Aumône
FRANCE
Tel: +44 (0)1926 457618
Email: a.table@la-cornue.com
Web: www.lacornue.co.uk

The La Cornue Château range is the flagship of our know-how. The luxurious materials, the quality of manufacture and the culinary performance – worthy of the best professional cooking ranges – do not suffer compromise. The cookers are timeless, rare and prestigious objects. A legend has accompanied La Cornue Châteaux through the years. One you can believe in – today as in the past – single cookers of the highest quality built to order.

KITCHEN ITALIA LTD
Unit 4 Spring Valley Business Centre
Porterswood
St Albans
AL3 6PD
www.kitchenitalia.com
email: sales@kitchenitalia.com
Tel: 01727 843 840
Fax: 01727 843 432

KITCHENS INTERNATIONAL
East Mains Industrial Estate
11 Youngs Rd
Broxburn
EH56 5LY
email: sales@kitchensinternational.co.uk
Tel: 0845 0740022

MARTIN MOORE & COMPANY
Altrincham
Old Amersham
Esher, Halifax And Fulham
www.martinmoore.com
Tel: 0161 928 2643

MICHAEL REED DESIGN
Arch 12
Kingsdown Close
London, W10 6SW
www.arch12.com
email: info@arch12.com
Tel: 020 72295391

MUSIC IN EVERY ROOM LTD
16 The Sidings
Guiseley
Leeds
LS20 8BX
www.musicineveryroom.co.uk
email: sales@musicineveryroom.co.uk
Tel: 0845 094 1857
Fax: 01943 872768

PINCUS

Exclusive - Boutique - Furniture

PINCUS DESIGN LTD
10 Woodfield Road, Altrincham,
Cheshire, WA14 4EU
Tel: 0161 941 6444
info@pincusdesign.co.uk
www.pincusdesign.co.uk
www.kitchendesignexpert.co.uk

Pincus is a bespoke furniture and spatial
design company creating handmade
kitchens, bedrooms, cinema rooms,
home studies and individual
commissions. Working in partnership
with both the domestic market and
architects, Pincus provides a boutique
service with full project management in
contemporary, classical, traditional and
modernist styles. Serving the Cheshire,
Lancashire and Manchester areas.

NEW FROM OLD
The Engine House
White House Road
Little Ouse, CB7 4TG
www.newfromold.co.uk
email: rick.forward@newfromold.co.uk
Tel: 01353 676227

SIEMATIC UK LTD
Osprey House, Primett Road,
Stevenage, SG1 3EE
www.siematic.co.uk
email: sales@siematic.co.uk
Tel: 01438 369 251
Fax: 01438 368 920

SIGMA 3 (KITCHENS) LTD
Llantrisant Business Park
Llantrisant
Mid Glamorgan
CF72 8LF
www.sigma3.co.uk
email: sales@sigma3.co.uk
Tel: 01443 237732
Fax: 01443 237343

THE MYERS TOUCH LTD
29 Springvale Road
Kings Worthy, Winchester, SO23 7ND
www.themyerstouch.co.uk
email: info@themyerstouch.co.uk
Tel: 0800 011 2585
Fax: 0870 446 5012

THE SYMPHONY GROUP PLC
Pen Hill Estate
Park Spring Road
Grimethorpe, S72 7EZ
www.symphony-group.co.uk
email: enquiries@symphony-group.co.uk
Tel: 01226 446000
Fax: 01226 711185

TIM WOOD LTD
29a Niton Street
Fulham
London, SW6 6NH
www.timwood.com
Tel: 020 7385 7228
Fax: 0870 063 5139

WS WESTIN LTD
Phoenix Mills, Leeds Road,
Huddersfield, HD1 6NG
www.westin.co.uk
email: sales@westin.co.uk
Tel: 01484 421 585
Fax: 01484 432420

KITCHEN APPLIANCES

BOSCH
Grand Union House
Old Wolverton Road, Wolverton
Milton Keynes
MK12 5PT
www.boschappliances.co.uk
Tel: 01908 328 500

BUYERS & SELLERS
120 - 122 Ladbroke Grove
London
W10 5NE
www.buyersandsellersonline.co.uk
email: lowestprices@buyers-sellers.co.uk
Tel: 02072 435400
Fax: 02072 214113

CAPLE
Fourth Way
Avonmouth
Bristol, BS11 8DW
www.caple.co.uk
Tel: 0117 938 1900
Fax: 0800 373 163

CDA
Harby Road, Langar,
Nottingham, NG13 9HY
Tel: 01949 862 010
Fax: 01949 862 001
Web: www.cda.eu

Based in Nottingham, CDA have been
manufacturing cutting edge, design
led appliances since 1991. The range
of around 300 models includes
everything needed for a modern,
energy saving kitchen at prices to suit
every budget from entry level to
luxury. CDA offers stylish, high
performance, reliable products
together with a 5 year guarantee for
complete peace of mind.

CUISINART
www.cuisinart.co.uk
Tel: 0870 240 6902

DE-DIETRICH KITCHEN APPLIANCES LTD
Intec 4, Wade Road,
Basingstoke, RG248NE
www.dedietrich.co.uk
email: enquiries-uk@fagorbrandt.com
Tel: 01256 308 000
Fax: 01256 843 024

DUALIT
County Oak Way, Crawley, West Sussex,
RH11 7ST
email: info@dualit.com
Tel: 01293 652 500

FISHER & PAYKEL APPLIANCES
Maidstone Road
Kingston, Milton Keynes, MK10 0BD
www.fisherpaykel.co.uk
email: customer.care@fisherpaykel.co.uk
Tel: 0845 0662200
Fax: 0845 3312370

LIEBHERR COOLECTRIC LTD
Interchange Point
Renny Park Road
Newport Pagnell, MK16 0HA
www.liebherr.co.uk
email: sales@coolectric.co.uk
Tel: 08444 122 655

LLOYTRON PLC
Laltex House, Leigh Commerce Park
Greenfold Way
Leigh, Lancashire, WN7 3XH
www.lloytron.com
email: lloytron@laltex.com
Tel: 01942 687040
Fax: 01942 687070

LA CORNUE
14, rue du Bois du Pont
95310 Saint Ouen L'Aumône
FRANCE
Tel: +44 (0)1926 457618
Email: a.table@la-cornue.com
Web: www.lacornue.co.uk

LA CORNUE
DEPUIS 1908

The La Cornue Château range is the flagship
of our know-how. The luxurious materials, the
quality of manufacture and the culinary
performance – worthy of the best professional
cooking ranges – do not suffer compromise.
The cookers are timeless, rare and prestigious
objects. A legend has accompanied La Cornue
Châteaux through the years. One you can
believe in – today as in the past – single
cookers of the highest quality built to order.

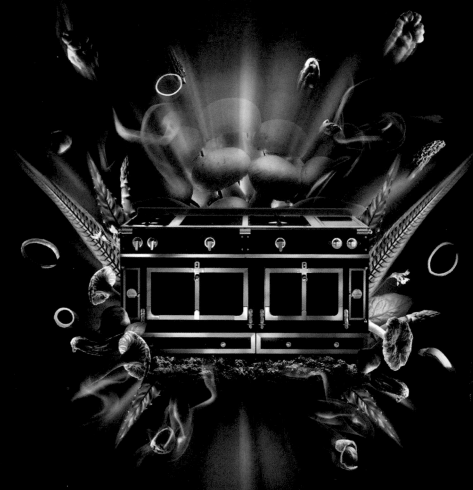

CHÂTEAU ULTRA BLACK 165

The La Cornue Château range is the flagship of our know-how.
A legend has accompanied La Cornue Châteaux through the years.
Today as in the past - single cookers of the highest quality built to order.

www.lacornue.co.uk
a.table@la-cornue.com

SHARP
4 Furzeground Way
Stockley Park
Uxbridge
UB11 1EZ
www.sharp.co.uk
email: martin.arnold@sharp-uk.co.uk
Tel: 0208 734 2000　0800 262 958

SILVERLINE BUILT IN APPLIANCES
Yilanli Ayazma Yolu, Yesil Plaza No:15 Kat:10
34010 Topkapi Istanbul Turkey
www.silverlineappliances.com
Tel: 0090 212 481 8144
Fax: 0090 212 481 4008

WHIRLPOOL UK
209 Purley Way
Croydon
CR9 4RY
www.whirlpool.co.uk
email: olivia_elliot@whirlpool.com
Tel: 020 8649 5000

WS WESTIN LTD
Phoenix Mills
Leeds Road
Huddersfield
HD1 6NG
www.westin.co.uk
email: sales@westin.co.uk
Tel: 01484 421 585
Fax: 01484 432420

KITCHENWARE

A. C. TOON LTD
Units 2-4 Warwick Street Ind. Estate
Storforth Lane
Chesterfield
S40 2TT
www.actoon.co.uk
email: sales@actoon.co.uk
Tel: 01246 223900
Fax: 01246 223901

CARRON PHOENIX
Carron Works
Stenhouse Road
Carron , Falkirk
FK2 8DW
www.carron.com
email: sales@carron.com
Tel: 01324 638 321
Fax: 01324 620 978

CATERINA FADDA STUDIO
201b Saga Centre,
326 Kensal Rd
London
W10 5BZ
www.caterinafadda.com
email: info@caterinafadda.com
Tel: 0208 9643725

DAVID MELLOR DESIGN
4 Sloane Square
London
SW1W 8EE
www.davidmellordesign.com
email: davidmellor@davidmellordesign.co.uk
Tel: 020 7730 4259
Fax: 020 7730 7240

ROBERT WELCH DESIGNS
Lower High Street
Chipping Campden
Glos
GL55 6DY
www.robertwelch.com
email: sales@welch.co.uk
Tel: 01386 840522
Fax: 01386 848804

TAPS & BRASSWARE

ABODE
Unit L Zenith Park
Whaley Road
Barnsley
S75 1HT
www.abode.eu
email: info@abode.eu
Tel: 01226 283434
Fax: 01226 282434

ABODE
Unit L Zenith Park
Whaley Road
Barnsley
S75 1HT
www.abode.eu
email: info@abode.eu
Tel: 01226 283434
Fax: 01226 282434

BLANCO
1 Victor Way,
Colney Street
St.albans , Herts
AL2 2FL
www.blanco.co.uk.
email: salesdesk@blanco.co.uk
Tel: 0844 912 0100

BRISTAN
Birch Coppice Business Park
Dordon
Tamworth
B78 1SG
www.bristan.com
email: enquire@bristan.com
Tel: 0844 701 6274
Fax: 0808 1611002

CAPLE
Fourth Way
Avonmouth
Bristol
BS11 8DW
www.caple.co.uk
Tel: 0117 938 1900
Fax: 0800 373 163

CARRON PHOENIX
Carron Works
Stenhouse Road
Carron , Falkirk
FK2 8DW
www.carron.com
email: sales@carron.com
Tel: 01324 638 321
Fax: 01324 620 978

CHARTLEY LTD
Attn Lisa Landells
Opal Business Centre
Opal Way, Stone, Staffs
ST15 0SS
www.chartley.com
email: sales@chartley.com
Tel: 01785 811836
Fax: 01785 811837

CONSULTO COLLECTION LTD
Unit B 33-36 Victoria Road
Victoria Industrial Estate
Burgess Hill, West Sussex
RH15 9LR
www.consultocollection.com
email: info@consultocollection.com
Tel: 01444 241296
Fax: 01444 247234

DORNBRACHT
Unit 8
Fletchworth Gate
Coventry
CV5 6SP
www.dornbracht.com
email: sales@dornbracht.com
Tel: 02476 717129
Fax: 02476 718907

DOUGLAS DELABIE
7 Henderson House
Hithercroft Road
Wallingford, Oxfordshire
OX10 9DG
www.douglasdelabie.co.uk
email: sales@douglasdelabie.co.uk
Tel: 01491 824449
Fax: 01491 825727

FANSKI GROUP INC
M&E Industrial Zone, Yuhuan County, Zhejiang
Provice, 317600 Pr China
317600
www.fanski.com
email: fanski@fanski.com
Tel: 86 576 87276781
Fax: 86 576 87276797

GROHE LTD
Blays House
Wick Road
Englefield Green, Egham
TW20 0HJ
www.grohe.co.uk
email: info-uk@grohe.com
Tel: 0871 200 3414
Fax: 0871 200 3415

HUDSON REED
Widow Hill Rd
Heasandford Industrial Estate
Burnley Lancs
BB10 2BE
www.hudsonreed.co.uk
email: info-ultra-group.co.uk
Tel: 01282 418 000
Fax: 01282 428915

IB RUBINETTERIE
Via Dei Pianotti 3
25068
www.ibrubinetterie.it
email: info@ibrubinetterie.it
Tel: 0039 0308 02101
Fax: 0039 0308 03097

J ËNI J BATHROOMS
12 Handsworth Crescent
Eastern Green
Coventry
CV5 7GE
www.jnjbathrooms.co.uk
email: sales@jnjbathrooms.co.uk
Tel: 024 7646 8850
Fax: 024 7646 8830

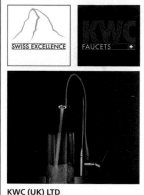

KWC (UK) LTD
149 Balham Hill, London, SW12 9DJ
Tel: 020 8675 9335
sales@swisslinelondon.co.uk
www.kwc-uk.com

A Swiss company with a long and proud
history of invention and precision
engineering, KWC Faucets is at the
forefront of design and technological
innovation in taps, creating beautiful,
highly-functional and reliable fittings that
are a must-have for the high spec kitchen.
KWC is the top kitchen designer's choice.

KEUCO (UK) LTD
Amersham House
Mill Street
Berkhamsted, Herts, HP4 2DT
www.keuco.de
email: klaus@keuco.co.uk
Tel: 01442 865220
Fax: 01442 865260

MM2 LTD
Orchard House
Church Road
Ramsden Bellhouse, Billericay, CM11 1RH
www.mm2ltd.com
email: sales@mm2ltd.com
Tel: 01268 712801
Fax: 01268 712803

PYRAMIS UK LTD
Unit 20-22,Haddenham Business Park,
Haddenham,
Bucks, HP178LJ
www.pyramisgroup.com
email: julianpyramis@talktalk.net
Tel: 01844 295882
Fax: 01844 291892

SMR BATHROOMS
Unit Q, Fishers Grove
Farlington, Portsmouth, PO6 1RN
www.smrbathrooms.co.uk
email: general-enquiry@smrbathrooms.co.uk
Tel: 08452 255045
Fax: 08452 255046

STEPHEN EINHORN
210 Upper Street
London, N1 1RL
www.stepheneinhorn.co.uk
email: info@stepheneinhorn.co.uk
Tel: 020 7359 4977
Fax: 020 7354 0953

SURESTOP LTD
Unit 3, Century Park
Starley Way
Bickenhill, B37 7HF
www.surestop.co.uk
email: sales @surestop.co.uk
Tel: 0845 643 1800
Fax: 0845 643 1801

THOMAS CRAPPER & COMPANY LTD
The Stable Yard, Alscot Park,
Stratford On Avon,
Warwickshire., CV37 8BL
www.thomas-crapper.com
email: wc@thomas-crapper.com
Tel: 01789 450522
Fax: 01789 450523

TRIFLOW CONCEPTS
Unit 1, Gateway Xiii
Ferry Lane
Rainham, RM13 9JY
www.triflowconcepts.com
email: marketing@triflowconcepts.com
Tel: 01708 526361
Fax: 01708 550220

TWYFORD BATHROOMS
Lawton Road
Alsager, Stoke-On-Trent, ST7 2DF
www.twyfordbathrooms.com
email: twyford.sales@twyfordbathrooms.com
Tel: 01270 879777
Fax: 01270 873864

WORK SURFACES

A. C. TOON LTD
Units 2-4 Warwick Street Ind. Estate
Storforth Lane
Chesterfield
S40 2TT
www.actoon.co.uk
email: sales@actoon.co.uk
Tel: 01246 223900
Fax: 01246 223901

BLANCO
1 Victor Way,
Colney Street
St.albans , Herts
AL2 2FL
www.blanco.co.uk.
email: salesdesk@blanco.co.uk
Tel: 0844 912 0100

BOTTLE ALLEY GLASS
1 Tills Courtyard
High St
Battle
TN33 0AE
www.bottlealleyglass.co.uk
email: info@bottlealleyglass.co.uk
Tel: 0845 643 2733
Fax: 0709 237 3521

CAESARSTONE
Gorrels Way
Trans-Pennine Industrial Estate
WF3 3LY
www.caesarstone.uk.com
email: info@ebor.co.uk
Tel: 01706 863 600

CAVENDISH EQUIPMENT LTD
Unit 10 Monro Industrial Estate
Station Approach
Waltham Cross
HERTS
www.cavendishequipment.co.uk
email: sales@cavendishequipment.co.uk
Tel: 01992 767105
Fax: 01992 716927

COUNTER PRODUCTION LTD
Red Kite Works, Watlington Industrial Estate,
Cuxham Road, Watlington, Oxon
OX49 5LU
www.counterproduction.co.uk
email: sales@counterproduction.co.uk
Tel: 01491 615470
Fax: 01494 615471

DIAPOL GRANITE LTD
Kasesalu 4
Saue
76505 - ESTONIA
www.diapol.co.uk
email: jason@diapol.co.uk
Tel: 020 8099 7828
Fax: 020 7012 1297

FORMICA LIMITED
11 Silver Fox Way
Cobalt Business Park
Newcastle Upon Tyne
NE27 0QJ
www.formica.com
email: info@formica.co.uk
Tel: 0191 259 3100
Fax: 0191 259 2648

FRANCIS N LOWE LTD
The Marble Works
New Road
Middleton
DE4 4NA
www.lowesmarble.com
email: info@lowesmarble.com
Tel: 01629 822216
Fax: 01629 824348

GEC ANDERSON
Oakengrove
Shire Lane
Hastoe, Tring, Hertfordshire
HP23 6LY
www.gecanderson.co.uk
email: info@gecanderson.co.uk
Tel: 01442 826 999
Fax: 01442 825 999

GLASSECO LTD
Unit 5 ,Highams Farm
Sheepbarn Lane, Warlingham
Surrey
CR6 9PQ
www.glasseco.co.uk
email: info@glasseco.co.uk
Tel: 01959 576897
Fax: 01959 575902

H & L MARBLE LTD
Unit 2 Abbey Wharf
Mount Pleasant
Wembley
HA0 1NR
www.hlmarble.co.uk
email: sales@hlmarble.co.uk
Tel: 02089 035811
Fax: 02089 033930

JAMES LATHAM
www.lathams.co.uk
Tel: 0116 257 3415

JRO DESIGN KITCHENS WORKS
220 Great Western Road
Glasgow
G4 9EJ
www.kitchenworksglasgow.co.uk
email: jrokitworks@aol.com
Tel: 01413 339602
Fax: 01413 339604

KITCHEN ITALIA LTD
Unit 4 Spring Valley Business Centre
Porterswood
St Albans
AL3 6PD
www.kitchenitalia.com
email: sales@kitchenitalia.com
Tel: 01727 843 840
Fax: 01727 843 432

MASS CONCRETE
Black Hill Rd Holton Heath Ind Estate
Poole Dorset
BH16 6LS
www.mass-concrete.com
email: sales@mass-concrete.com
Tel: 01202 628 140
Fax: 01202 628 149

PFLEIDERER INDUSTRIE LTD
Oakfield House
Springwood Way
Tytherington Business Park, Macclesfield
SK10 2XA
www.duropal.co.uk
email: info@pfleiderer.co.uk
Tel: 01625 660 410
Fax: 01625 617 301

PIANOFORTE/QUARELLA
Via Passo Napoleone No 19
Domegliara, Verona
Italy
37015
www.pianofortequartz.co.uk
email: info@pianofortequartz.co.uk
Tel: 0800 107 7870
Fax: 01625 850220

SIEMATIC UK LTD
Osprey House
Primett Road
Stevenage
SG1 3EE
www.siematic.co.uk
email: sales@siematic.co.uk
Tel: 01438 369 251
Fax: 01438 368 920

SNOWDONIA SLATE & STONE
North Wales
www.snowdoniaslate.co.uk
email: richard@snowdoniaslate.co.uk
Tel: 01766 832525
Fax: 01766 832404

STONE THEATRE LTD
Newnham Terrace
Hercules Road
Waterloo, London
SE1 7DR
www.stonetheatre.com
email: london@stonetheatre.com
Tel: 020 7021 0020
Fax: 0207 021 0049

STONEHOUSE TILES LTD
2-10 Ossory Road
London
SE1 5AN
www.stonehousetiles.co.uk
email: sales@stonehousetiles.co.uk
Tel: 0207 237 5375
Fax: 0207 231 7597

SYLMAR TECHNOLOGY LTD
Azalea Close
Clover Nook Ind Park
Alfreton
DE55 4QX
www.sylmarsolidsurfaces.com
email: info@sylmar.co.uk
Tel: 01773 521300
Fax: 01773 836837

TBS FABRICATIONS LTD
Martens Road
Northbank Industrial Park
Irlam, Manchester
M44 5AX
www.tbs-fabrications.com
email: info@tbs-fabrications.com
Tel: 0161 775 1871
Fax: 0161 775 8929

TOUCHSTONE WORKTOPS LTD
Unit 2 Chase Rd. Trading Est.
51 Chase Rd.
London
NW10 6LG
www.touchstoneworktops.com
email: sales@touchstoneworktops.com
Tel: 020 8963 7450
Fax: 020 8963 7455

TRESPA UK
Grosvenor House
Hollinswood Road
Central Park, Telford
TF2 9TW
www.trespa.com
email: info@trespa.co.uk
Tel: 01952 290707
Fax: 01952 290101

WILSONART
Lambton Street Industrial Estate
Shildon
County Durham
DL4 1PX
Tel: 01388 774 661
Fax: 01388 774 861

Lighting

ACTULITE
Aura House
30 Sedgley Road
Penn Common, Wolverhampton
WV4 5LE
www.actulite.com
email: designer@actulite.com
Tel: 01902 332352
Fax: 01902 332 341

AUTHENTIC MODELS
24 Lintot Sq.
Fairbank Rd
Southwater, West Sussex
RH13 9LA
www.authenticmodels.com
email: info@am-uk.eu
Tel: 01403 734 999
Fax: 01403 734888

DESIGN WRIGHT
Lf3.4, The Leathermarket
11/13 Weston St
London
SE1 3ER
www.designwright.co.uk
email: studio@designwright.co.uk
Tel: 020 7357 7788

FLAIRLIGHT
12 Hillcrest Close
Epsom
KT18 5JY
www.flairlight.co.uk
email: sales@flairlight.co.uk
Tel: 01372 807661
Fax: 01372 807660

INGO MAURER GMBH
Kaiserstrasse 47
Munich
Germany
80801
www.ingo-maurer.com
email: info@ingo-maurer.com
Tel: 0049 89 381 606-0
Fax: 0049 89 381 606-30

MOOOI
Minervum 7003
4817 ZL BREDA
www.moooi.com
email: info@moooi.com
Tel: 0031 765784444
Fax: 0031 765710621

OBEROI BROTHERS LIGHTING LTD
29 Humbleton Drive,
Mackworth Estate
Derby
DE22 4AU
www.sales@lightsuk.com
email: sales@lightsuk.com
Tel: 01332 341027/728676
Fax: 01332 293863

PJR ENGINEERING
Collingbourne Ducis
Nr. Marlborough
Wiltshire
SN8 3EH
www.pjrengineering.co.uk
email: sales@pjrengineering.co.uk
Tel: 01264 850763
Fax: 01264 850632

SHIU KAY KAN
34 Lexington Street
London
W1F 0LH
www.skk.net
email: sales@skk.org.uk
Tel: 020 7434 4095
Fax: 0207 734 0901

SILL LIGHTING
3 Thame Park Business Centre
Wenman Road
Thame, Oxfordshire
OX9 3XA
www.sill-uk.com
email: sales@sill-uk.com
Tel: 01844 260 006
Fax: 01844 260 760

TAG FURNITURE CONSULTANCY
Tel: 0151 924 6036

THE LIGHTING ASSOCIATION
Stafford Park 7
Telford
Shropshire
TF3 3BQ
www.lightingassociation.com
email: enquiries@lightingassociation.com
Tel: 01952 290905
Fax: 01952 290906

ANTIQUE & TRADITIONAL LIGHTING

CHANTELLE LIGHTING LTD
Unit 36
Lomeshaye Business Village
Nelson
BB97DR
www.chantellelighting,co.uk
email: info@chantellelighting.co.uk
Tel: 01282 877877
Fax: 01282 877888

CHELSOM LTD
Heritage House
Clifton Road, Blackpool
Lancashire
FY4 4QA
www.chelsom.co.uk
email: marketing@chelsom.co.uk
Tel: 01253 831400
Fax: 01253 791341

CRYSTAL LITE CHANDELIERS
Unit 1 Oak Farm
Cattlegate Rd.
Crews Hill
EN2 9DS
www.chandeliersltd.com
email: admin@chandeliersltd.com
Tel: 0208 367 6766
Fax: 08701 391165

DICKINSON'S PERIOD HOUSE SHOPS
141 Corve Street, Ludlow Sy8 2pg
65 Wyle Cop, Shrewsbury Sy1 1ux
66 Market Place, Warwick Cv34 4sd
www.periodhouseshops.com &
www.periodlightingshop.com
email: periodhouseshop@yahoo.co.uk
Tel: 01584 877276
Fax: 01584 875411

FRITZ FRYER ANTIQUE LIGHTING
23 Station Street
Ross On Wye
HR9 7AG
www.fritzfryer.co.uk
email: enquiries@fritzfryer.co.uk
Tel: 01989 567416
Fax: 01989 566742

HOWE
93 Pimlico Road
Belgravia
London
SW1W 8PH
www.howelondon.com
email: design@howelondon.com
Tel: 02(0) 7730 7987
Fax: 02(0) 7730 0157

JIM LAWRENCE
The Ironworks
Lady Lane Industrial Estate
Hadleigh
IP7 6BQ
www.jim-lawrence.co.uk
email: sales@jim-lawrence.co.uk
Tel: 01473 828176
Fax: 01473 824074

ODEON DESIGN LTD
76-78 St Edward Street
Leek
Staffordshire
ST13 5 DL
odeonantiques.co.uk
email: odeonantiques@hotmail.com
Tel: 01538 378188
Fax: 01538 384235

QUALITY LIGHTING DESIGN
164 Bridge St West
Newtown
Birmingham
B19 2YX
www.qualitylights.com
email: helen@qualitylights,com
Tel: 0121 359 5556
Fax: 0121 359 5557

W.SITCH & COMPANY (ANTIQUES) LTD
48 Berwick Street
Oxford Street
London, W1F 8JD
Tel: 020 7437 3776
Fax: 020 7437 5707
E-mail: info@wsitch.co.uk
Web: www.wsitch.co.uk

This company has been specialising in the reproduction and renovation of antique light fittings for over 200 years, and also carries a vast stock of antique fittings for sale, as well as a range of reproductions manufactured using traditional techniques. We run a full repair, rewiring & renovation service for clients' own fittings.

REINDEER ANTIQUES
81 Kensington Church Street
London
W8 4BG
www.reindeerantiques.co.uk
email: london@reindeerantiques.co.uk
Tel: 02079 373754
Fax: 02079 377199

REMAINS LIGHTING
420 The Chambers
Chelsea Harbour
London
SW10 0XF
www.remains.com
email: london@remains.com
Tel: +44 (0)20 7349 0643

ROCHAMP LTD
Unit5, Shaftesbury Centre
The Runnings
Cheltenham
GL519NH
www.rochamp.com
email: david@rochamp.com
Tel: 01242 525385
Fax: 01242 227546

ARCHITECTURAL LIGHTING

ADVANCED LEDS LTD
Unit 1, Bow Court
Fletchworth Gate, Burnsall Road
Coventry
CV5 6SP
www.advanced-led.com
email: sales@advanced-led.com
Tel: 0247 6716151
Fax: 0247 6712161

AKTIVA
10 Spring Place
London
NW5 3BH
www.aktiva.co.uk
email: info@aktiva.co.uk
Tel: 02074 289325
Fax: 02074 289882

AMOS LIGHTING
Bridford Road
Marsh Barton
Exeter
EX2 8QX
www.amoslighting.co.uk
email: info@amoslighting.co.uk
Tel: 01392 677030
Fax: 01392 662744

AQUA CREATIONS
Ben Zvi Road
Tel Aviv
68103
email: albi@aquagallery.com
Tel: 0097 23551227
Fax: 00972 35151223

ARTEMIDE GB LTD
106 Great Russell Street
London
WC1B 3NB
www.artemide.com
email: showroom@artemide.co.uk
Tel: 02076 315200
Fax: 02076 315222

BETA-CALCO INC.
107 Bell St.
London
NW1 6TL
email: sales@betacalco.co.uk
Tel: 08701 657481
Fax: 08701 657482

CHAOS DESIGN CONSULTANTS LTD
14 Queen Square
Bath
Somerset
BA1 2HN
www.chaosdc.co.uk
email: sonja@chaosdc.co.uk
Tel: 01225 780044
Fax: 01225 780087

COLITE INTERNATIONAL
Po Box 4380
Worthing
West Sussex
BN13 2WE
www.coite.com
email: info@colite.co.uk
Tel: 01903 694925
Fax: 01803 9359003

COMMERCIAL LIGHTING SYSTEMS LTD
Tel: 01489 581002
Fax: 01489 576262

CRESCENT LIGHTING LTD
8 Rivermead
Pipers Lane
Thatcham, Berkshire
RG13 4EP
www.crescent.co.uk
email: sales@crescent.co.uk
Tel: 01635 878888
Fax: 01635 873888

DAVEY LIGHTING LTD
Unit 2 Martlesham Creek Ind Park
Sandy Lane
Woodbridge, Suffolk
IP12 4SD
www.davey-lighting.co.uk
email: sales@davey-lighting.co.uk
Tel: 01394 386768
Fax: 01394 387228

DOPPLER ASSOCIATES
16 Boston Parade
Boston Road
London
W7 2DG
www.dopplerassociates.com
email: sales@doppler.uk.net
Tel: 020 8840 6560
Fax: 020 8840 6560

IDEALS (GB) LTD
Unit 3
Brookside Centre
Sumpters Way, Southend On Sea
SS2 5RR
www.idealsgb.co.uk
email: sales@idealsgb.co.uk
Tel: 01702 460 855
Fax: 01702 460655

IGUZZINI ILLUMINAZIONE UK
Astolat Business Park
Off Old Portsmouth Road
Guildford, Surrey
GU3 1NE
www.iguzzini.co.uk
email: info@iguzzini.co.uk
Tel: 01483 468 000
Fax: 01483 468 001

KEMPS ARCHITECTURAL LIGHTING LTD
Unit 2 Matrix Court
Middleton Grove
Leeds
LS11 5WB
www.kempslighting.com
email: sales@kempslighting.com
Tel: 01132 715777
Fax: 01132 715666

KREON
5 St Saviours Wharf
Mill Street
London
SE1 2BE
www.kreon.com
email: salesuk@kreon.com
Tel: +44 20 7740 2112
Fax: +44 20 7740 2923

LIGHT PROJECTS GROUP
23 Jacob Street
London
SE1 2BG
Tel: 020 7231 8282
Fax: 020 7237 4342

LIGHTING DESIGN INTERNATIONAL
3 Hammersmith Studios
55a Yeldham Road
London
W6 8AF
T: 020 8600 5777
F: 020 8600 5778
design@ldi-uk.com
www.lightingdesigninternational.com

LUXO U K LTD
Unit 1 Abbey Industrial Estate
24 Willow Lane
Mitcham
CR4 4NA
www.luxo.co.uk
email: office@luxo.co.uk
Tel: 0208 687 3370
Fax: 0208 687 3371

MIKE STOANE LIGHTING
www.mikestoanelighting.com
email: sales@mikestoanelighting.com
Tel: 0131 440 1313
Fax: 0131 440 0049

MODULAR LIGHTING INSTRUMENTS
22-24 St Giles High Street
London
WC2H 8TA
www.modular-lighting.co.uk
email: sales@modular-lighting.co.uk
Tel: 020 7681 9933
Fax: 020 7681 9943

OMC (UK) LTD.
Candela House
Cardew Industrial Estate
Redruth, Cornwall
TR15 1SS
www.omc-uk.com
email: omc-sales@omc-uk.com
Tel: 01209 215424
Fax: 01209 215197

ORA LIGHTING
16, Boston Parade
Boston Road
London
W7 2DG
www.dopplerassociates.com
email: sales@doppler.uk.net
Tel: 020 8840 6560
Fax: 020 8840 6560

REMAINS LIGHTING
420 The Chambers
Chelsea Harbour
London
SW10 0XF
www.remains.com
email: london@remains.com
Tel: +44 (0)20 7349 0643

SHIU KAY KAN
34 Lexington Street
London
W1F 0LH
www.skk.net
email: sales@skk.org.uk
Tel: 020 7434 4095
Fax: 0207 734 0901

SILL LIGHTING
3 Thame Park Business Centre
Wenman Road
Thame, Oxfordshire
OX9 3XA
www.sill-uk.com
email: sales@sill-uk.com
Tel: 01844 260 006
Fax: 01844 260 760

SON ET LUMIERE AV & LIGHTING CONSULTANTS
Design House
39a High Street
East Malling
ME19 6AJ
www.son-et-lumiere.co.uk
Tel: 01732 521111

TINDLE LIGHTING
162 Wandsworth Bridge Road, London
www.tindle-lighting.co.uk
email: info@tindle-lighting.com
Tel: 020 7384 1485

TORNADO LIGHTING
2 Stable Yard, Danemere St,
London, SW15 1LT
www.tornado.co.uk
email: sales@tornado.co.uk
Tel: 02087 882324
Fax: 02087 857017

BATHROOM LIGHTING

COMPLETE LITE SOLUTIONS
5,Greystoke Rd
Rawcliffe, YO305FD
www.cls-ltd.com
email: rob@cls-ltd.com
Tel: 0190 469 1009/0844 249 2328
Fax: 0190 469 3664

EGLO UK LTD
Blenheim House
Eversley Way
Egham, TW20 8RY
www.eglo.com
email: info-greatbritain@eglo.com
Tel: 01784 430230
Fax: 01784 430235

FRANKLITE LTD
Snowdon Drive
Winterhill
Milton Keynes, MK6 1AP
www.franklite.net
email: sales@franklite.ltd.uk
Tel: 01908 443090
Fax: 01908 691939

ASTRO LIGHTING LTD
Unit G2
River Way
Harlow
Essex
CM20 2DP
Tel: 01279 427001
Fax: 01279 427002
Web: www.astrolighting.co.uk

Astro Lighting produces a wide range of lighting for all areas of the home, inside and out, but with a specialism in bathroom lighting. With a reputation for innovative designs, high quality manufacture and reliable performance, products are available from lighting specialist outlets, online shops and leading department stores.

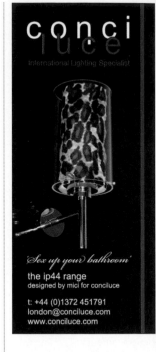

JCC LIGHTING PRODUCTS
Lamplighter House
Beeding Close, Southern Cross Trading Estate,
Bognor Regis, PO22 9TS
www.jcc-lighting.co.uk
email: sales@jcc-lighting.co.uk
Tel: 01243 838999

LIGHTING DESIGN INTERNATIONAL
3 Hammersmith Studios
55a Yeldham Road, London, W6 8AF
T: 020 8600 5777
F; 020 8600 5778
design@ldi-uk.com
www.lightingdesigninternational.com

BESPOKE LIGHTING

2D:3D
263 Abbeydale Road
Wembley, London, HA0 1TW
www.2d3d.co.uk
email: rob@2d3d.co.uk
Tel: 0208 998 3199
Fax: 0208 998 7767

ALBION COURT LTD
The Idea Works
New Road, Gillingham, SP8 4JH
www.albioncourt.co.uk
email: info@albioncourt.co.uk
Tel: 01747 822 818
Fax: 01747 824 469

BOB CROOKS: FIRST GLASS
Thelbridge Cross Farm
Thelbridge Crediton, Devon, EX17 5SH
www.bobcrooks.com
email: sales@bobcrooks.com
Tel: 01884 860037

BOWLES & LINARES
www.bowlesandlinares.co.uk
email: info@bowlesandlinares.co.uk
Tel: 0207 229 9886

CHANTELLE LIGHTING LTD
Unit 36
Lomeshaye Business Village
Nelson
BB97DR
www.chantellelighting,co.uk
email: info@chantellelighting.co.uk
Tel: 01282 877877
Fax: 01282 877888

CHAOS DESIGN CONSULTANTS LTD
14 Queen Square
Bath
Somerset
BA1 2HN
www.chaosdc.co.uk
email: sonja@chaosdc.co.uk
Tel: 01225 780044
Fax: 01225 780087

CRYSTAL LITE CHANDELIERS
Unit 1 Oak Farm
Cattlegate Rd.
Crews Hill
EN2 9DS
www.chandeliersltd.com
email: admin@chandeliersltd.com
Tel: 0208 367 6766
Fax: 08701 391165

CTO LIGHTING
Unit 208 Belgravia Workshops
157-163 Marlborough Road
London
N19 4NF
www.cto-lighting.co.uk
email: info@cto-lighting.co.uk
Tel: 020 7686 8700
Fax: 020 7686 8701

CUBE LIGHTING LTD
Unit 7 River Park
Billet Lane
Berkhamsted
HP4 1HL
www.cubelighting.com
email: sales@cubelighting.com
Tel: 01442 876676
Fax: 01442 876756

DISPLAY LIGHTING LTD
Cedar Technology Centre
Atlantic Street
Altrincham
WA14 5DZ
www.display-lighting.com
email: sales@display-lighting.com
Tel: 0161 929 3355
Fax: 0121 929 3356

DOPPLER ASSOCIATES
16 Boston Parade
Boston Road
London
W7 2DG
www.dopplerassociates.com
email: sales@doppler.uk.net
Tel: 020 8840 6560
Fax: 020 8840 6560

GLASSCASTS LTD
299 Haggerston Rd, London E8 4en
E8 4EN
www.glasscasts.co.uk
email: jeff@glasscasts.co.uk
Tel: 0207 2758 481
Fax: 0207 275 8481

INTERNATIONAL COMPONENTS
Hixon Industrial Estate
Church Lane, Hixon
Staffordshire
ST18 0PY
www.internationalcomponents.co.uk
email: sales@internationalcomponents.co.uk
Tel: 01889 271135
Fax: 01889 271183

KEMPS ARCHITECTURAL LIGHTING LTD
Unit 2 Matrix Court
Middleton Grove
Leeds
LS11 5WB
www.kempslighting.com
email: sales@kempslighting.com
Tel: 01132 715777
Fax: 01132 715666

LAMPHOLDER 2000 LTD
Unit 3, T U House
Thorpe Underwood
Northampton
NN6 9PA
www.lampholder.co.uk
email: sales@lampholder.co.uk
Tel: 01536 713642
Fax: 01536 713994

LAZULI LTD
The Dove House
Astwood, Newport Pagnell
Bucks
MK16 9JX
www.lazuliltd.com
email: info@lazuliltd.com
Tel: 01234 391156

LUXO U K LTD
Unit 1 Abbey Industrial Estate
24 Willow Lane
Mitcham
CR4 4NA
www.luxo.co.uk
email: office@luxo.co.uk
Tel: 0208 687 3370
Fax: 0208 687 3371

MIKE STOANE LIGHTING
www.mikestoanelighting.com
email: sales@mikestoanelighting.com
Tel: 0131 440 1313
Fax: 0131 440 0049

ORA LIGHTING
16, Boston Parade
Boston Road
London
W7 2DG
www.dopplerassociates.com
email: sales@doppler.uk.net
Tel: 020 8840 6560
Fax: 020 8840 6560

PAUL CARRUTHERS DESIGN
Spartan Works
534 Attercliffe Road
Sheffield
S9 3QP
email: paul@paulcarruthersdesign.co.uk
Tel: 0114 242 5440
Fax: 0114 242 5440

PHILLIPS & WOOD
4 Wilson Walk
Off Prebend Gardens
London
W4 1TP
www.phillipsandwood.co.uk
email: info@phillipsandwood.co.uk
Tel: 020 8222 8117
Fax: 020 8748 9752

PJR ENGINEERING
Collingbourne Ducis
Nr. Marlborough
Wiltshire
SN8 3EH
www.pjrengineering.co.uk
email: sales@pjrengineering.co.uk
Tel: 01264 850763
Fax: 01264 850632

PR LIGHTING SYSTEMS LTD
Unit B, Horsted Keynes Industrial Park
Cinder Hill
Horsted Keynes
RH17 7BA
www.prlightingsystems.co.uk
email: sales@prlightingsystems.co.uk
Tel: 01342 811555
Fax: 01342 811888

QUALITY LIGHTING DESIGN
164 Bridge St West
Newtown
Birmingham
B19 2YX
www.qualitylights.com
email: helen@qualitylights,com
Tel: 0121 359 5556
Fax: 0121 359 5557

REMAINS LIGHTING
420 The Chambers
Chelsea Harbour
London
SW10 0XF
www.remains.com
email: london@remains.com
Tel: +44 (0)20 7349 0643

TANNER LIGHTING LTD
Unit 4, Brunel Court
Enterprise Drive, Four Ashes
Wolverhampton
WV10 7DF
www.tanner-lighting.co.uk
email: enquiries@tanner-lighting.co.uk
Tel: 01902 791386
Fax: 01902 791493

WIZARD LIGHTING
Springfieldschurch Lane
Bisley
Woking
GU24 9EA
wizardlighting.co.uk
email: wizlightin@aol.com
Tel: 01483 489080
Fax: 01473 489030

COMMERCIAL LIGHTING

AMOS LIGHTING
Bridford Road
Marsh Barton
Exeter
EX2 8QX
www.amoslighting.co.uk
email: info@amoslighting.co.uk
Tel: 01392 677030
Fax: 01392 662744

ANSELL (SALES & DISTRIBUTION) LTD
Units 32/37, Somerton Industrial Park
Dargan Crescent
Belfast
BT3 9JP
www.anselluk.com
email: sales@anselluk.com
Tel: 028 9077 3750
Fax: 028 9077 3783

ANSELL ELECTRICAL PRODUCTS LTD
Unit 6b Yew Tree Way
Stone Cross Park, Golborne
Warrington
WA3 3JD
www.anselluk.com
email: saleswarrington@anselluk.com
Tel: 01942 433 339
Fax: 01942 433 430

CHANNEL SAFETY SYSTEMS LTD
Bedford Road
Petersfield
Hampshire
GU32 3QA
www.channelsafety.co.uk
email: sales@channelsafety.co.uk
Tel: 0845 884 7000
Fax: 0845 884 6000

CMD LTD, POWERPLAN
Brockholes Way
Claughton-On-Brock
Preston
PR3 0PZ
www.powerplan.co.uk
email: enquiries@powerplan.co.uk
Tel: 01995 640844
Fax: 01995 640798

COMMERCIAL LIGHTING SYSTEMS LTD
Tel: 01489 581002
Fax: 01489 576262

DISPLAY LIGHTING LTD
Cedar Technology Centre
Atlantic Street
Altrincham
WA14 5DZ
www.display-lighting.com
email: sales@display-lighting.com
Tel: 0161 929 3355
Fax: 0121 929 3356

DOPPLER ASSOCIATES
16 Boston Parade
Boston Road
London
W7 2DG
www.dopplerassociates.com
email: sales@doppler.uk.net
Tel: 020 8840 6560
Fax: 020 8840 6560

EYE LIGHTING EUROPE LTD
Unit 2, Eskdale Road
Uxbridge
Middlesex
UB8 2RT
www.eyelighting.co.uk
email: sales@eyelighting.co.uk
Tel: 01895 814418
Fax: 01895 814666

FLUOREL LIGHTING
Tel: 02085 049691
Fax: 02085 061792

IDEALS (GB) LTD
Unit 3
Brookside Centre
Sumpters Way, Southend On Sea
SS2 5RR
www.idealsgb.co.uk
email: sales@idealsgb.co.uk
Tel: 01702 460 855
Fax: 01702 460655

IGUZZINI ILLUMINAZIONE UK
Astolat Business Park
Off Old Portsmouth Road
Guildford, Surrey
GU3 1NE
www.iguzzini.co.uk
email: info@iguzzini.co.uk
Tel: 01483 468 000
Fax: 01483 468 001

KREON
5 St Saviours Wharf
Mill Street
London
SE1 2BE
www.kreon.com
email: salesuk@kreon.com
Tel: +44 20 7740 2112
Fax: +44 20 7740 2923

LUXO U K LTD
Unit 1 Abbey Industrial Estate
24 Willow Lane
Mitcham
CR4 4NA
www.luxo.co.uk
email: office@luxo.co.uk
Tel: 0208 687 3370
Fax: 0208 687 3371

MODULAR LIGHTING INSTRUMENTS
22-24 St Giles High Street
London
WC2H 8TA
www.modular-lighting.co.uk
email: sales@modular-lighting.co.uk
Tel: 020 7681 9933
Fax: 020 7681 9943

ORA LIGHTING
16, Boston Parade
Boston Road
London
W7 2DG
www.dopplerassociates.com
email: sales@doppler.uk.net
Tel: 020 8840 6560
Fax: 020 8840 6560

PJR ENGINEERING
Collingbourne Ducis
Nr. Marlborough
Wiltshire
SN8 3EH
www.pjrengineering.co.uk
email: sales@pjrengineering.co.uk
Tel: 01264 850763
Fax: 01264 850632

PR LIGHTING SYSTEMS LTD
Unit B, Horsted Keynes Industrial Park
Cinder Hill
Horsted Keynes
RH17 7BA
www.prlightingsystems.co.uk
email: sales@prlightingsystems.co.uk
Tel: 01342 811555
Fax: 01342 811888

TANNER LIGHTING LTD
Unit 4, Brunel Court
Enterprise Drive, Four Ashes
Wolverhampton
WV10 7DF
www.tanner-lighting.co.uk
email: enquiries@tanner-lighting.co.uk
Tel: 01902 791386
Fax: 01902 791493

THE LIGHTING ASSOCIATION
Stafford Park 7
Telford
Shropshire
TF3 3BQ
www.lightingassociation.com
email: enquiries@lightingassociation.com
Tel: 01952 290905
Fax: 01952 290906

CONTEMPORARY LIGHTING

AKTIVA
10 Spring Place
London
NW5 3BH
www.aktiva.co.uk
email: info@aktiva.co.uk
Tel: 02074 289325
Fax: 02074 289882

AMOS LIGHTING
Bridford Road
Marsh Barton
Exeter
EX2 8QX
www.amoslighting.co.uk
email: info@amoslighting.co.uk
Tel: 01392 677030
Fax: 01392 662744

BLUE MARMALADE LTD
32-36 Dalmeny Street
Edinburgh
EH6 8RG
www.bluemarmalade.co.uk
email: info@bluemarmalade.co.uk
Tel: 0131 5537766
Fax: 0131 5536659

BOWLES & LINARES
www.bowlesandlinares.co.uk
email: info@bowlesandlinares.co.uk
Tel: 0207 229 9886

nlimited **Light** manufactures a wide range of fibre optic lighting kits to reate stunning effects in your home.Enjoy them yourself or install them to et your property apart from others. White light, static colour, colour hange (choose from 15 vibrant colours) and remote control available.

call 01890883522 or shop online at www.unlimitedlight.com

BRAND VAN EGMOND BV
Nikkelstraat 41
NL-1411 AH Naarden
tel: +31 (0)35 692 12 59
fax: +31 (0)35 691 17 25
info@brandvanegmond.co.uk
press@brandvanegmond.com
www.brandvanegmond.com

Since 20 years the Dutch design studio
BRAND VAN EGMOND designs
handmade unique and sensual lighting
sculptures that stimulate the fantasy.
Their lighting sculptures light up many
prestigious projects and the houses of
the rich and famous. The creations are
available both in a standard collection
and as 'Haute Couture' and custom
made for boutiques, hotels, clubs and
restaurants… From London to Shanghai.

CATERINA FADDA STUDIO
201b Saga Centre,
326 Kensal Rd
London, W10 5BZ
www.caterinafadda.com
email: info@caterinafadda.com
Tel: 0208 9643725

CHAPLINS FURNITURE LTD
477-507 Uxbridge Rd
Hatch End
Middlesex, HA5 4JS
www.chaplins.co.uk
email: sales@chaplins.co.uk
Tel: 020 84211779
Fax: 020 84213872

CHELSOM LTD
Heritage House
Clifton Road, Blackpool
Lancashire, FY4 4QA
www.chelsom.co.uk
email: marketing@chelsom.co.uk
Tel: 01253 831400
Fax: 01253 791341

CRYSTAL LITE CHANDELIERS
Unit 1 Oak Farm
Cattlegate Rd.
Crews Hill, EN2 9DS
www.chandeliersltd.com
email: admin@chandeliersltd.com
Tel: 0208 367 6766
Fax: 08701 391165

CTO LIGHTING
Unit 208 Belgravia Workshops
157-163 Marlborough Road, London, N19 4NF
www.cto-lighting.co.uk
email: info@cto-lighting.co.uk
Tel: 020 7686 8700
Fax: 020 7686 8701

CUBE LIGHTING LTD
Unit 7 River Park
Billet Lane
Berkhamsted
HP4 1HL
www.cubelighting.com
email: sales@cubelighting.com
Tel: 01442 876676
Fax: 01442 876756

DESIGNHEURE
10 Bis Rue De La Savonnerie
34200 SÈTE - FRANCE
www.designheure.com
email: contact@designheure.com
Tel: 0033 04675 19199
Fax: 0033 04880 49604

DIX HEURES DIX
5 Rue De La Toscane Bp 4308
Erdre Active
La Chapelle Sur Erdre Cedex
FR-44243
www.dixheuresdix.com
email: info@dixheuresdix.com
Tel: 00 33 240 99 85 00
Fax: 00 33 240 35 26 22

DO SHOP LIMITED
G/F And Basement
47 Beak Street
London
W1F 9SE
www.do-shop.com
email: info@do-shop.com
Tel: 020 7494 9090
Fax: 020 7494 9090

EGLO UK LTD
Blenheim House
Eversley Way
Egham
TW20 8RY
www.eglo.com
email: info-greatbritain@eglo.com
Tel: 01784 430230
Fax: 01784 430235

EYE LIGHTING EUROPE LTD
Unit 2, Eskdale Road
Uxbridge
Middlesex
UB8 2RT
www.eyelighting.co.uk
email: sales@eyelighting.co.uk
Tel: 01895 814418
Fax: 01895 814666

JOCELYN WARNER LTD
23 Links Yard
Spelman Street
London, United Kingdom
E1 5LX
www.jocelynwarner.com
Tel: 0207 3753754

JOHN CULLEN LIGHTING
561-563 Kings Road
London
SW6 2EB
www.johncullenlighting.co.uk
email: design@johncullenlighting.co.uk
Tel: 020 7371 5400
Fax: 020 7371 7799

KAREN LAWRENCE GLASS
Unit F 272, Riverside Business Centre
Brendon Valley
Wandsworth, London
SW18 4UQ
www.karenlawrenceglass.com
email: karen@karenlawrenceglass.com
Tel: 020 8874 7955

LAMPHOLDER 2000 LTD
Unit 3, T U House
Thorpe Underwood
Northampton
NN6 9PA
www.lampholder.co.uk
email: sales@lampholder.co.uk
Tel: 01536 713642
Fax: 01536 713994

LLOYTRON PLC
Laltex House, Leigh Commerce Park
Greenfold Way
Leigh, Lancashire
WN7 3XH
www.lloytron.com
email: lloytron@laltex.com
Tel: 01942 687040
Fax: 01942 687070

MIKE STOANE LIGHTING
www.mikestoanelighting.com
email: sales@mikestoanelighting.com
Tel: 0131 440 1313
Fax: 0131 440 0049

MODULAR LIGHTING INSTRUMENTS
22-24 St Giles High Street
London, WC2H 8TA
www.modular-lighting.co.uk
email: sales@modular-lighting.co.uk
Tel: 020 7681 9933
Fax: 020 7681 9943

MARK BRAZIER-JONES

Hyde Hall Barn
Sandon
Buntingford
Herts, SG9 0RU
Tel: 01763 273599
Fax: 01763 273410
Web: www.brazier-jones.com
Email: studio@brazier-jones.com

Mark Brazier-Jones has been creating
furniture and lighting for over 20
years. Working with precious metals
such as bronze and aluminium, and
glass lenses and crystals on his
lighting, Mark's design has influenced
many. As well as bespoke pieces
unique to individual clients
requirements, Mark has a collection of
work that can be made to order.

NEUESLICHT
www.neueslicht.com
email: info@neueslicht.de
Tel: 04991 3193 22658

OPEN GALLERY
375 City Road
London
EC1V 1NB
www.opengallery.co.uk
email: will@opengallery.co.uk
Tel: 020 7837 3000
Fax: 020 7833 2185

PAUL CARRUTHERS DESIGN
Spartan Works
534 Attercliffe Road
Sheffield
S9 3QP
email: paul@paulcarruthersdesign.co.uk
Tel: 0114 242 5440
Fax: 0114 242 5440

PAVILION RATTAN LTD
The Ulvers Building
Budby Road
Cuckney, Nr. Mansfield
NG20 9JP
www.pavilionrattan.co.uk
email: sales@pavilionrattan.co.uk
Tel: 01623 847030
Fax: 0870 706 2159

PREMIER HOUSEWARES LLP
Premier Business Park
55 Jordanvale Avenue
Glasgow
G14 0QP
www.premierhousewares.co.uk
email: info@premierhousewares.co.uk
Tel: 0141 579 2000
Fax: 0141 579 2005

**PANESAR ELECTRICAL CO &
PEC LIGHTS**
362-364 High St North,
Manor Park, London, E12 6PH
Tel: 020 8503 4314
Tel: 020 8472 1873
Fax: 020 8471 6271
Email: info@peclights.com
Web: www.peclights.com

PEC Lights distribute a high-end
collection of contemporary Downlights
and LED Downlights. Our lights
represent excellence and innovation.
The versatility of our lights is aimed to
break the convention of 'bog' standard
downlights by offering a touch of
sophistication and excitement. Give life
to you're ceiling space. Contact us today
for your catalogue.

PLACESANDSPACES

PLACES AND SPACES
30 Old Town,
Clapham,
London, SW4 0LB
Tel: 02074980998
Email: contact@placesandspaces.com
Web: www.placesandspaces.com

Lighting can make a space! We are a
retail shop that offers a wide selection
of brands and bespoke makers for all
lighting requirements. We can work
with you on a brief and then find the
light that suits your requirements so
do ask for more information.

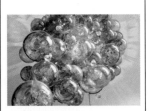

ROAST DESIGNS LTD
327 Croxted Road
London
SE24 9DB
Tel: 0208 671 6595
Mob: 07828 034208
Email: roastdesigns@aol.com
Web: www.roastdesigns.co.uk

Roast design and handcraft bespoke
chandeliers from individually blown
glass spheres. Totally unique, these
stunning glass sculptures look
fabulous in traditional and
contemporary settings. We have
completed large scale commercial and
residential commissions and our work
is sold by Selfridges and Liberty. We
have been featured in many
prestigious publications.

RASMUS
12-13 Royal Parade
Harrogate
North Yorkshire
HG1 2SZ
www.rasmusdesign.co.uk
email: info@rasmusdesign.co.uk
Tel: 01423 560050
Fax: 01423 875087

ROCHAMP LTD
Unit5, Shaftesbury Centre
The Runnings
Cheltenham
GL519NH
www.rochamp.com
email: david@rochamp.com
Tel: 01242 525385
Fax: 01242 227546

TAY LIGHTING
Unit Yo1 Access House
443 Norwood Road
London
SE27 9DQ
www.taylighting.com
email: info@taylighting.com
Tel: 020 8766 0500
Fax: 020 8766 0500

TINDLE LIGHTING
162 Wandsworth Bridge Road
London
www.tindle-lighting.co.uk
email: info@tindle-lighting.com
Tel: 020 7384 1485

TORNADO LIGHTING
2 Stable Yard
Danemere St
London
SW15 1LT
www.tornado.co.uk
email: sales@tornado.co.uk
Tel: 02087 882324
Fax: 02087 857017

VESSEL
114 Kesington Park Road
Notting Hill
London
W112PW
www.vesselgallery.com
email: info@vesselgallery.com
Tel: 02077 278001
Fax: 02077 278661

WESTERN LIGHTS
Duchy Road, Heathpark Industrial Estate,
Honiton, Devon, EX14 1YD
Tel: 01404 435888
email: sales@westernlights.co.uk

WITHIN4WALLS LTD
Stratford Lodge
29 Leam Terrace
Royal Leamington Spa
CV31 1BQ
www.within4walls.co.uk
email: info@within4walls.co.uk
Tel: 01926 772217

DECORATIVE LIGHTING

BETA-CALCO INC.
107 Bell St.
London
NW1 6TL
email: sales@betacalco.co.uk
Tel: 08701 657481
Fax: 08701 657482

BRABIN & FITZ
22 Bridge Street Row
Chester
CH1 1NN
www.brabinandfitz.co.uk
Tel: 01244 314 838
Fax: 01244 349 756

CARLOS REMES LIGHTING CO
10 New Quebec Street
London
W1H 7RN
www.carlosremes.co.uk
email: carlos@remes.demon.co.uk
Tel: 020 7262 9963
Fax: 020 7262 9227

CHELSOM LTD
Heritage House
Clifton Road, Blackpool
Lancashire
FY4 4QA
www.chelsom.co.uk
email: marketing@chelsom.co.uk
Tel: 01253 831400
Fax: 01253 791341

CONTRACT LIGHTING & DESIGN
Unit 17 Branksome Business Park
Bourne Valley Road
Poole , Dorest
BH12 1DW
www.contractlighting.co.uk
email: tim@contractlighting.co.uk
Tel: 0845 270 0773
Fax: 0845 270 0776

DESIGNHEURE
10 Bis Rue De La Savonnerie
34200 SÈTE - FRANCE
www.designheure.com
email: contact@designheure.com
Tel: 0033 04675 19199
Fax: 0033 04880 49604

DIX HEURES DIX
5 Rue De La Toscane Bp 4308
Erdre Active
La Chapelle Sur Erdre Cedex
FR-44243
www.dixheuresdix.com
email: info@dixheuresdix.com
Tel: 00 33 240 99 85 00
Fax: 00 33 240 35 26 22

FEBLAND GROUP
Ashworth Road
Marton
Blackpool, Lancs
FY4 4UN
www.febland.co.uk
email: info@febland.co.uk
Tel: 01253 600 600
Fax: 01253 792211

FRANKLITE LTD
Snowdon Drive
Winterhill
Milton Keynes, Milton Keynes
MK6 1AP
www.franklite.net
email: sales@franklite.ltd.uk
Tel: 01908 443090
Fax: 01908 691939

INGO MAURER GMBH
Kaiserstrasse 47
Munich
Germany
80801
www.ingo-maurer.com
email: info@ingo-maurer.com
Tel: 0049 89 381 606-0
Fax: 0049 89 381 606-30

INTERNATIONAL COMPONENTS
Hixon Industrial Estate
Church Lane, Hixon
Staffordshire
ST18 0PY
www.internationalcomponents.co.uk
email: sales@internationalcomponents.co.uk
Tel: 01889 271135
Fax: 01889 271183

KEMPS ARCHITECTURAL LIGHTING LTD
Unit 2 Matrix Court
Middleton Grove
Leeds
LS11 5WB
www.kempslighting.com
email: sales@kempslighting.com
Tel: 01132 715777
Fax: 01132 715666

KONEPT DESIGN
Bismarckstr.90
20253 HAMBURG
www.buegelbrett.net
email: info@buegelbrett.net
Tel: 0049 1724 055486
Fax: 0049 721 151 34 35 32

LAMPHOLDER 2000 LTD
Unit 3, T U House
Thorpe Underwood
Northampton
NN6 9PA
www.lampholder.co.uk
email: sales@lampholder.co.uk
Tel: 01536 713642
Fax: 01536 713994

LAZULI LTD
The Dove House
Astwood, Newport Pagnell
Bucks
MK16 9JX
www.lazuliltd.com
email: info@lazuliltd.com
Tel: 01234 391156

LIGHT ENGINEERING
64 Eden Road
London
E17 9JY
www.light-engineering.com
email: info@light-engineering.com
Tel: 02085 202336
Fax: 02085 091332

MARTIN DANNELL & CO LTD
Md House, 13 Abbeymead Industrial Park
Brooker Road
Waltham Abbey
EN9 1HU
www.martin-dannell.co.uk
email: enquiries@martin-dannell.co.uk
Tel: 01992 700311
Fax: 01992 769521

OBEROI BROTHERS LIGHTING LTD
29 Humbleton Drive,
Mackworth Estate
Derby
DE22 4AU
www.sales@lightsuk.com
email: sales@lightsuk.com
Tel: 01332 341027/728676
Fax: 01332 293863

OPTI
38 Cromwell Road
Luton
LU3 1DN
email: optiuk@optikinetics.com
Tel: 01582 411413
Fax: 01582 400613

PHILLIPS & WOOD
4 Wilson Walk
Off Prebend Gardens
London
W4 1TP
www.phillipsandwood.co.uk
email: info@phillipsandwood.co.uk
Tel: 020 8222 8117
Fax: 020 8748 9752

PUFF-BUFF DESIGN
Ul.sniegockiej 10/40a, 00430 Warsaw
Ul.podgorna 46, 87100 Torun
www.puff-buff.com
email: sales@puff-buff.com
Tel: 04822 6210834
Fax: 04822 6210834

QUALITY LIGHTING DESIGN
164 Bridge St West
Newtown
Birmingham
B19 2YX
www.qualitylights.com
email: helen@qualitylights,com
Tel: 0121 359 5556
Fax: 0121 359 5557

SARAH WALKER ARTSHADES
Selsdon House
80 Wells Road
Malvern
WR14 4PA
www.artshades.co.uk
email: sarah@artshades.co.uk
Tel: 01684 575756

SMART FIRE LTD
Lyon House
160-166 Borough High St
SE1 1JR
www.ecosmartfire.com
email: uk(at)ecosmartfire.com
Tel: 020 7173 5000
Fax: 020 7173 5001

SPINA DESIGN
12 Kingsgate Place
London
NW6 4TA
www.spinadesign.co.uk
email: info@spinadesign.co.uk
Tel: 0207 328 5274
Fax: 0207 624 2078

TANNER LIGHTING LTD
Unit 4, Brunel Court
Enterprise Drive, Four Ashes
Wolverhampton
WV10 7DF
www.tanner-lighting.co.uk
email: enquiries@tanner-lighting.co.uk
Tel: 01902 791386
Fax: 01902 791493

THE FRENCH BEDROOM COMPANY
www.frenchbedroomcompany.co.uk
Tel: 08456 448022

THE LIGHTING ASSOCIATION
Stafford Park 7
Telford
Shropshire
TF3 3BQ
www.lightingassociation.com
email: enquiries@lightingassociation.com
Tel: 01952 290905
Fax: 01952 290906

TP24 LTD
Seymour House
12 Station Road
Chatteris , Cambridgeshire
PE16 6AG
www.tp24.com
email: sales@tp24.com
Tel: 01354 694 591
Fax: 01354 695 879

WOKA LAMPS VIENNA
Singerstrasse 16
Vienna
A-1010
www.woka.com
Tel: 00 43 1 513 2912
Fax: 00 43 1 513 8505

DESIGNER LIGHTING

ACCENT APS
www.accent.dk
Tel: 0045 2087 9049

AGUSTIN OTEGUI
www.agustin-otegui.com
email: agustin@nos-id.com
Tel: 005255 44399655

ALBION COURT LTD
The Idea Works
New Road
Gillingham
SP8 4JH
www.albioncourt.co.uk
email: info@albioncourt.co.uk
Tel: 01747 822 818
Fax: 01747 824 469

AQUA CREATIONS
Ben Zvi Road
Tel Aviv
68103
email: albi@aquagallery.com
Tel: 0097 23551227
Fax: 00972 35151223

CHANTELLE LIGHTING LTD
Unit 36
Lomeshaye Business Village
Nelson
BB97DR
www.chantellelighting,co.uk
email: info@chantellelighting.co.uk
Tel: 01282 877877
Fax: 01282 877888

arturo alvarez
San Miguel de Sarandón, 9.
15886 Vedra. A Coruña (Spain)
Tel: +34 981 81 46 00
Fax: +34 981 50 20 00
Mail: calor-color@arturo-alvarez.com
Web: www.arturo-alvarez.com

arturo alvarez designs and manufactures all kind of decorative lighting with high-quality and personality. All products are entirely handmade in Spain, passing very strict quality controls and they are made with the best raw materials. Our main aim is to innovate, surprise and create illusions.

CONTRACT LIGHTING & DESIGN
Unit 17 Branksome Business Park
Bourne Valley Road
Poole , Dorest, BH12 1DW
www.contractlighting.co.uk
email: tim@contractlighting.co.uk
Tel: 0845 270 0773
Fax: 0845 270 0776

FRANKLITE LTD
Snowdon Drive
Winterhill
Milton Keynes, MK6 1AP
www.franklite.net
email: sales@franklite.ltd.uk
Tel: 01908 443090
Fax: 01908 691939

IDEALS (GB) LTD
Unit 3
Brookside Centre
Sumpters Way, Southend On Sea, SS2 5RR
www.idealsgb.co.uk
email: sales@idealsgb.co.uk
Tel: 01702 460 855
Fax: 01702 460655

INFORM FURNITURE LIMITED
99 St John's Hill
London, W11 1SY
www.informfurniture.co.uk
email: info@informfurniture.co.uk
Tel: 020 7228 3335
Fax: 020 7924 5955

INGO MAURER GMBH
Kaiserstrasse 47
Munich, Germany, 80801
www.ingo-maurer.com
email: info@ingo-maurer.com
Tel: 0049 89 381 606-0
Fax: 0049 89 381 606-30

JOE EARLEY DESIGN
Mallards Cottage, South Gren Road
Fingringhoe, Colchester
Essex
CO5 DR
www.earleybrothers.com
email: joe@earleybrothers.com
Tel: 07909994860

LASERPOD
Highmoor Park
Highmoor
Henley On Thames
RG9 5DH
www.laserpod.com
email: andy@laserpod.com
Tel: 01491 641 000

LAZULI LTD
The Dove House
Astwood, Newport Pagnell
Bucks
MK16 9JX
www.lazuliltd.com
email: info@lazuliltd.com
Tel: 01234 391156

NEO DESIGN
Herdeckerstr. 26
58453 WITTEN
www.neo-studios.de
email: info@neo-studios.de
Tel: 0049 2302 202 76 28
Fax: 0049 2302 202 76 28

NORMANN COPENHAGEN
Osterbrogade 70
Copenhagen
Denmark
2100
www.normann-copenhagen.com
email: normann@normann-copenhagen.com
Tel: 0045 35 554 459
Fax: 0045 35 554 439

OBEROI BROTHERS LIGHTING LTD
29 Humbleton Drive,
Mackworth Estate
Derby
DE22 4AU
www.sales@lightsuk.com
email: sales@lightsuk.com
Tel: 01332 341027/728676
Fax: 01332 293863

PAUL CARRUTHERS DESIGN
Spartan Works
534 Attercliffe Road
Sheffield
S9 3QP
email: paul@paulcarruthersdesign.co.uk
Tel: 0114 242 5440
Fax: 0114 242 5440

PHILLIPS & WOOD
4 Wilson Walk
Off Prebend Gardens
London
W4 1TP
www.phillipsandwood.co.uk
email: info@phillipsandwood.co.uk
Tel: 020 8222 8117
Fax: 020 8748 9752

SIMPLY SCANDINAVIAN
70 Flaxman Road
London
SE5 9DH
www.simply-scandinavian.co.uk
Tel: 0207 095 8400
Fax: 07766 663960

SKEELS
www.skeels.co.uk
email: rebecca@skeels.co.uk
Tel: 07715093690

T BAC DESIGN
AUSTRALIA
www.tbacdesign.com
email: troy@tbacdesign.com
Tel: 0061 39417 6595

TAY LIGHTING
Unit Yo1 Access House
443 Norwood Road
London
SE27 9DQ
www.taylighting.com
email: info@taylighting.com
Tel: 020 8766 0500
Fax: 020 8766 0500

TWENTYTWENTYONE
18c River Street
London
EC1R 1XN
www.twentytwentyone.com
email: mail@twentytwentyone.com
Tel: 02078 371900
Fax: 02078 371908

WITHIN4WALLS LTD
Stratford Lodge
29 Leam Terrace
Royal Leamington Spa
CV31 1BQ
www.within4walls.co.uk
email: info@within4walls.co.uk
Tel: 01926 772217

WOKA LAMPS VIENNA
Singerstrasse 16
Vienna
A-1010
www.woka.com
Tel: 00 43 1 513 2912
Fax: 00 43 1 513 8505

EMERGENCY LIGHTING

CHANNEL SAFETY SYSTEMS LTD
Bedford Road
Petersfield
Hampshire
GU32 3QA
www.channelsafety.co.uk
email: sales@channelsafety.co.uk
Tel: 0845 884 7000
Fax: 0845 884 6000

FLUOREL LIGHTING
Tel: 02085 049691
Fax: 02085 061792

FIBRE OPTICS

CRESCENT LIGHTING LTD
8 Rivermead
Pipers Lane
Thatcham, Berkshire
RG13 4EP
www.crescent.co.uk
email: sales@crescent.co.uk
Tel: 01635 878888
Fax: 01635 873888

LIGHT ENGINEERING
64 Eden Road
London, E17 9JY
www.light-engineering.com
email: info@light-engineering.com
Tel: 02085 202336
Fax: 02085 091332

LIGHT PROJECTS GROUP
23 Jacob Street
London, SE1 2BG
Tel: 020 7231 8282
Fax: 020 7237 4342

NEUESLICHT
www.neueslicht.com
email: info@neueslicht.de
Tel: 04991 3193 22658

HOME LIGHTING

CARLOS REMES LIGHTING CO
10 New Quebec Street, London, W1H 7RN
www.carlosremes.co.uk
email: carlos@remes.demon.co.uk
Tel: 020 7262 9963
Fax: 020 7262 9227

COMPLETE LITE SOLUTIONS
5,Greystoke Rd, Rawcliffe, YO305FD
www.cls-ltd.com
email: rob@cls-ltd.com
Tel: 0190 469 1009/0844 249 2328
Fax: 0190 469 3664

DIX HEURES DIX
5 Rue De La Toscane Bp 4308
Erdre Active
La Chapelle Sur Erdre Cedex, FR-44243
www.dixheuresdix.com
email: info@dixheuresdix.com
Tel: 00 33 240 99 85 00
Fax: 00 33 240 35 26 22

JOHN CULLEN LIGHTING
561-563 Kings Road, London, SW6 2EB
www.johncullenlighting.co.uk
email: design@johncullenlighting.co.uk
Tel: 020 7371 5400
Fax: 020 7371 7799

DECORLIGHT (UK) LTD
Decorlight Building, 68b Pier Avenue,
Clacton-on-Sea, Essex, CO15 1NH
Tel: 01255 421818
Fax: 01255 474147
enquiries@decorlightuk.com
www.decorlightuk.com

We have a range of contemporary
table, floor and large arc lamps which
complement both modern and classic
interiors. We pride ourselves with
competitive prices and excellent
service.

MARTIN DANNELL & CO LTD
Md House, 13 Abbeymead Industrial Park
Brooker Road
Waltham Abbey
EN9 1HU
www.martin-dannell.co.uk
email: enquiries@martin-dannell.co.uk
Tel: 01992 700311
Fax: 01992 769521

SARAH WALKER ARTSHADES
Selsdon House
80 Wells Road
Malvern
WR14 4PA
www.artshades.co.uk
email: sarah@artshades.co.uk
Tel: 01684 575756

TP24 LTD
Seymour House
12 Station Road
Chatteris , Cambridgeshire
PE16 6AG
www.tp24.com
email: sales@tp24.com
Tel: 01354 694 591
Fax: 01354 695 879

LAMPS & SHADES

ALBION COURT LTD
The Idea Works
New Road
Gillingham
SP8 4JH
www.albioncourt.co.uk
email: info@albioncourt.co.uk
Tel: 01747 822 818
Fax: 01747 824 469

BRABIN & FITZ
22 Bridge Street Row
Chester
CH1 1NN
www.brabinandfitz.co.uk
Tel: 01244 314 838
Fax: 01244 349 756

CANDLES DIRECT
55 Marine Drive
Paignton
TQ3 2NS
www.candlesdirect.uk.com
email: james@candlesdirect.uk.com
Tel: 01803 525365
Fax: 01803 528865

CARLOS REMES LIGHTING CO
10 New Quebec Street
London
W1H 7RN
www.carlosremes.co.uk
email: carlos@remes.demon.co.uk
Tel: 020 7262 9963
Fax: 020 7262 9227

CATHERINE HAMMERTON
Cockpit Arts, Cockpit Yard
Northington Street
London
WC1N 2NP
www.catherinehammerton.com
email: info@catherinehammerton.com
Tel: ex directory.

CTO LIGHTING
Unit 208 Belgravia Workshops
157-163 Marlborough Road
London, N19 4NF
www.cto-lighting.co.uk
email: info@cto-lighting.co.uk
Tel: 020 7686 8700
Fax: 020 7686 8701

JACK AND ROSE
Unit 1, Solhampton Farm Business Park
Astley, Stourport On Severn, DY13 0RR
www.jackandrose.co.uk
email: info@jackandrose.co.uk
Tel: 01299 828930
Fax: 01299 829786

JUDY HOLME LIMITED
The Watermark
9-15 Ribbleton Lane
Preston, PR1 5EZ
www.judyholme.com
email: sales@judyholme.com
Tel: 0845 389 3131
Fax: 0845 389 3121

ROCHAMP LTD
Unit5, Shaftesbury Centre
The Runnings
Cheltenham, GL519NH
www.rochamp.com
email: david@rochamp.com
Tel: 01242 525385
Fax: 01242 227546

SARAH WALKER ARTSHADES
Selsdon House
80 Wells Road
Malvern, WR14 4PA
www.artshades.co.uk
email: sarah@artshades.co.uk
Tel: 01684 575756

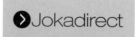

SHADES OF JAPAN
www.shadesofjapan.net
email: glennjoachim@ntlworld.com
Tel: 01476 594603

TAY LIGHTING
Unit Yo1 Access House
443 Norwood Road
London
SE27 9DQ
www.taylighting.com
email: info@taylighting.com
Tel: 020 8766 0500
Fax: 020 8766 0500

THE CUBE COLLECTION
Po Box 188,
TQ9 9AY
www.thecube.uk.com
email: info@thcube.uk.com
Tel: 01803 712388
Fax: 01803 712388

LED LIGHTING

ADVANCED LEDS LTD
Unit 1, Bow Court
Fletchworth Gate, Burnsall Road
Coventry
CV5 6SP
www.advanced-led.com
email: sales@advanced-led.com
Tel: 0247 6716151
Fax: 0247 6712161

ANSELL (SALES & DISTRIBUTION) LTD
Units 32/37, Somerton Industrial Park
Dargan Crescent
Belfast
BT3 9JP
www.anselluk.com
email: sales@anselluk.com
Tel: 028 9077 3750
Fax: 028 9077 3783

ANSELL ELECTRICAL PRODUCTS LTD
Unit 6b Yew Tree Way
Stone Cross Park, Golborne
Warrington
WA3 3JD
www.anselluk.com
email: saleswarrington@anselluk.com
Tel: 01942 433 339
Fax: 01942 433 430

ARTEMIDE GB LTD
106 Great Russell Street
London
WC1B 3NB
www.artemide.com
email: showroom@artemide.co.uk
Tel: 02076 315200
Fax: 02076 315222

AUSTIN LUCE & COMPANY LTD
Elm Trees House
Effingham Road
Copthorne
RH10 3HX
www.austinluce.co.uk
email: enquiries@austinluce.co.uk
Tel: 01342 713310
Fax: 01342 718097

AV INSPIRATIONS LTD
Units 8 - 10 Shorade Ind Est
Watling Street, Bridgtown
Cannock
WS11 0DH
email: tracey@avinspirations.co.uk
Tel: 01543 506766

BDC
Bdc Head Office
550 White Hart Lane
London
N17 7RQ
www.bdc.co.uk
email: sales@bdc.co.uk
Tel: 0844 811 0040
Fax: 0844 811 0041

BETA-CALCO INC.
107 Bell St.
London
NW1 6TL
email: sales@betacalco.co.uk
Tel: 08701 657481
Fax: 08701 657482

CANDLES DIRECT
55 Marine Drive
Paignton
TQ3 2NS
www.candlesdirect.uk.com
email: james@candlesdirect.uk.com
Tel: 01803 525365
Fax: 01803 528865

CHANNEL SAFETY SYSTEMS LTD
Bedford Road
Petersfield
Hampshire
GU32 3QA
www.channelsafety.co.uk
email: sales@channelsafety.co.uk
Tel: 0845 884 7000
Fax: 0845 884 6000

CHAOS DESIGN CONSULTANTS LTD
14 Queen Square
Bath
Somerset
BA1 2HN
www.chaosdc.co.uk
email: sonja@chaosdc.co.uk
Tel: 01225 780044
Fax: 01225 780087

COLITE INTERNATIONAL
Po Box 4380
Worthing
West Sussex
BN13 2WE
www.coite.com
email: info@colite.co.uk
Tel: 01903 694925
Fax: 01803 9359003

COMPLETE LITE SOLUTIONS
5,Greystoke Rd
Rawcliffe
YO305FD
www.cls-ltd.com
email: rob@cls-ltd.com
Tel: 0190 469 1009/0844 249 2328
Fax: 0190 469 3664

CONTRACT LIGHTING & DESIGN
Unit 17 Branksome Business Park
Bourne Valley Road
Poole , Dorest
BH12 1DW
www.contractlighting.co.uk
email: tim@contractlighting.co.uk
Tel: 0845 270 0773
Fax: 0845 270 0776

Koncept believes in smart design. Smart design brings together form and function in startling ways. Our new high power LED lamps combine high performance LEDs with fully articulating bodies in stunningly slim profiles. Effortless poses, available dimming and a choice of warm or cool white light give you control over every aspect of your light. Graceful form and energy-efficient LEDs impact your senses instead of the environment.

CRESCENT LIGHTING LTD
8 Rivermead
Pipers Lane
Thatcham, Berkshire
RG13 4EP
www.crescent.co.uk
email: sales@crescent.co.uk
Tel: 01635 878888
Fax: 01635 873888

CUBE LIGHTING LTD
Unit 7 River Park
Billet Lane, Berkhamsted, HP4 1HL
www.cubelighting.com
email: sales@cubelighting.com
Tel: 01442 876676
Fax: 01442 876756

DISPLAY LIGHTING LTD
Cedar Technology Centre
Atlantic Street, Altrincham, WA14 5DZ
www.display-lighting.com
email: sales@display-lighting.com
Tel: 0161 929 3355
Fax: 0121 929 3356

FLAIRLIGHT
12 Hillcrest Close
Epsom, KT18 5JY
www.flairlight.co.uk
email: sales@flairlight.co.uk
Tel: 01372 807661
Fax: 01372 807660

INTERNATIONAL COMPONENTS
Hixon Industrial Estate
Church Lane, Hixon
Staffordshire, ST18 0PY
www.internationalcomponents.co.uk
email: sales@internationalcomponents.co.uk
Tel: 01889 271135
Fax: 01889 271183

KONCEPT

**PROGRESSIVE CONSUMER
ELECTRONICS LTD**
Unit 2 Pulborough Way
Hounslow
Middlesex
TW4 6DE
Tel: 0208 754 6200
Fax: 0208 754 6201
Email: info@konceptech.co.uk
Web: www.konceptech.co.uk

California design house Koncept
Technologies have developed a range of
innovative and affordable lighting. With a
sleek and elegant design, the collection
of desk and floor lamps use high
powered, economic, environmentally
friendly LED bulbs. A stylish and practical
addition to any space.

JCC LIGHTING PRODUCTS
Lamplighter House
Beeding Close
Southern Cross Trading Estate, Bognor Regis
PO22 9TS
www.jcc-lighting.co.uk
email: sales@jcc-lighting.co.uk
Tel: 01243 838999

LIGHTING DESIGN INTERNATIONAL
3 Hammersmith Studios
55a Yeldham Road
London
W6 8AF
T: 020 8600 5777
F; 020 8600 5778
design@ldi-uk.com
www.lightingdesigninternational.com

LIGHT ENGINEERING
64 Eden Road
London
E17 9JY
www.light-engineering.com
email: info@light-engineering.com
Tel: 02085 202336
Fax: 02085 091332

NEUESLICHT
www.neueslicht.com
email: info@neueslicht.de
Tel: 04991 3193 22658

OMC (UK) LTD.
Candela House
Cardew Industrial Estate
Redruth, Cornwall
TR15 1SS
www.omc-uk.com
email: omc-sales@omc-uk.com
Tel: 01209 215424
Fax: 01209 215197

PR LIGHTING SYSTEMS LTD
Unit B, Horsted Keynes Industrial Park
Cinder Hill
Horsted Keynes
RH17 7BA
www.prlightingsystems.co.uk
email: sales@prlightingsystems.co.uk
Tel: 01342 811555
Fax: 01342 811888

PUFF-BUFF DESIGN
Ul.sniegockiej 10/40a, 00430 Warsaw
Ul.podgorna 46, 87100 Torun
www.puff-buff.com
email: sales@puff-buff.com
Tel: 04822 6210834
Fax: 04822 6210834

SHIU KAY KAN
34 Lexington Street
London
W1F 0LH
www.skk.net
email: sales@skk.org.uk
Tel: 020 7434 4095
Fax: 0207 734 0901

SILL LIGHTING
3 Thame Park Business Centre
Wenman Road
Thame, Oxfordshire
OX9 3XA
www.sill-uk.com
email: sales@sill-uk.com
Tel: 01844 260 006
Fax: 01844 260 760

LIGHTING ACCESSORIES

FOCUS SB LTD
Napier Road
Castleham Industrial Estate
St Leonards-on-Sea
East Sussex, TN38 9NY
Tel: 01424 858060
Fax: 01424 853862.
Email: sales@focus-sb.co.uk
Web: www.focus-sb.co.uk

As switches and sockets form an
integral part of the interior design
scheme, UK manufacturer, Focus SB,
offers a wide choice of plate styles for
top end projects, along with lighting
control solutions.
They also manufacture bespoke plates
with no requirement for long lead times
or minimum order charges.

MARTIN DANNELL & CO LTD
Md House, 13 Abbeymead Industrial Park
Brooker Road
Waltham Abbey
EN9 1HU
www.martin-dannell.co.uk
email: enquiries@martin-dannell.co.uk
Tel: 01992 700311
Fax: 01992 769521

NEO DESIGN
Herdeckerstr. 26
58453 WITTEN
www.neo-studios.de
email: info@neo-studios.de
Tel: 0049 2302 202 76 28
Fax: 0049 2302 202 76 28

RAKO CONTROLS LTD
Knight Road
Rochester
Kent
ME2 2AH
www.rakocontrols.com
email: sales@rakocontrols.com
Tel: 01634 226666
Fax: 01634 226667

OUTDOOR LIGHTING

ADVANCED LEDS LTD
Unit 1, Bow Court
Fletchworth Gate, Burnsall Road
Coventry
CV5 6SP
www.advanced-led.com
email: sales@advanced-led.com
Tel: 0247 6716151
Fax: 0247 6712161

ANSELL (SALES & DISTRIBUTION) LTD
Units 32/37, Somerton Industrial Park
Dargan Crescent
Belfast
BT3 9JP
www.anselluk.com
email: sales@anselluk.com
Tel: 028 9077 3750
Fax: 028 9077 3783

ANSELL ELECTRICAL PRODUCTS LTD
Unit 6b Yew Tree Way
Stone Cross Park, Golborne
Warrington
WA3 3JD
www.anselluk.com
email: saleswarrington@anselluk.com
Tel: 01942 433 339
Fax: 01942 433 430

ARTEMIDE GB LTD
106 Great Russell Street
London
WC1B 3NB
www.artemide.com
email: showroom@artemide.co.uk
Tel: 02076 315200
Fax: 02076 315222

COMMERCIAL LIGHTING SYSTEMS LTD
Tel: 01489 581002
Fax: 01489 576262

DAVEY LIGHTING LTD
Unit 2 Martlesham Creek Ind Park
Sandy Lane
Woodbridge, Suffolk
IP12 4SD
www.davey-lighting.co.uk
email: sales@davey-lighting.co.uk
Tel: 01394 386768
Fax: 01394 387228

DW WINDSOR LIGHTING
Pindar Road, Hodderson, Herts
EN11 0DX
www.dwwindsor.co.uk
email: info@dwwindsor.co.uk
Tel: 01992 474 600
Fax: 01992 474 601

EGLO UK LTD
Blenheim House
Eversley Way
Egham
TW20 8RY
www.eglo.com
email: info-greatbritain@eglo.com
Tel: 01784 430230
Fax: 01784 430235

EYE LIGHTING EUROPE LTD
Unit 2, Eskdale Road
Uxbridge
Middlesex
UB8 2RT
www.eyelighting.co.uk
email: sales@eyelighting.co.uk
Tel: 01895 814418
Fax: 01895 814666

FLAIRLIGHT
12 Hillcrest Close
Epsom
KT18 5JY
www.flairlight.co.uk
email: sales@flairlight.co.uk
Tel: 01372 807661
Fax: 01372 807660

FRITZ FRYER ANTIQUE LIGHTING
23 Station Street
Ross On Wye
HR9 7AG
www.fritzfryer.co.uk
email: enquiries@fritzfryer.co.uk
Tel: 01989 567416
Fax: 01989 566742

IGUZZINI ILLUMINAZIONE UK
Astolat Business Park
Off Old Portsmouth Road
Guildford, Surrey
GU3 1NE
www.iguzzini.co.uk
email: info@iguzzini.co.uk
Tel: 01483 468 000
Fax: 01483 468 001

JCC LIGHTING PRODUCTS
Lamplighter House
Beeding Close
Southern Cross Trading Estate, Bognor Regis
PO22 9TS
www.jcc-lighting.co.uk
email: sales@jcc-lighting.co.uk
Tel: 01243 838999

JOHN CULLEN LIGHTING
561-563 Kings Road
London
SW6 2EB
www.johncullenlighting.co.uk
email: design@johncullenlighting.co.uk
Tel: 020 7371 5400
Fax: 020 7371 7799

LIGHT PROJECTS GROUP
23 Jacob Street
London
SE1 2BG
Tel: 020 7231 8282
Fax: 020 7237 4342

SECURITY LIGHTING
DANLERS LTD
Danlers Business Centre
Vincients Road
Chippenham
SN14 6NQ
www.danlers.co.uk
email: sales@danlers.co.uk
Tel: 01249 443377
Fax: 01249 443388

Spa Facilities

HYDROTHERAPY

CHESHIRE SPAS & POOLS
Clayhill Industrial Estate
Neston
Cheshire
CH64 3RU
www.cheshirewellnessuk.com
email: sales@cheshire-spas-pools.co.uk
Tel: 01513 363417
Fax: 01513 36 8671

HERITAGE POOLS LTD
Heritage House
Worplesdon Road
Guildford, Surrey
GU2 9XN
www.heritagepools.co.uk
email: info@heritagepools.co.uk
Tel: 01483 235858
Fax: 01483 233483

SPLASH DISTRIBUTION
email: info@splashdistribution.co.uk
Tel: 01444 473355

TERETE HOT TUBS
Osmotherley
North Yorkshire
England
DL6 3BB
www.teretehottubs.co.uk
email: mike@teretehottubs.co.uk
Tel: 01609 883103
Fax: 06109 883103

THE TUB COMPANY
10 Mercerd Rd
www.thetubcompany.co.uk
Tel: 01284 733888
Fax: 01284 733888

TYLO
Fishleigh Rd
Roundswell Commercial Park West
Barnstaple, Devon
EX31 3UA
www.tylolife.co.uk
email: tylo@goldenc.com
Tel: 01271 371676
Fax: 01271 371699

JACUZZIS

HERITAGE POOLS LTD
Heritage House
Worplesdon Road
Guildford, Surrey
GU2 9XN
www.heritagepools.co.uk
email: info@heritagepools.co.uk
Tel: 01483 235858
Fax: 01483 233483

NORPE SAUNAS LTD
47 Maltese Road
Chelmsford
Essex
CM1 2PB
www.norpesaunas.co.uk
email: info@norpesaunas.co.uk
Tel: 01245 344432
Fax: 05603 130898

TERETE HOT TUBS
Osmotherley
North Yorkshire
England
DL6 3BB
www.teretehottubs.co.uk
email: mike@teretehottubs.co.uk
Tel: 01609 883103
Fax: 06109 883103

THE TUB COMPANY
10 Mercerd Rd
www.thetubcompany.co.uk
Tel: 01284 733888
Fax: 01284 733888

SAUNAS

NORPE SAUNAS LTD
47 Maltese Road
Chelmsford
Essex
CM1 2PB
www.norpesaunas.co.uk
email: info@norpesaunas.co.uk
Tel: 01245 344432
Fax: 05603 130898

TERETE HOT TUBS
Osmotherley
North Yorkshire
England
DL6 3BB
www.teretehottubs.co.uk
email: mike@teretehottubs.co.uk
Tel: 01609 883103
Fax: 06109 883103

TYLO
Fishleigh Rd
Roundswell Commercial Park West
Barnstaple, Devon
EX31 3UA
www.tylolife.co.uk
email: tylo@goldenc.com
Tel: 01271 371676
Fax: 01271 371699

STEAM ROOMS

CHESHIRE SPAS & POOLS
Clayhill Industrial Estate
Neston
Cheshire
CH64 3RU
www.cheshirewellnessuk.com
email: sales@cheshire-spas-pools.co.uk
Tel: 01513 363417
Fax: 01513 36 8671

NORPE SAUNAS LTD
47 Maltese Road
Chelmsford
Essex
CM1 2PB
www.norpesaunas.co.uk
email: info@norpesaunas.co.uk
Tel: 01245 344432
Fax: 05603 130898

TYLO
Fishleigh Rd
Roundswell Commercial Park West
Barnstaple, Devon, EX31 3UA
www.tylolife.co.uk
email: tylo@goldenc.com
Tel: 01271 371676
Fax: 01271 371699

SWIMMING POOLS

BURLINGTON SLATE LTD
Cavendish House
Kirkby In Furness, Cumbria, LA17 7UN
burlingtonstone.co.uk
email: sales@burlingtonstone.co.uk
Tel: 01229 889661
Fax: 01229 889466

CHESHIRE SPAS & POOLS
Clayhill Industrial Estate
Neston, Cheshire, CH64 3RU
www.cheshirewellnessuk.com
email: sales@cheshire-spas-pools.co.uk
Tel: 01513 363417
Fax: 01513 36 8671

HERITAGE POOLS LTD
Heritage House
Worplesdon Road, Guildford, Surrey, GU2 9XN
www.heritagepools.co.uk
email: info@heritagepools.co.uk
Tel: 01483 235858
Fax: 01483 233483

NIRVANA CHAIRS
Trippet Villa, Sunnyway, Bosham, W.sussex.
United Kingdom.
PO18 8HQ
www.nirvanachairs.com
email: sales@nirvanachairs.com
Tel: 01243 575446
Fax: 01243 575446

PINELOG LTD
Riverside Business Park
Bakewell
Derbyshire
DE45 1GS
www.pinelog.co.uk
email: admin@pinelog.co.uk
Tel: 01629 814481
Fax: 01629 814634

TILES OF STOW LTD
Langston Priory Workshops
Station Road
Kingham
OX7 6UP
www.tilesofstow.co.uk
email: info@tilesofstow.co.uk
Tel: 01608 658993
Fax: 01608 658951

Wall Finishes

PERUCCHETTI PLASTERING
Cemex House
15 Townmead Road
London, SW6 2QL
Tel: 020 7371 5497
Fax: 020 7371 5842
E-mail: office@perucchetti.com
Web: www.perucchetti.com

Perucchetti maintain a traditional method of application, using the finest ingredients that are amalgamated achieving spectacular results through the techniques used. With many textures, an infinite colour range suiting classical or contemporary projects. The finishes attain a depth, beauty and durability unrivalled by ready-mixed products. The versatility of the Marmorino is limitless.

LINTON MAYERS DESIGN
Specialist Decorating Company
117 Dowson Road, Gee Cross
Hyde, Cheshire, SK14 5HJ
www.lintonmayersdesign.co.uk
email: linton@lintonmayersdesign.co.uk
Tel: 0161 367 9495

THE TILE ASSOCIATION
Forum Court, 83 Copers Cope Road,
Beckenham, BR3 1NR
www.tiles.org.uk
email: info@tiles.org.uk
Tel: 020 8663 0946
Fax: 020 8663 0949

UNIQUE PLASTER FINISHES LTD
59 Wentworth Way
Rainham, Essex, RM13 9NM
Tel: 01708 550970. 07970403909
Fax: 01708 550970

ANTIQUED MIRROR GLASS

DE FERRANTI
E1 The Engineering Offices
2 Michael Road,
London, SW6 2AD
www.deferranti.com
email: ask@deferranti.com
Tel: 0870 321 0511
Fax: 0870 321 0512

BESPOKE WALLPAPER

55MAX
6 Lonsdale Road, Queens Park,
London, NW6 6RD
www.55max.com
email: info@55max.com
Tel: 020 7625 3774
Fax: 020 7625 3776

ARCHITECTURAL TEXTILES LTD
Shardelows Farm,
New England Lane,
Cowlinge, SB8 9HP
www.architecturaltextiles.co.uk
email: sales@architecturaltextiles.co.uk
Tel: 01638 500 338

DOMINIC CRINSON
274 Richmond Road,. E8 3QW
www.crinson.com
email: info@crinson.com
Tel: 0207 241 7467
Fax: 02076 132783

FROMENTAL
The Saga Centre
326 Kensal Road
London
W10 5BZ
www.fromental.co.uk
email: info@fromental.co.uk
Tel: 020 8960 8899
Fax: 020 7681 2343

HAMILTON • WESTON WALLPAPERS & DESIGN

HAMILTON WESTON WALLPAPERS
Marryat Courtyard, 88 Sheen Road,
Richmond, Surrey, TW9 1UF
Tel: + 44 (0) 20 8940 4850
Fax: + 44 (0) 20 8332 0296
E-mail: info@hamiltonweston.com
Web: www.hamiltonweston.com

Founded in 1981, Hamilton Weston are wallpaper specialists. The Company's historic designs available to order date from late 17th to 20th C. The colourings may be individually customised for contemporary interiors. Unique wallpapers by Marthe Armitage, hand lino block printed by the Artist, are available to order. Services include architectural and historical analysis, interior design and space planning.

HOME & BOOK
Studio 1, 46-52 Church Road
London, SW13 0DQ
www.homeandbook.com
email: youngskim71@gmail.com
Tel: 07865 046266

JAMES BRINDLEY
FABRICS & WALLCOVERINGS
Hookstone Park
Harrogate, HG2 7DB
Tel: 01423 880400
www.jamesbrindley.com

JOHN ANTHONY SIGNS LTD
Claydons Lane, Rayleigh,
Essex, SS6 7UU
www.askjas.co.uk
email: info@askjas.co.uk
Tel: 01268 777333
Fax: 01268 777193

SELTEX INTERIORS LTD
1 Horizon Trade Park
Ring Way
London
N11 2NW
www.seltex.co.uk
email: sales@seltex.co.uk
Tel: 020 8211 3107
Fax: 020 8368 0838

THE STENCIL LIBRARY
Stocksfield Hall
Stocksfield
Northumberland
NE43 7TN
www.stencil-library.com
email: info@stencil-library.com
Tel: 01661 844844
Fax: 01661 843984

TONES SPECIALIST PAPER HANGERS
3 Stocks Lane Gamlingay
Sandy
Bedfordshire
SG19 3JP
tones-specialist-paperhangers.com
email: tonesdecoration@btopenworld.com
Tel: 01767 650277
Fax: 01767 650277

ZARDI & ZARDI
Podgwell Barn
Edge
Gloucestershire
GL6 6NJ
www.zardiandzardi.co.uk
email: enquiries@zardiandzardi.co.uk
Tel: 01452 814777
Fax: 01452 814 433

COLOURED GLASS
BOTTLE ALLEY GLASS
1 Tills Courtyard
High St
Battle
TN33 0AE
www.bottlealleyglass.co.uk
email: info@bottlealleyglass.co.uk
Tel: 0845 643 2733
Fax: 0709 237 3521

DAEDALIAN GLASS LTD
The Old Smithy,
Cold Row,
Carr Lane,
Stalmine,
Poulton - Le - Fylde,
FY6 9DW
www.daedalian-glass.co.uk
email: chris@daedalian-glass.co.uk
Tel: 01253 702531
Fax: 01253 702532

INTERSTYLE CERAMIC & GLASS
3625 Brighton Ave
Burnaby,
Bc Canada, V5A 3H5
www.interstyle.ca
email: info@interstyle.ca
Tel: 1 604 421 7229
Fax: 1 604 421 7544

LEAD & LIGHT
35a Hartland Road NW1 8DB
Tel: 02074 850997
Fax: 02072 842660

MOSQUITO / AMY CUSHING
62 Lower Ham Road,
Kingston,
Surrey, KT2 5AW
www.mosquito-design.com
email: amycushing@mosquito-design.com
Tel: 07957 258 620

RUPERT SCOTT LTD
The Glass Studio
Broadlands Enterprise Park
St Davids, SA62 6BR
www.rupertscott.com
email: glass@rupertscott.com
Tel: 0845 450 7684
Fax: 0845 017 7685

Opticolour Ltd
Tel: 01225 464343
E-mail: sales@opticolour.co.uk
Web: www.opticolour.co.uk

Opticolour's spectacular glass wall
coverings are available in a wide range of
colours and printed designs. The 6mm
thick glass is toughened for impact and
heat resistance. It stays clean, involves no
grouting and is used in many
applications including; architectural
features in public buildings, restaurants,
shops, office areas, nightclubs, kitchens
and bathrooms.

SASHA WARD GLASS
19 Salisbury Road
Marlborough, Wiltshire, SN8 4AD
email: sasha@artward.org.uk
Tel: 01672 515638
Fax: 01672 516738

STAINED GLASS STUDIO
The Meadows Off Blanche Lane
South Mimms
Herts
EN6 3PD
stainedglassstudio.co.uk
email: matthew@stainedglassstudio.co.uk
Tel: 01707 66 11 77
Fax: 01707 66 11 77

SVAJA LIMITED
The Circlefifteen
Emily Davison Drive
Epsom
KT18 5QH
www.svaja.com
email: nigelb@svaja.com
Tel: 0870 444 6860
Fax: 0870 444 6861

ZENITH MOSAIC & TILES LTD
Zenith House, Units 5-6 Monarch Industrial
Estate
198 Kings Road, Tyseley
Birmingham
B11 2AP
www.zenithtiles.com
email: info@zenithtiles.com
Tel: 0121 706 6456
Fax: 0121 706 7509

DECORATIVE PANELS

ANDREA MAFLIN
44 Albert Road
Stroud Green
London
N4 3RP
www.andreamaflin.co.uk
email: design@andreamaflin.co.uk
Tel: 0207 272 7972

ANDREW MOOR ASSOCIATES
14 Chamberlain Street
London
NW1 8XB
www.andrewmoor.co.uk
email: andrew@andrewmoor.co.uk
Tel: 02075 868181
Fax: 02075 868484

ARYMA
Tel: 01597 825505
Fax: 01597 824484

ECONOWALL
Joyces Farm Buildings
Southminster Road
Mayland
CM3 6EB
www.econowall.co.uk
email: sales@econowall.co.uk
Tel: 0845 0942 751
Fax: 0845 0942 761

FABRIC ARCHITECTURE
Unit B4 Nexus
Hurricane Rd
Brockworth, Glos
GL3 4AG
www.fabricarchitecture.co.uk
email: info@fabarc.co.uk
Tel: 01452 612 800
Fax: 01452 621 200

FORMICA LIMITED
11 Silver Fox Way
Cobalt Business Park
Newcastle Upon Tyne
NE27 0QJ
www.formica.com
email: info@formica.co.uk
Tel: 0191 259 3100
Fax: 0191 259 2648

FROMENTAL
The Saga Centre
326 Kensal Road
London
W10 5BZ
www.fromental.co.uk
email: info@fromental.co.uk
Tel: 020 8960 8899
Fax: 020 7681 2343

HOME & BOOK
Studio 1, 46-52 Church Road
London
SW13 0DQ
www.homeandbook.com
email: youngskim71@gmail.com
Tel: 07865 046266

ION GLASS LTD
Po Box 284
Burgess Hill
West Sussex
RH15 0WP
www.ionglass.co.uk
email: sales@ionglass.co.uk
Tel: 0845 658 9988
Fax: 0845 658 9989

JAPP DECORATIVE ARTS & INTERIORS
83 Rectory Rd
Worthing
West Sussex
BN14 7PD
email: davidjapp@ntlworld.com
Tel: 01903 203491
Fax: 01903 203491

LA DRAPE INTERNATIONAL LTD
Internet House
Aston Lane North
Preston Brook
WA7 3PE
www.thequiltedwall.co.uk
email: info@ladrape.co.uk
Tel: 01928 713 330
Fax: 01928 713 094

LALIQUE LTD
47 Conduit Street
London
W1S 2YP
www.cristallalique.fr
email: shop.london.cs@lalique.fr
Tel: 0207 292 0444
Fax: 02074 937249

MOLLIE REGAN TEXTILES
The Studio
99 Dorchester Road, Oakdale
Poole, Dorset
BH15 3QZ
www.mollieregantextiles.co.uk
email: rosalyn@mollieregantextiles.co.uk
Tel: 01202 675944
Fax: 01202 675944

MOSAIC WORKSHOP LTD
Unit 2 Harry Day Mews
1 Chestnut Rd
London, SE27 9EZ
www.mosaicworkshop.com
email: sales@mosaicworkshop.com
Tel: 0208 6704466
Fax: 0208 6704466

STEVENSONS OF NORWICH LIMITED
Roundtree Way
Norwich
Norfolk, NR7 8SQ
www.stevensonsofnorwich.com
email: info@stevensonsofnorwich.com
Tel: 01603 400 824
Fax: 01603 405113

STEWARD DESIGN PANELS BV
P.o. Box 96
Gorinchem
Netherlands, 4200 AB
www.designpanels.com
email: info@designpanels.com
Tel: 0031 1835 89099
Fax: 0031 1835 89823

TONY SANDLES GLASS LTD
Unit 6, Park Farm, Park Road, Great
Chesterford, Essex
CB10 1RN
www.sandles-glass.co.uk
email: tony@sandles-glass.co.uk
Tel: 01799 531516
Fax: 01799 531516

TRESPA UK
Grosvenor House
Hollinswood Road
Central Park, Telford
TF2 9TW
www.trespa.com
email: info@trespa.co.uk
Tel: 01952 290707
Fax: 01952 290101

WILTON STUDIOS
Jackson Place
Wilton Road Ind. Est.
Grimsby, N E Lincolnshire
DN36 4AS
www.wiltonstudios.co.uk
email: postbox@wiltonstudios.co.uk
Tel: 01472 210820
Fax: 01472 812602

YOUR WHITE SPACE
66 Brackendale Rd
Bournemouth
Dorset
BH8 9HZ
www.yourwhitespace.com
email: david@yourwhitespace.com
Tel: 01202 251126

PAINT & COATINGS

BONA LIMITED
www.bona.com
email: info.uk@bona.com
Tel: 01908 399740
Fax: 01908 232722

CONSTRUCTION SPECIALTIES (U K) LTD
1010 Westcott Venture Park
Westcott
Buckinghamshire, HP18 0XB
www.c-sgroup.co.uk
email: info@c-sgroup.co.uk
Tel: 01296 652800
Fax: 01296 652888

LIQUID PLASTICS
Iotech House, Miller Street,
Preston, PR1 1EA
www.liquidplastics.co.uk
email: info@liquidplastics.co.uk
Tel: 01772 255022
Fax: 01772 255691

NCS COLOUR CENTRE
71 Ancastle Green
Henley On Thames
Oxfordshire, United Kingdom, RG9 1TS
www.ncscolour.co.uk
Tel: 0149 141 1717
Fax: 0149 141 1231

NUTSHELL NATURAL PAINTS
Unit 3 Leigham Units
Silverton Rd
Matford Park, Exeter, EX2 8HY
www.nutshellpaints.com
email: enquires@nutshellpaints.co.uk
Tel: 01392 823 760
Fax: 01392 824437

STO LTD.
2 Gordon Avenue
Hillington Park
Glasgow, G52 4TG
www.sto.co.uk
email: info.uk@stoeu.com
Tel: 0141 892 8000
Fax: 0141 404 9001

TEFCOTE SURFACE SYSTEMS
20-28 Cotlands Road
Bournemouth
Dorset, BH1 3RS
www.tefcote.co.uk
email: office@tefcote.co.uk
Tel: 01202 551212
Fax: 01202 559090

THE LITTLE GREENE PAINT COMPANY LIMITED
Wood Street, Openshaw,
Manchester, M11 2FB
Tel: 0845 880 5855
Fax: 0845 880 5877
E-mail: mail@thelittlegreene.com
Web: www.thelittlegreene.com

Little Greene environmentally friendly paints and coordinating wallpapers bring fabulous colour and elegant design to your home. The extensive Colours of England palette combines historic English Heritage colours with striking contemporary shades, whilst advanced formulations using up to 40% more pigment than ordinary paint ensure an unrivalled, lasting finish.

THURLOW DECORATION
112 Saffron Road, Wigston, Leicester
LE18 4UN
email: pthurlow@btconnect.com
Tel: 01162 477941
Fax: 01162 779356

PANELLING

AAZTEC CUBICLES
Tel: 01423 326400
Fax: 01423 325115

ARYMA
Tel: 01597 825505
Fax: 01597 824484

BYLAW THE FURNITURE MAKERS
The Workshop
Norwich Road
Lenwade
NR9 5SH
www.bylaw.co.uk
email: info@bylaw.co.uk
Tel: 01603 30 80 90
Fax: 01603 872 122

CASADOR
Tel: 0049 30 78991854
Fax: 0049 30 78991855

DREAMWALL
18 Glebe Road Scartho
Grimsby
North East Lincolnshire
DN33 2HL
www.dreamwall.co.uk
email: info@dreamwall.co.uk
Tel: 01472 750552
Fax: 01472 750552

DUFAYLITE DEVELOPMENT LTD
Cromwell Road
St Neots
Cambridgeshire
PE19 1QW
www.ultraboard.co.uk
email: enquiries@dufaylite.com
Tel: 01480 215000
Fax: 01480 405526

MARTIN OAKLEY
43 Sandfield Road
Oxford
OX3 7RN
www.martinoakley.co.uk
email: sales@martinoakley.co.uk
Tel: 01865 742111

MASS CONCRETE
Black Hill Rd Holton Heath Ind Estate
Poole Dorset, BH16 6LS
www.mass-concrete.com
email: sales@mass-concrete.com
Tel: 01202 628 140
Fax: 01202 628 149

SPECIALIST PAINT FINISHES

HUNG, DRAWN & CORDED
1 Tudor Close, Dean Court Road
Rottingdean, Brighton
BN2 7DF
hungdrawnandcorded.com
email: ally_pollock@hotmail.com
Tel: 01273 390070
Fax: 01273 390070

JAPP DECORATIVE ARTS & INTERIORS
83 Rectory Rd
Worthing
West Sussex
BN14 7PD
email: davidjapp@ntlworld.com
Tel: 01903 203491
Fax: 01903 203491

KARIN MOORHOUSE INTERIORS
1 School Lane
Arundel
West Sussex
BN18 9DR
www.karinmoorhousedesign.com
email: karin@karinmoorhouse.co.uk
Tel: 07801 613334

MARK HORNAK
email: hornax@hotmail.com
Tel: 07930 205 350

STO LTD.
2 Gordon Avenue
Hillington Park
Glasgow, G52 4TG
www.sto.co.uk
email: info.uk@stoeu.com
Tel: 0141 892 8000
Fax: 0141 404 9001

TEFCOTE SURFACE SYSTEMS
20-28 Cotlands Road
Bournemouth
Dorset
BH1 3RS
www.tefcote.co.uk
email: office@tefcote.co.uk
Tel: 01202 551212
Fax: 01202 559090

THE STENCIL LIBRARY
Stocksfield Hall
Stocksfield
Northumberland
NE43 7TN
www.stencil-library.com
email: info@stencil-library.com
Tel: 01661 844844
Fax: 01661 843984

THURLOW DECORATION
112 Saffron Road, Wigston, Leicester
LE18 4UN
email: pthurlow@btconnect.com
Tel: 01162 477941
Fax: 01162 779356

TILES

AMARESTONE
Hogwood Farm Industrial Estate
Sheerlands Road
Finchampstead
RG40 4QY
www.amarestone.com
email: sales@amarestone.com
Tel: 0845 260 8070
Fax: 01189 760371

AQUAVISION WATERPROOF TELEVISIONS
Ibroc House
Essex Road
Hoddesdon
EN11 0QS
www.aquavision.co.uk
email: info@aquavision.co.uk
Tel: 01992 708333
Fax: 01992 708308

CERAMIQUE INTERNATIONALE LTD
Unit 1 Royds Lane
Lower Wortley Ring Road
Leeds
LS12 6DU
www.tilesandmosaics.co.uk
email: info@ceramiqueinternationale.co.uk
Tel: 01132 310218
Fax: 01132 310353

DOMINIC CRINSON
274 Richmond Road
E8 3QW
www.crinson.com
email: info@crinson.com
Tel: 0207 241 7467
Fax: 02076 132783

H & E SMITH LTD
Broom Street
Hanley
Stoke-On-Trent, ST1 2ER
www.hesmith.co.uk
email: sales@hesmith.co.uk
Tel: 01782 281617
Fax: 01782 269882

INTERSTYLE CERAMIC & GLASS
3625 Brighton Ave
Burnaby, Bc
Canada, V5A 3H5
www.interstyle.ca
email: info@interstyle.ca
Tel: 1 604 421 7229
Fax: 1 604 421 7544

JASBA MOSAIK GMBH
Im Petersborn 2
D-56244
www.jasba.de
email: info@jasba.de
Tel: +49 2602 682-0

JOHNSON TILES
Harewood Street
Tunstall
Stoke On Trent, ST6 5JZ
www.johnson-tiles.com
email: sales@johnson-tiles.com
Tel: 01782 575575
Fax: 01782 524138

LUBNA CHOWDHARY
162 Sunnyhill Road
London, SW16 2UN
www.lubnachowdhary.co.uk
Tel: 020 8769 1142
Fax: 020 8769 1142

MARLBOROUGH TILES
www.marlboroughtiles.com
Tel: 01672 512422
Fax: 01672 515791

MOSAIC WORKSHOP LTD
Unit 2 Harry Day Mews
1 Chestnut Rd
London
SE27 9EZ
www.mosaicworkshop.com
email: sales@mosaicworkshop.com
Tel: 0208 6704466
Fax: 0208 6704466

MOSAIK PIERRE MESGUICH
10 Kensington Square
London
W8 5EP
www.mesguichmosaik.co.uk
email: ann@mesguichmosaik.co.uk
Tel: 02077 956253
Fax: 02073 769495

RAK CERAMICS UK LTD
Paris House,
Frenchmans Road,
Petersfield, Hampshire, GU32 3AW.
Tel: 01730 237850
Email: info@rakceramics.co.uk
Web: www.rakceramics.co.uk

R.I.M TILE AND MOSAIC BOUTIQUE
Unit 311 Design Centre Chelsea Harbour
London
SW10 0XE
www.rim.ru
email: info@rimdesign.co.uk
Tel: 020 7376 5820

RYE POTTERY LTD
Wish Ward, Rye Tn31 7dh
www.ryepottery.co.uk
email: sales@ryepottery.co.uk
Tel: 01797 223038
Fax: 01797 225802

STONEHOUSE TILES LTD
2-10 Ossory Road
London
SE1 5AN
www.stonehousetiles.co.uk
email: sales@stonehousetiles.co.uk
Tel: 0207 237 5375
Fax: 0207 231 7597

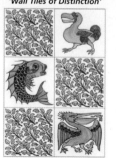

VICTORIAN CERAMICS
'Wall Tiles of Distinction'

Tel: 0044 (0)1952 759246
www.victorianceramics.com
david@victorianceramics.com
Contact: David Franklin

Victorian Ceramics hand decorates wall
tiles, specialising in the reproduction of
William Morris and William De Morgan
designs. These timeless designs are
ideally suited for kitchens, bathrooms
and fireplaces in both period and
contemporary settings. An extensive
range of colours and accessories are
also available.

THE TILE ASSOCIATION
orum Court, 83 Copers Cope Road,
eckenham, BR3 1NR
www.tiles.org.uk
mail: info@tiles.org.uk
el: 020 8663 0946
ax: 020 8663 0949

ILES OF STOW LTD
angston Priory Workshops,
tation Road, Kingham, OX7 6UP
www.tilesofstow.co.uk
mail: info@tilesofstow.co.uk
el: 01608 658993
ax: 01608 658951

WAXMAN CERAMICS LTD
Grove Mills
lland, West Yorkshire, HX5 9DZ
www.waxmanceramics.co.uk
mail: sales@waxmanceramics.co.uk
el: 01422 311331
ax: 01422 310654

WILTON STUDIOS
ackson Place
Wilton Road Ind. Est.
Grimsby, N E Lincolnshire
N36 4AS
www.wiltonstudios.co.uk
mail: postbox@wiltonstudios.co.uk
el: 01472 210820
ax: 01472 812602

ENITH MOSAIC & TILES LTD
enith House, Units 5-6 Monarch Industrial
state,198 Kings Road, Tyseley,
irmingham, B11 2AP
www.zenithtiles.com
mail: info@zenithtiles.com
el: 0121 706 6456
ax: 0121 706 7509

WALL CLADDING

CONSTRUCTION SPECIALTIES (U K) LTD
1010 Westcott Venture Park
Westcott, Buckinghamshire, HP18 0XB
www.c-sgroup.co.uk
email: info@c-sgroup.co.uk
Tel: 01296 652800
Fax: 01296 652888

DREAMWALL
18 Glebe Road Scartho
Grimsby
North East Lincolnshire, DN33 2HL
www.dreamwall.co.uk
email: info@dreamwall.co.uk
Tel: 01472 750552
Fax: 01472 750552

FAIROAKS TIMBER PRODUCTS
Tel: 01722 716779
Fax: 01722 716761

FEEK BVBA
Fao Sofie Couwenberg
Klapdorp 52, B-2000
Antwerp, Belgium
B-2000
www.feek.be
email: info@feek.be
Tel: 0032 3475 1765

FRANCIS N LOWE LTD
The Marble Works
New Road
Middleton
DE4 4NA
www.lowesmarble.com
email: info@lowesmarble.com
Tel: 01629 822216
Fax: 01629 824348

KIRKSTONE
Skelwith Bridge
Ambleside
Cumbria
LA22 9NN
www.kirkstone.com
email: info:kirkstone.com
Tel: 01539 433296
Fax: 015394 34006

SAS INTERNATIONAL
31 Suttons Business Park
London Road
Reading
RG6 1AZ
www.sasint.co.uk
email: enquiries@sasint.co.uk
Tel: 0118 929 0900
Fax: 0118 929 0901

SPM INTERNATIONAL LTD
Unit 4 Houndhill Park
Bolton Road
Wath Upon Dearne
S63 7JY
www.spm-international.com
email: stephen_woodhead@hotmail.com
Tel: 01709 871111
Fax: 01709 871122

SSQ GROUP
301 Elveden Road
Park Royal
London
NW10 7SS
www.ssqgroup.com
email: info@ssq.co.uk
Tel: 020 8961 7725
Fax: 020 8965 7013

STEWARD DESIGN PANELS BV
P.o. Box 96
Gorinchem
Netherlands
4200 AB
www.designpanels.com
email: info@designpanels.com
Tel: 0031 1835 89099
Fax: 0031 1835 89823

STONE THEATRE LTD
Newnham Terrace
Hercules Road
Waterloo, London
SE1 7DR
www.stonetheatre.com
email: london@stonetheatre.com
Tel: 020 7021 0020
Fax: 0207 021 0049

TRESPA UK
Grosvenor House
Hollinswood Road
Central Park, Telford
TF2 9TW
www.trespa.com
email: info@trespa.co.uk
Tel: 01952 290707
Fax: 01952 290101

VICTORIAN WOODWORKS
Redhouse, Lower Dunton Road
Bulphan, Upminster
Essex
RM14 3TD
www.victorianwoodworks.co.uk
email: sales@victorianwoodworks.co.uk
Tel: 020 8534 1000
Fax: 020 8434 2000

WALLPAPER

ALHAMBRA UK
126 Whitby Street South
Hartlepool
Cleveland
TS24 7LP
email: joanne@norfolhouse-uk.com
Tel: 01429 260860
Fax: 01429 224418

ANNA FRENCH
36 Hinton Road
London
SE24 0HJ
www.annafrench.co.uk
email: enquiries@annafrench.co.uk
Tel: 02077 376555

ARC COLLECTIONS LIMITED
1 Andrew Place
London
SW8 4RA
www.arccollections.com
email: sales@arccollections.com
Tel: 020 7720 1628
Fax: 020 7622 6214

ARCHITECTURAL TEXTILES LTD
Shardelows Farm
New England Lane
Cowlinge
SB8 9HP
www.architecturaltextiles.co.uk
email: sales@architecturaltextiles.co.uk
Tel: 01638 500 338

BRIAN YATES (INTERIORS) LTD
Lansil Way
Caton Road
Lancaster
LA1 3QY
www.brian-yates.co.uk
email: sales@brian-yates.co.uk
Tel: 01524 35035
Fax: 01524 32232

BRUNO TRIPLET LTD
23 Elystan Street
SW3 3NT
www.brunotriplet.com
email: info@brunotriplet.com
Tel: 02078 239990
Fax: 02078 239989

CASAMANCE LTD
Greytown House
221-227 High Street
Orpington, Kent
BR6 0NZ
www.casamance.co.uk
email: d.wilson@texdecor.com
Tel: 0844 369 0104
Fax: 0844 369 0103

CATHERINE HAMMERTON
Cockpit Arts, Cockpit Yard
Northington Street
London
WC1N 2NP
www.catherinehammerton.com
email: info@catherinehammerton.com
Tel: ex directory.

COLEFAX AND FOWLER
19/23 Grosvenor Hill
LONDON W1K 3QD
Tel: 020 7493 2231
Fax: 020 7318 6043

DE GOURNAY
112 Old Church Street
London, United Kingdom
SW3 6EP
www.degournay.com
email: info@degournay.com
Tel: 0207 352 9988
Fax: 0207 795 0447

ERICA WAKERLY
Studio 5
96 De Beauvoir Road
London N1 4EN
www.printpattern.com
email: info@printpattern.com
Tel: 07940 577 620

HARLEQUIN HARRIS
Tel: 0844 5430100
Fax: 0844 5430101

HOME & BOOK
Studio 1, 46-52 Church Road
London
SW13 0DQ
www.homeandbook.com
email: youngskim71@gmail.com
Tel: 07865 046266

JOCELYN WARNER LTD
23 Links Yard
Spelman Street
London, United Kingdom
E1 5LX
www.jocelynwarner.com
Tel: 0207 3753754

KNOWLES & CHRSITOU
116 Lots Road
Chelsea
London
SW10 0RN
www.knowles-christou.com
email: info@knowles-christou.com
Tel: 02073 527000
Fax: 02073 528877

LOOPHOUSE
88 Southwark Bridge Road
London
SE1 0EX
www.loophouse.com
email: info@loophouse.com
Tel: 020 7207 7619
Fax: 020 7207 7834

MARK FINZEL DESIGN & PHOTOGRAPHY
www.markfinzel.co.uk
email: mark@markfinzel.co.uk
Tel: 0771 259 0706

MURASPEC LTD
74-78 Wood Lane End
Hemel Hempstead
Hertfordshire
HP2 4RF
www.muraspec.com
email: customerservices@muraspec.com
Tel: 08705 117 118
Fax: 08705 329 020

NAMA ROCOCO
New York
USA
www.namarococo.com
email: info@namarococo.com
Tel: 001 413 652 2312

NATASHA MARSHALL FABRICS AND WALLCOVERINGS
The Printworks, 10 Otago Street
Glasgow
G12 8JH
www.natashamarshall.com
email: info@natashamarshall.com
Tel: 01413 390120

PENBRICE INTERIORS
4 Kingsway
West Wickham
Kent
BR4 9JF
www.penbriceinteriors.co.uk
email: info@penbriceinteriors.co.uk
Tel: 0208 462 8787

PRESTIGIOUS TEXTILES
4 Cross Lane
Westgate Hill Street
Bradford BD4 0SG
www.prestigious.co.uk
email: mail@prestigious.co.uk
Tel: 01274 688 448
Fax: 01274 689 560

ROGER DAVIS INTERIORS LTD
43, Tentercroft Street
Lincoln
Lincolnshire
LN5 7DB
www.roger-davis-interiors.co.uk
email: info@roger-davis-interiors.co.uk
Tel: 01522 531371
Fax: 01522 528349

ROMO LTD
Lowmoor Road
Kirkby-In-Ashfield
Nottinghamshire
NG17 7DE
www.romo.com
email: sales@romo.com
Tel: 01623 750005
Fax: 01623 750031

SELTEX INTERIORS LTD
1 Horizon Trade Park
Ring Way
London
N11 2NW
www.seltex.co.uk
email: sales@seltex.co.uk
Tel: 020 8211 3107
Fax: 020 8368 0838

STICKYUPS
1-6 Clay Street
London
W1U 6DA
www.stickyups.com
email: sales@stickyups.com
Tel: 0845 257 0642

THE ART SURGERY
33-35 Tib Street
Northern Quarter
Manchester
M4 1LX
www.theartsurgery.co.uk
email: info@theartsurgery.co.uk
Tel: 0161 8192888

THE CECIL BEATON FABRIC COLLECTION
The Square
Tisbury
Wiltshire
SP3 6JP
www.cecilbeatonfabrics.com
email: beaton@beaudesert.co.uk
Tel: 0845 838 8720
Fax: 01747 871016

THE LITTLE GREENE PAINT COMPANY
Wood Street
Openshaw
Manchester
M11 2FB
www.thelittlegreene.com
email: mail@thelittlegreene.com
Tel: 0161 230 0880
Fax: 0161 223 3208

THURLOW DECORATION
112 Saffron Road, Wigston, Leicester
LE18 4UN
email: pthurlow@btconnect.com
Tel: 01162 477941
Fax: 01162 779356

TODAY INTERIORS
Hollis Road
Grantham
Lincolnshire
NG31 7QH
www.todayinteriors.com
email: info@today-interiors.co.uk
Tel: 01476 574 401
Fax: 01476 590208

notes...

notes...

notes...

notes...